Essential Maths

Book 7C

David Rayner, Michael White

Elmwood Press

First published 2008 by
Elmwood Press
80 Attimore Road
Welwyn Garden City
Herts. AL8 6LP
Tel. 01707 333232

ISBN 9781 902 214 740

Numerical answers are published in a separate book

Typeset and illustrated by Domex e-Data Pvt. Ltd.
Printed and bound by Mateu Cromo

PREFACE

Essential Maths Book 7C has been written for pupils who are working towards National Curriculum Level 5. Level 4 work is consolidated and then developed further.

Although there is no set path through the books, the topics appear in the order suggested in the National Numeracy Strategy guide. Broadly speaking, the book is split into 6 units. Each unit of work can be used during one half-term with appropriate revision material at the end of the unit. Many topics are reviewed later in the book, in line with the NNS guide.

Puzzle activities and mental arithmetic tasks can be found between the units, to be used whenever appropriate. Investigations appear regularly throughout the book. Ideas for discussing and exploring themes from the 'history of mathematics' are included between each pair of units.

The authors believe that children learn mathematics most effectively by *doing* mathematics. Many youngsters who find mathematics difficult derive much more pleasure and enjoyment from the subject when they are doing questions which help them build up their confidence. Pupils feel a greater sense of satisfaction when they work in a systematic way and when they can appreciate the purpose and the power of the mathematics they are studying.

No textbook will have the 'right' amount of material for every class. The authors believe that it is preferable to have too much material rather than too little. Opportunities for functional maths are incorporated into activities throughout the book.

Most work is broken down into two parts. 'M' exercises are aimed at all children at this level. 'E' exercises provide extension work. Pupils may move naturally onto this work after an 'M' exercise or teachers may judge that a number of students should *only* tackle 'E' exercise.

Pupil self-assessment is a very important part of assessment for learning. Regular 'check yourself' sections appear throughout the book. Answers to these parts only are provided at the back of the book for immediate feedback.

David Rayner and Michael White

CONTENTS

UNIT 1

1.1 Whole number arithmetic

In section 1.1 you will learn how to:

- use place value to write whole numbers in words or figures

- add with whole numbers

- subtract with whole numbers

- multiply with whole numbers

Place value

- Whole numbers are made up from units, tens, hundreds, thousands and so on.

- For the number 8625 we write 'eight thousand, six hundred and twenty-five'.

Exercise 1M

1 The figure 2 in the number 73296 stands for 2 hundreds or 200.
  What do these figures stand for?

   (a) the 3   (b) the 9   (c) the 7

2 Starting with the number 85607, write down the number you get when you

   (a) add 100   (b) add 1000   (c) add 10
   (d) add 10 000   (e) add 1   (f) add 100 000

3 State the value of the figure underlined

   (a) 5<u>1</u>7   (b) 60<u>3</u>7   (c) <u>6</u>7 318   (d) 5<u>8</u>14
   (e) 4<u>7</u> 318   (f) <u>3</u>50 609   (g) 4 6<u>5</u>8 100   (h) <u>6</u> 500 000

4 Do these questions in your head

   (a) add 100 to 5735   (b) add 1000 to 48 500
   (c) add 10 to 2193   (d) add 10 000 to 535 000

In questions ⑤ to ⑪ write down the number which goes in each box.

⑤ 393 = ☐ + 90 + 3

⑥ 527 = 500 + ☐ + 7

⑦ 834 = 800 + ☐ + 4

⑧ 699 = ☐ + 90 + 9

⑨ 7317 = ☐ + 300 + 10 + 7

⑩ 5043 = 5000 + ☐ + 3

⑪ 65 317 = ☐ + 5000 + 300 + ☐ + 7

⑫ Write down the number which is

(a) 1 less than 300

(b) 1 less than 6700

(c) 10 less than 4500

(d) 10 less than 500

(e) 100 less than 7000

(f) 1 less than 6500

⑬ What number is shown by each arrow?

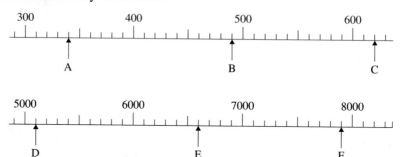

⑭ Write these numbers in figures.

(a) Four hundred and nine.

(b) Six thousand, four hundred and one.

(c) Sixteen thousand, two hundred and eleven.

(d) Half a million.

(e) Four hundred thousand and fifty.

(f) Three and a half thousand.

⑮ Here are four number cards:

(a) Use all the cards to make the largest possible number.

(b) Use all the cards to make the smallest possible number.

16 Here are five number cards:

4 5 0 9 6

(a) Use all the cards to make the largest possible number.

(b) Use all the cards to make the smallest possible number. Do not use 0 as the first card.

17 Read this news item which appeared in a newspaper.
When the cheese was cut and used to make sandwiches
there were 675 000 visits to the website.

(a) Write this number in words.

(b) Try to think of a website which might appeal to the
same sort of people.

> **Cheese web frenzy**
>
> More than 400,000 cheese-lovers have visited the website www.cheddarvision.tv to watch the maturing process of a round of Cheddar cheese. Viewing is expected to reach a frenzy tomorrow as the 44lb (20kg) cheese is subjected to its first quality check. The project is based at a farm in Shepton Mallet, Somerset.

Exercise 1E

1 Copy and complete the addition squares

(a)

+	100	10	1	1000
1437				
499				
2917				
6043				

(b)

+	20	300	5	100
380				
796				
905				
32				

2 Start at 579

(a) + 1

(b) + 100

(c) + 1000

3 Start at 2683

(a) + 20

(b) – 300

(c) – 1000

4 On a cheque you have to write the
amount of money in both words and
figures.
Write the words for the number on
this cheque.

5 Show how you can use the numbers **547**, **1000** and **100** to make the number 1447 by adding and subtracting.

6 Write these numbers in words.

   (a) 6200   (b) 90 000   (c) 25 010

   (d) 610 400   (e) 7 010 000

7 Here are five number cards:

6   3   4   8   9

   (a) Use all the cards to make the largest possible *odd* number.

   (b) Use all the cards to make the smallest possible *even* number.

8 Write down the number that is ten more than:

   (a) 351   (b) 399   (c) 7025

9 Write down the number that is one thousand more than:

   (a) 425   (b) 6423   (c) 24100

10 (a) Lisa puts a 2 digit whole number into her calculator. She multiplies the number by 10.

     Fill in *one* other digit which you know must now be on the calculator.

   (b) Lisa starts again with the same 2 digit number and this time she multiplies it by 1000.

     Fill in all five digits on the calculator this time.

11 Write down the numbers in order, from the smallest to the largest.

   (a) 2142   2290   2058   2136

   (b) 5329   5029   5299   5330

   (c) 25 117   25 200   25 171   25 000   25 500

12 Find a number n so that $5 \times n + 7 = 507$.

13 Find a number P so that $6 \times P + 8 = 68$.

14 Find a pair of numbers a and b for which $8 \times a + b = 807$.

15 Find a pair of numbers P and q for which $7 \times P + 5 \times q = 7050$.

And finally...

A taxi driver who spent six years writing out every number from one to a million in an attempt to win a place in the Guinness Book of records has been told he may have to start again.

The compilers have a rule that the numbers should be in words rather than digits!

Addition

Exercise 2M

1. 126
    + 37

2. 48
    + 173

3. 9
    17
    + 193

4. 28
    63
    + 205

5. 355
    + 278

6. 573
    + 209

7. 301
    99
    + 257

8. 114
    9
    + 867

9. 501
    397
    + 124

10. 634
    769
    + 127

11. 389
    193
    + 624

12. 371
    567
    + 462

In Questions 13 to 32 set the problems out correctly in columns.

13. 3 + 12 + 109

14. 27 + 260

15. 584 + 617

16. 39 + 357

17. 3 + 109 + 61

18. 5034 + 69

19. 201 + 76 + 40

20. 679 + 63 + 4

21. 54 + 507 + 2704

22. 2030 + 69 + 5

23. 6006 + 708 + 99

24. 842 + 67 + 2011

25 1089 + 891 + 19 + 9   **26** 5867 + 321 + 45 + 9   **27** 8647 + 198

28 873 + 2316 + 473   **29** 2644 + 55685   **30** 26 514 + 749

31 45 609 + 20 047   **32** 67 508 + 95 607 + 436

Exercise 2E

Copy the following cross number puzzle onto squared paper.
Complete the puzzles.

Clues across

1. 19 + 38
3. 871 + 105
5. 67 + 24
6. 261 + 548
7. 356 + 55
8. 314 + 250
9. 17 + 26
12. 288 + 471
14. 143 + 274
16. 213 + 504
17. 210 + 109
18. 62 + 27

Clues down

1. 163 + 419
2. 36 + 34
4. 257 + 387
5. 822 + 92
8. 518 + 67
10. 746 + 201
11. 354 + 579
12. 703 + 66
13. 899 + 79
15. 162 + 567

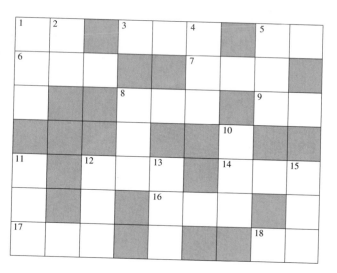

Game

This is a game for 2 or 3 players.
You need cards numbered 0 to 9 which are placed
face down on the table.

Each player draws a grid like this ...

Now turn over one of the cards and then
each person writes that number somewhere
on their own grid.

For example,

Sue put the 5 here

and Sami put the 5 here

Now turn over four more cards, one at a time, and write each new number somewhere on the grid.

Finally add together the two numbers.

The winner is the person with the highest total

In the game between Sue and Sami

Sue got

	4	2
+	8	5	7

   8 9 9

and Sami got

		7	5
+	8	4	2

   9 1 7

So Sami was the winner

Subtraction

(a)
$$
\begin{array}{r}
5\ 8\ 3 \\
-\ 1\ 4\ 7 \\
\end{array}
$$

Exchange ten from 80 to make 13

$$
\begin{array}{r}
5\ {}^7\!8\ {}^1 3 \\
-\ 1\ \ 4\ \ 7 \\
\hline
4\ \ 3\ \ 6 \\
\end{array}
$$

(b)
$$
\begin{array}{r}
6\ 7\ 4\ 3 \\
-\ 3\ 9\ 2\ 7 \\
\end{array}
$$

Exchange in two places

$$
\begin{array}{r}
{}^5\!6\ {}^1 7\ {}^3\!4\ {}^1 3 \\
-\ 3\ 9\ \ 2\ 7 \\
\hline
2\ 8\ \ 1\ 6 \\
\end{array}
$$

Exercise 3M

1.
$$
\begin{array}{r} 59 \\ -\ 23 \end{array}
$$

2.
$$
\begin{array}{r} 85 \\ -\ 8 \end{array}
$$

3.
$$
\begin{array}{r} 83 \\ -\ 65 \end{array}
$$

4.
$$
\begin{array}{r} 72 \\ -\ 37 \end{array}
$$

5.
$$
\begin{array}{r} 60 \\ -\ 37 \end{array}
$$

6.
$$
\begin{array}{r} 523 \\ -\ 118 \end{array}
$$

7.
$$
\begin{array}{r} 376 \\ -\ 95 \end{array}
$$

8.
$$
\begin{array}{r} 571 \\ -\ 363 \end{array}
$$

9.
$$
\begin{array}{r} 850 \\ -\ 264 \end{array}
$$

10.
$$
\begin{array}{r} 965 \\ -\ 575 \end{array}
$$

In Questions 11 to 20 write the numbers in columns and then subtract.

11. $33 - 16$
12. $24 - 7$
13. $57 - 19$
14. $40 - 13$
15. $167 - 78$

16. $319 - 234$
17. $743 - 517$
18. $800 - 342$
19. $965 - 877$
20. $2001 - 416$

Find the missing numbers.

21
```
   7 8 4
 - 6 2 7
 ─────────
   □ □ □
```

22
```
   6 3 5
 - □ 2 9
 ─────────
   2 □ □
```

23
```
   6 8 7 4
 -   5 9 □
 ─────────
   □ □ □ 2
```

Exercise 3E

Work out

1 153 increased by 61

2 165 greater than 180

3 41 less than 796

4 1759 take away 466

5 428 plus 535

6 decrease 640 by 280

7 538 and 617 added together

8 take 666 from 700

9 the difference between 65 and 450

10 249 more than 826

Copy and complete.

11 3700 plus □ is 5600

12 411 is □ more than 203

13 □ take away 17 is 89

14 □ is 240 less than 655

15 $3684 + □ = 4816$

16 $367 - □ = 248$

17 4155 plus □ is 5230

18 □ subtract 17 is 815

19 □ decreased by 213 is 48

20 $1234 - □ = 416$

21 In April a company made 4367 masks
In May production increased by 1292.
How many masks were made in May?

22 45 660 copies of a magazine were printed but only 38 880
were sold. How many copies were not sold?

23 In one week 2569 children used a swimming pool.
The total number of tickets sold was 4185. How many
adults used the pool?

24 Copy and complete this addition square.

+	18			
		100		65
			114	
17	35			49
		81	67	

25 One subtraction, using the digits 2, 3, 4, 5, 6, is $\boxed{642 - 35}$.

Which subtraction using all the digits 2, 3, 4, 5, 6 has the smallest positive answer?

Magic squares

In a magic square the sum of the numbers in each column, row and main diagonal are equal. Here is an example of a magic square. The sum of each column, row and diagonal is 18.

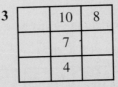

9	5	4
1	6	11
8	7	3

Copy and complete the following magic squares

1

4	3	
	5	
		6

2

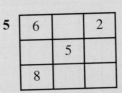

		3
	6	
9		4

3

	10	8
	7	
	4	

4

		11
5	12	7

5

6		2
	5	
8		

6

6	7	
13	8	
	9	

7

	6	10	15
16		5	4
	12	8	
		11	

8

9	14		
		16	7
12	3	15	8
6			

9

11			10
2	13	16	
		4	
7	12		6

Multiplying

- Multiplying is a quick way of adding together the same number...
  $8 + 8 + 8 + 8 + 8 + 8$ is the same as 8×6 and $8 \times 6 = 48$.

  You need to know your multiplication tables.

Exercise 4M   Part A

Write down the answer only.

1 7×2
2 5×2
3 2×8
4 9×2
5 6×2

6 8×3
7 5×3
8 6×3
9 3×9
10 3×7

11 4×4
12 7×4
13 5×4
14 4×8
15 4×6

16 3 × 5   17 7 × 5   18 8 × 5   19 5 × 5   20 5 × 9

21 4 × 6   22 7 × 6   23 8 × 6   24 6 × 6   25 6 × 9

26 3 × 7   27 5 × 7   28 6 × 7   29 7 × 4   30 7 × 7

31 3 × 8   32 7 × 8   33 8 × 8   34 8 × 9   35 8 × 6

36 1 × 9   37 0 × 9   38 7 × 9   39 6 × 9   40 9 × 9

Part B

Copy and complete the grids below. Time yourself on grid 1. Try to improve your time on grid 2.

Grid 1

×	7	2	12	8	6	3	11	9	4	5
7	49									
2										
12										
8										
6				48						
3								9		
11										
9										
4										
5										

Grid 2

×	2	9	6	3	5	11	12	8	7	4
2										
9										
6										
3										
5										
11										
12										
8										
7										
4										

Exercise 4E

1 Copy and complete the multiplication squares. The numbers outside the square are always 2, 3, 4, 5, 6, 7, 8, 9.

(a)

	8	2	7
5			35
		32	
3	27		
6			

(b)

	4	7	3	8
5				
			42	
2				

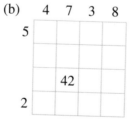

(c)

		5	8	2
	28		56	
6				
9				

(d)

	4		3	
			45	72
			30	
7		35		

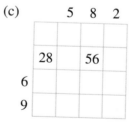

(e)   7   9

	7		9
24	32		
		18	
	42		

(f)   5   7

	5	7	
	40	32	
3			
6	12		

(g)

	35	40	15
			18
18			27

(h)   8

	8		
			27
	56		
	40	30	
			36

(i)   3

	3		
7	42		
	24		
45		72	

(j)

18	14		
45		20	
54			48

(k)

		10	16
	24		48
63			72

(l)

		40	
	18		
18		30	42

---

2 In the next three squares you may have the same number at the top and along the side of the square.

(a)   4

			4	
		56		
				15
		36		
	14	49		
30				25

(b)

			18	48
		49		
			9	
	45			40
16		28		

(c)

	42	28		
	48		64	
15			40	
				81
			24	

Multiplying larger numbers

```
      5 2
   ×    7
   3 6 4
     ↑
   carry
```

```
    3 0 4
    ×   9
   2 7 3 6
       3
       ↑
     carry
```

```
     7 4 3
   ×     6
   4 4 5 8
     2 1
     ↖ ↗
     carry
```

Exercise 5M

1. 34
    × 5

2. 63
    × 4

3. 45
    × 5

4. 49
    × 3

5. 51
    × 8

6. 64
    × 9

7. 85
    × 7

8. 73
    × 6

Copy and complete.

9.   23
     × 4
     □ 2
      1

10. 27
     × 3
     □ 1
      2

11. 16
     × 7
     1 □ 2
       4

12. 25
     × □
     100

13. 19
     × 4
     □□

14. 45
     × 4
     □□□
       2

15. 342
     × 3

16. 465
     × 6

17. 529
     × 7

18. 644
     × 8

19. 607
     × 9

20. 370
     × 6

21. 4216
     ×   7

22. 3614
     ×   8

23. 2016
     ×   4
     □□6□

24. 875
     × 7
     □ 1 □□

Exercise 5E

1. If you have 4 video tapes each of 180 minutes duration, how many minutes of taping can you do?

2. Each month an office worker earns £2150. How much does she earn in 6 months?

3. How many hours are there in 5 days?

4. Eight racks of CDs each contained 22 CDs. How many CDs were there altogether?

5. Sami sends a postcard with a 34p stamp every day for 7 days. How much does she spend on stamps altogether?

6 In one week the average daily audience at a cinema was 627 people. How many people watched films at the cinema during that week?

7 There are 52 playing cards in a 'deck'. How many cards are there altogether in nine decks?

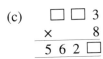

8 The perimeter of a square garden is 36 m. What is the area of the garden?

9 Find the missing digits.

(a) □ 7
   ×   5
   ‾‾‾‾‾‾
   2 3 □

(b) □ □ 6
   ×   7
   ‾‾‾‾‾‾‾‾
   2 2 8 □

(c) □ □ 3
   ×   8
   ‾‾‾‾‾‾‾‾
   5 6 2 □

10 Answer true or false:

(a) $3 + 4 + 5 + 6 + 7 = 5 \times 5$

(b) $77 + 78 + 79 = 3 \times 78$

11 Mike knows that $221 \times 31 = 6851$. Explain how he can use this information to work out 222×31.

12 Given that $357 \times 101 = 36\,057$, work out 358×101 without multiplying.

1.2 Short division

In section 1.2 you will learn how to:

● divide a whole number by another whole number

● solve mixed problems involving remainders

Division is the inverse (reverse) operation of multiplication.

When you know one × or ÷ fact $9 \times 7 = 63$ $7 \times 9 = 63$

you know 3 related facts. $63 \div 7 = 9$ $63 \div 9 = 7$

Exercise 1M

1 Write the answers only.

(a) $10 \div 2$ (b) $12 \div 3$ (c) $18 \div 9$ (d) $24 \div 3$

(e) $36 \div 4$ (f) $40 \div 5$ (g) $60 \div 6$ (h) $32 \div 8$

(i) $35 \div 7$ (j) $81 \div 9$ (k) $22 \div 2$ (l) $36 \div 6$

(m) $45 \div 9$ (n) $110 \div 10$ (o) $16 \div 1$ (p) $9 \div 9$

(q) $0 \div 6$ (r) $56 \div 8$ (s) $63 \div 7$ (t) $72 \div 8$

2   Copy and complete.

(a) $77 \div \square = 7$

(b) $\square \div 8 = 6$

(c) $42 \div \square = 7$

(d) $54 \div \square = 6$

(e) $24 \div \square = 12$

(f) $500 \div \square = 50$

(g) $\square \div 9 = 9$

(h) $\square \div 7 = 7$

(i) $\square \div 7 = 8$

(j) $40 \div \square = 5$

(k) $\square \div 8 \square = 9$

(l) $30 \div \square = 15$

(m) $\square \div 7 = 6$

(n) $200 \div \square = 5$

(o) $80 \div \square = 10$

3   For each statement write three related × or ÷ statements.

(a) $15 \div 3 = 5$ [Hint: one fact is $15 \div 5 = 3$]

(b) $5 \times 15 = 75$

(c) $12 \times 8 = 96$

(d) $96 \div 6 = 16$

4   What number, when divided by 8 and then multiplied by 6, gives an answer of 30?

5   What number, when divided by 8 and then multiplied by 7, gives an answer of 56?

Exercise 1E

1   Write down each statement and write 'true' or 'false'.

(a) $45 \div 5 = 9$

(b) $60 \div 6 = 9$

(c) $7 \div 1 = 1 \div 7$

(d) $20 \div 2 = 10$

(e) $84 \div 4 = 12$

(f) $9 \div 9 = 0$

2   Write each statement and find the missing number.

(a) $80 \div 10 = \square$

(b) $24 \div \square = 3$

(c) $36 \div \square = 9$

(d) $\square \div 7 = 4$

(e) $\square \div 6 = 7$

(f) $8 \div \square = 1$

3   What number, when multiplied by 3 and then divided by 4, gives an answer of 6?

4   What number, when multiplied by 6 and then divided by 3, gives an answer of 14?

5   Copy and complete: $(3 + \square) \div 5 = 4$

Copy and complete these multiplication squares.

6

×			9		
		54		36	
	35		15		
				48	
		36	27		
7	49				

7

×					
	40			64	
	35		42		
			12		14
		12			
		27		63	

8

×					
		49			
	30			40	
					36
		21		24	
	36		54		24

Dividing larger numbers

- The order in which you divide numbers *is* important. For example $12 \div 3$ is *not* the same as $3 \div 12$.

- Here is a 'pencil and paper' method for dividing.

(a) $625 \div 5$

$$\begin{array}{r} 1\ 2\ 5 \\ 5\overline{)\ 6^12^25} \end{array}$$

(b) $936 \div 4$

$$\begin{array}{r} 2\ 3\ 4 \\ 4\overline{)\ 9^13^16} \end{array}$$

(c) $3073 \div 7$

$$\begin{array}{r} 0\ 4\ 3\ 9 \\ 7\overline{)3^30^27^63} \end{array}$$

Exercise 2M

Work out

1. $3\overline{)\ 99}$
2. $2\overline{)\ 42}$
3. $4\overline{)\ 48}$
4. $7\overline{)\ 84}$

5. $5\overline{)\ 65}$
6. $6\overline{)\ 72}$
7. $7\overline{)\ 847}$
8. $9\overline{)\ 558}$

9. $8\overline{)\ 128}$
10. $9\overline{)\ 729}$
11. $2\overline{)\ 678}$
12. $6\overline{)\ 3372}$

13. $3\overline{)\ 729}$
14. $5\overline{)\ 725}$
15. $4\overline{)\ 1028}$
16. $8\overline{)\ 1856}$

Exercise 2E

Work out

1. $8\overline{)\ 2056}$
2. $5\overline{)\ 1025}$
3. $6\overline{)\ 7776}$
4. $7\overline{)\ 5082}$

5. $3050 \div 10$
6. $1387 \div 1$
7. $38\ 199 \div 7$
8. $14\ 032 \div 8$

9. $31\ 386 \div 6$
10. $3490 \div 5$
11. $28\ 926 \div 9$
12. $15\ 638 \div 7$

13 Eight tins of pears weigh 3200g. How much does each tin weigh?

14 336 children are divided into four equal teams. How many children are in each team?

15 Books are sold in boxes of 8. How many boxes are needed for 184 books?

16 Cinema tickets cost £6. How many tickets can be bought for £162?

17 Six crocodiles each laid the same number of eggs. Altogether there are 138 eggs. How many eggs did each crocodile lay?

Remainders

Suppose you need to share 267 cakes between 5 people.

Work out 267 ÷ 5:

$$
\begin{array}{r}
5\ 3 \ \ \textit{remainder 2} \\
5\overline{)\ 2\ 6^1\ 7}
\end{array}
$$

Each person gets 53 cakes and there are 2 left over.

Exercise 3M

Write the answer with a remainder.

1 $5\overline{)\,432}$ 2 $4\overline{)\,715}$ 3 $6\overline{)\,895}$ 4 $3\overline{)\,164}$

5 $8\overline{)\,514}$ 6 $9\overline{)\,375}$ 7 $5\overline{)\,2642}$ 8 $2\overline{)\,7141}$

9 $4079 \div 7$ 10 $2132 \div 5$ 11 $4013 \div 8$ 12 $235 \div 6$

13 $657 \div 10$ 14 $8327 \div 10$ 15 $85\,714 \div 6$ 16 $4826 \div 9$

17 $2007 \div 7$ 18 $9998 \div 9$ 19 $6732 \div 11$ 20 $84\,563 \div 7$

Rounding remainders up or down

(a) How many teams of 5 can you make from 113 people?

Work out 113 ÷ 5.

$$
\begin{array}{r}
2\ 2 \ \ \textit{remainder 3} \\
5\overline{)\ 1\ 1^13}
\end{array}
$$

Here we round *down*. You can make 22 teams and there will be 3 people left over.

(b) An egg box holds 6 eggs. How many boxes do you need for 231 eggs?

Work out $231 \div 6$.

$$\begin{array}{r} 3\ 8 \quad \textit{remainder 3} \\ 6\overline{)2\ 3^5\ 1} \end{array}$$

Here we round *up* because you must use complete boxes. You need 39 boxes altogether.

Exercise 3E

In these questions you will get a remainder. Decide whether it is more sensible to round *up* or to round *down*.

1. Train tickets cost £5. How many tickets can be bought for £88?

2. A car can carry 3 children as passengers. How many cars are needed to carry 40 children?

3. There are 23 children in a class. How many teams of 4 can be made?

4. Eggs are packed six in a box. How many boxes do I need for 200 eggs?

5. Tickets cost £6 each and I have £80. How many tickets can I buy?

6. I have 204 plants and one tray takes 8 plants. How many trays do I need?

7. There are 51 children in the dining room and a table seats 6. How many tables are needed to seat all the children?

8. I have 100 cans of drink. One box holds 8 cans. How many boxes can I fill?

9. Five people can travel in one car and there are altogether 93 people to transport. How many cars are needed?

10. There are 332 children in a school. One coach holds 50 children. How many coaches are needed for a whole school trip?

11. Tins of spaghetti are packed 8 to a box. How many boxes are needed for 913 tins?

12. A prize consists of 10 000 one pound coins. The prize is shared between 7 people. How many pound coins will each person receive?

13. How many 9p stamps can I buy with a £5 note?

14. Find the missing numbers

(a)
$$\begin{array}{r} 7\ 1\ 4\ r\ \square \\ 8\overline{)5\ 7\ 1\ 4} \end{array}$$

(b)
$$\begin{array}{r} 5\ 6\ \ r\ 4 \\ 7\overline{)3\ 9\ \square} \end{array}$$

(c)
$$\begin{array}{r} 8\ 1\ \ 2\ \ r\ 7 \\ 9\overline{)7\ 3\ 1\ \square} \end{array}$$

CHECK YOURSELF ON SECTIONS 1.1 AND 1.2

1   Using place value to write whole numbers in words and figures

Write these numbers in figures

(a) Two thousand and eleven

(b) Twenty-three thousand, two hundred and one

(c) Nine and a half thousand

2   Adding with whole numbers

Work out

(a) $60214 + 20$

(b) $8007 + 200$

(c) $314 + 5273$

(d) $6592 + 617$

(e) $234 + 51 + 618$

3   Subtracting with whole numbers

Work out

(a) $578 - 45$

(b) $614 - 332$

(c) $422 - 53$

(d) $2510 - 304$

(e) $1000 - 25$

4   Multiplying with whole numbers

Work out

(a) 9×7

(b) 74×7

(c) 328×6

(d) How many hours are there in seven days?

5   Dividing a whole number by another whole number

Copy and complete

(a) $54 \div 6 = \square$

(b) $45 \div \square = 9$

(c) $252 \div 7 = \square\square$

(d) $\square\square\square \div 9 = 46$

(e)
```
    6 4
4)2 □ 6
```

(f)
```
    2 7
8)2 □ 6
```

6   Solving mixed problems involving remainders

(a) A calculator costs £7. How many can I buy with £90?

(b) Tins of blackcurrants are packed 6 to a box. How many boxes are needed for 70 tins?

1.3 Long multiplication and division

In section 1.3 you will learn how to:

- multiply by a two or three digit number
- divide by a two digit number
- solve mixed problems

Long multiplication

- Using grids

  35 × 41

  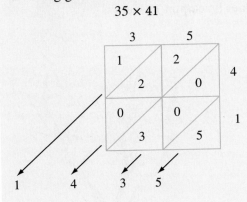

- Other method

  $$\begin{array}{r} 35 \\ \times\ \ 41 \\ \hline 35 \\ 1400 \\ \hline 1435 \end{array}$$
  (35 × 1)
  (35 × 40)

Exercise 1M

In questions 1 to 6 copy and complete the grids and then add along the diagonals to obtain the answer.

1   2   7

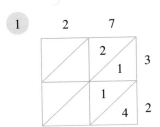

2   1   6

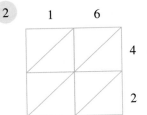

3   3   5

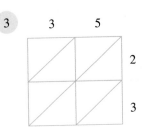

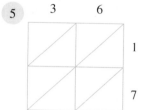

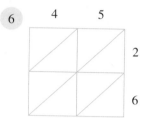

Work out

7 36 × 27   8 49 × 24   9 36 × 25   10 38 × 44

11 92 × 47   12 28 × 17   13 82 × 37   14 18 × 87

15 Each week a shop assistant earns £84. How much does he earn in 15 weeks?

16 Gold-plated trees cost € 69 each. How much would 81 of these trees cost?

17 A film company hires 94 extras to film crowd scenes. They are paid £75 each. What is the total wage bill?

Exercise 1E

In questions 1 to 3 copy and complete the grids and then find the answer.

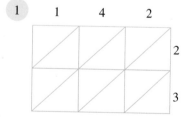

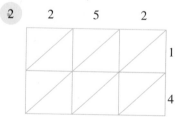

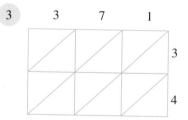

4   326 × 15   5   208 × 24   6   36 × 79   7   27 × 281

8   472 × 11   9   897 × 36   10   141× 27   11   324 × 213

12   A delivery van uses an average of 43 litres of petrol per day. How much does the van use in 14 days?

13   In a car park there are 25 rows of 42 cars. How many cars are in the car park?

14   An aircraft holds 174 people. The aircraft was full on every trip for three days. How many people did it carry in total over the three days?

Day	Number of trips
Fri	16
Sat	22
Sun	18

15   How many hours are there in eleven weeks?

16   Fill in the boxes with the digits 2, 3, 4, 5 to make the answer correct.

$$\begin{array}{r} \square\ \square \\ \times\ \square\ \square \\ \hline 8\ 4\ \ 0 \end{array}$$

17   Fill in the boxes with the digits 1, 2, 3, 4, 5 to make the answer correct. This is not easy but it can be done!

$$\begin{array}{r} \square\ \square\ \square \\ \times\ \square\ \square \\ \hline 5\ 5\ 2\ 5 \end{array}$$

Long division

With ordinary short division, you divide and find remainders. The method for 'long' division is really the same but you set it out so that the remainders are easier to find.

Work out   864 ÷ 36

$$\begin{array}{r} 2\ 4 \\ 36)\overline{8\ 6\ 4} \\ -7\ 2\ \downarrow \\ \hline 1\ 4\ 4 \\ -1\ 4\ 4 \\ \hline 0 \end{array}$$

32 into 86 goes 2 times

2 × 36 = 72

86 – 72 = 14

bring down 4

36 into 144 goes 4 times

Exercise 2M

1 Work out.

(a) $7 \overline{)3374}$

(b) $13 \overline{)702}$

Work out. There are no remainders in these questions.

2 $286 \div 13$	3 $360 \div 15$	4 $672 \div 21$	5 $621 \div 23$
6 $888 \div 24$	7 $992 \div 32$	8 $810 \div 18$	9 $644 \div 46$
10 $1224 \div 51$	11 $1035 \div 45$	12 $612 \div 36$	13 $1769 \div 29$

Exercise 2E

There are remainders in some of the divisions.

1 $450 \div 14$	2 $515 \div 15$	3 $851 \div 23$	4 $580 \div 13$
5 $775 \div 31$	6 $1128 \div 24$	7 $830 \div 36$	8 $945 \div 41$

9 A hammer costs £14. How many hammers can be bought with £355?

10 A rugby team has 15 players. How many teams can be made from 187 players?

11 How many 32 cm lengths of string can be cut from 60 metres?

12 A school hall can fit 28 chairs into one row. How many rows are needed to seat 1000 people?

13 Each box contains 25 pills. How many boxes can be filled from 6040 pills?

14 Copy and complete

(a) $23 \times \boxed{} = 391$

(b) $\boxed{} \times 35 = 840$

(c) $1512 \div 42 = \boxed{}$

Questions 15 to 18 involve either division or multiplication.

15 On average a shop sells 32 chess sets a week. How many sets are sold in a year?

16 Jars of peaches are packed 18 to a box. How many boxes do you need for 625 jars?

17 The stairs on an escalator move up at a rate of 14 cm per second. How far will the stairs go up in three quarters of a minute?

18 There are 35 offices in a building and each office has 14 phones. The phones are delivered in boxes of 15. How many boxes are needed?

1.4 Using a calculator

In section 1.4 you will learn about:

- the order of operations $(+, -, \times, \div)$
- using a calculator with simple expressions
- using the 'bracket' keys on a calculator

Order of operations

Consider the possible answers to this question:

'Work out $5 + 7 \times 3$'

On some calculators, we get:

$$5 + 7 \times 3$$
$$= 12 \times 3 \quad \text{(adding first)}$$
$$= 36$$

On other calculators, we get:

$$5 + 7 \times 3$$
$$= 5 \times 21 \quad \text{(multiplying first)}$$
$$= 26$$

Both answers seem sensible but if we could get different answers to the same question people around the world would argue over who is correct. Another question comes when there are brackets in a calculation, for example $6 \times (8 - 3)$.

The rule we use is

'work out the brackets first and then multiply or divide before you add or subtract'.

The correct answers to the calculations above are

$$5 + 7 \times 3 = 26$$
$$6 \times (8 - 3) = 30$$

Later we will work with indices like 5^2 or 4^3 and when they are involved the complete rule is shown in the table below.

B rackets	$(\ )$	do first	'B'
I ndices	x^y	do next	'I'
D ivision M ultiplication	$\div$ $\times$	do this pair next	'D' 'M'
A ddition S ubtraction	$+$ $-$	do this pair next	'A' 'S'

Remember the word 'B I D M A S'

(a) $40 \div 5 \times 2$

$= 8 \times 2$

$= 16$

(c) $5 + 2 \times 3$

$= 5 + 6$

$= 11$

× before +

(b) $9 + 8 - 7$

$= 17 - 7$

$= 10$

(d) $10 - 8 \div 2$

$= 10 - 4$

$= 6$

÷ before −

Exercise 1M

Work out the following. Show every step in your working.

1 $5 + 3 \times 2$

2 $4 - 1 \times 3$

3 $7 - 4 \times 3$

4 $2 + 2 \times 5$

5 $9 + 2 \times 6$

6 $13 - 11 \times 1$

7 $7 \times 2 + 3$

8 $9 \times 4 - 12$

9 $2 \times 8 - 7$

10 $4 \times 7 + 2$

11 $13 \times 2 + 4$

12 $8 \times 5 - 15$

13 $6 + 10 \div 5$

14 $7 - 16 \div 8$

15 $8 - 14 \div 7$

16 $5 + 18 \div 6$

17 $5 + 18 \div 6$

18 $6 - 12 \div 4$

19 $20 \div 4 + 2$

20 $15 \div 3 - 7$

21 $24 \div 6 - 8$

22 $30 \div 6 + 9$

23 $8 \div 2 + 9$

24 $28 \div 7 - 4$

25 $13 + 3 \times 13$

26 $9 + 26 \div 13$

27 $10 \times 8 - 70$

28 $96 \div 4 - 4$

29 $36 \div 9 + 1$

30 $1 \times 2 + 3$

31 Copy each calculation and write in the missing number.

(a) $4 \times \boxed{} - 7 = 9$

(b) $20 - 3 \times \boxed{} = 5$

(c) $24 \div \boxed{} - 4 = 4$

(d) $(10 - \boxed{}) \times 4 = 36$

(e) $26 - (10 - \boxed{}) = 19$

(f) $36 \div (7 - \boxed{}) = 6$

(g) $(\boxed{} + 7) \times 5 = 65$

(h) $11 - \boxed{} \div 2 = 5$

(i) $\boxed{} + 7 \times 3 = 30$

(j) $44 + (24 \div \boxed{}) = 56$

(k) $(\boxed{} \times 7) - 21 = 0$

(l) $48 \div \boxed{} + 11 = 17$

(a) $8 + 3 \times 4 - 6$
$= 8 + (3 \times 4) - 6$
$= 8 + 12 - 6$
$= 14$

(b) $3 \times 2 - 8 \div 4$
$= (3 \times 2) - (8 \div 4)$
$= 6 - 2$
$= 4$

$\times$ and $\div$ before $+$ and $-$

Notice that we have put brackets in to make the working easier.

Exercise 1E

Evaluate the following. Show every step in your working.

1 $2 + 3 \times 4 + 1$

2 $4 + 8 \times 2 - 10$

3 $7 + 2 \times 2 - 6$

4 $25 - 7 \times 3 + 5$

5 $17 - 3 \times 5 + 9$

6 $11 - 9 \times 1 - 1$

7 $1 + 6 \div 2 + 3$

8 $6 - 28 \div 7 - 2$

9 $8 + 15 \div 3 - 5$

10 $5 - 36 \div 9 + 3$

11 $6 - 24 \div 4 + 0$

12 $8 - 30 \div 6 - 2$

13 $3 \times 4 + 1 \times 6$

14 $4 \times 4 + 14 \div 7$

15 $2 \times 5 + 8 \div 4$

16 $21 \div 3 + 5 \times 4$

17 $10 \div 2 + 1 \times 3$

18 $15 \div 5 + 18 \div 6$

19 $5 \times 5 - 6 \times 4$

20 $2 \times 12 - 4 \div 2$

21 $7 \times 2 - 10 \div 2$

22 $35 \div 7 - 5 \times 1$

23 $36 \div 3 - 1 \times 7$

24 $42 \div 6 - 56 \div 8$

25 $72 \div 9 + 132 \div 11$

26 $19 + 35 \div 5 - 16$

27 $50 - 6 \times 7 + 8$

28 $30 - 9 \times 2 + 40$

29 $4 \times 11 - 28 \div 7$

30 $13 \times 11 - 4 \times 8$

In questions 31 to 48 remember to perform the operation in the brackets first.

31 $3 + (6 \times 8)$

32 $(3 \times 8) + 6$

33 $(8 \div 4) + 9$

34 $3 \times (9 \div 3)$

35 $(5 \times 9) - 17$

36 $10 + (12 \times 8)$

37 $(16 - 7) \times 6$

38 $48 \div (14 - 2)$

39 $64 \div (4 \times 4)$

40 $81 + (9 \times 8)$

41 $67 - (24 \div 3)$

42 $(12 \times 8) + 69$

43 $(6 \times 6) + (7 \times 7)$

44 $(12 \div 3) \times (18 \div 6)$

45 $(5 \times 12) - (3 \times 9)$

46 $(20 - 12) \times (17 - 9)$

47 $100 - (99 \div 3)$

48 $1001 + (57 \times 3)$

Working backwards

Exercise 2M

Copy each question and write brackets so that each calculation gives the correct answer.

1 $3 + 4 \times 5 = 35$

2 $6 + 9 \times 7 = 69$

3 $7 \times 2 + 3 = 17$

4 $9 + 12 \times 5 = 105$

5 $6 \times 8 - 2 = 36$

6 $3 \times 8 - 6 = 18$

7 $19 - 6 \times 3 = 39$

8 $27 - 9 \div 3 = 24$

9 $51 \div 3 + 4 = 21$

10 $7 \times 24 - 5 = 133$

11 $6 + 14 \div 2 = 10$

12 $11 + 6 \times 4 = 68$

13 $12 \times 8 - 9 \times 7 = 33$

14 $8 \times 9 - 4 \times 7 = 44$

15 $5 \times 6 - 4 \div 2 = 13$

16 $81 \div 9 \times 12 - 4 = 72$

17 $3 + 5 \times 9 - 7 = 16$

18 $16 - 10 \div 18 \div 6 = 2$

19 $6 + 7 - 1 \div 2 = 6$

20 $5 + 7 \div 3 \times 0 = 0$

Jumble the numbers

Exercise 2E

Using each number once, find the calculation which gives the correct answer.

For example:

Numbers	Answer	Calculation
5, 3, 6	3	$(6 - 5) \times 3 = 3$

	Numbers			Answer	Calculation		Numbers			Answer	Calculation
1.	2	4	8	6		2.	2	3	5	21	
3.	7	2	3	3		4.	9	2	4	7	
5.	8	4	5	20		6.	20	2	3	6	
7.	7	2	4	30		8.	7	22	6	20	
9.	6	4	3	8		10.	8	40	3	8	
11.	8	36	4	5		12.	7	49	2	14	
13.	21	14	11	24		14.	16	3	9	57	
15.	12	4	16	7		16.	24	42	6	24	
17.	18	5	13	25		18.	40	6	16	4	
19.	7	8	6	50		20.	13	8	4	44	
21.	4	3	9	12		22.	7	9	3	21	
23.	45	4	3	11		24.	121	11	7	77	

25 Make up your own question to try on a friend. You may use as many numbers as you like.

Using a calculator

Division can be written with a horizontal line

$$8 \div 2 = \frac{8}{2} \qquad (4 + 6) \div 2 = \frac{4 + 6}{2} \qquad 4 + 6 \div 2 = 4 + \frac{6}{2}$$

$$12 \div (4 + 2) = \frac{12}{4 + 2} \qquad (8 - 3) \div (11 + 2) = \frac{8 - 3}{11 + 2}$$

Exercise 3M

1 Write the following expressions with a horizontal line.

(a) $8 + 6 \div 2$ (b) $10 \div 2 + 4$ (c) $12 - (8 \div 2)$

(d) $10 \div (3 + 1)$ (e) $(12 - 7) \div 2$ (f) $10 \div 5 - 1$

2 Work out without a calculator.

(a) $\frac{8 - 2}{3}$ (b) $12 - \frac{8}{2}$ (c) $\frac{14 - 8}{2}$ (d) $\frac{8}{4} + 1$

(e) $\frac{8}{3 + 1}$ (f) $\frac{12 - 8}{2}$ (g) $\frac{16}{1 + 3}$ (h) $15 + \frac{12}{3}$

In questions 3 to 14 use a calculator to find the answer.

3 2.5×1.67

4 $19.6 - 3.73$

5 $0.795 \div 0.25$

6 $0.13 + 8.9 - 3.71$

7 $2.4 \times 2.4 - 3.45$

8 $5.3 \times 1.7 + 3.7$

9 $0.71 \times 0.92 - 0.15$

10 $\frac{15.48}{1.72}$

11 $\frac{8.448}{1.32}$

12 $8.2 \times 0.4 - 3$

13 4.65×101

14 $8.17 - 1.56 + 7.4$

In questions 15 to 32 remember the correct order of operations.

15 $2.5 + 3.1 \times 2.4$

16 $7.81 + 0.7 \times 1.82$

17 $8.73 + 3.45 \div 0.5$

18 $11.7 \div 9 - 0.74$

19 $4.48 \div 0.32 + 1.15$

20 $2.6 + 5.2 \times 1.7$

21 $2.9 + \frac{6.039}{1.83}$

22 $1.6 \times 1.7 + 2.62$

23 $5.2 + \frac{4.995}{1.85}$

24 $9.64 + \frac{10.92}{0.42}$

25 $1.27 + 3.1 \times 4.4$

26 $\frac{1.5 \times 1.5}{25}$

27 $0.15 + 1.4 \times 9.2$

28 $1.7 \times 1.7 \times 1.7$

29 $8.2 + 3.2 \times 3.3$

30 $\dfrac{3.2 + 9.408}{6.72}$

31 $\dfrac{1.9 + 2.953}{2.3}$

32 $\dfrac{8.7 - 5.622}{1.14}$

Using brackets

For the calculation $14 - (8 \div 2)$ you press

| 1 | 4 | − | (| 8 | ÷ | 2 |) | = |

When the right hand bracket button is pressed you will see that the calculation inside the brackets has been performed. Try it.

Don't forget to press the = button at the end to give the final answer.

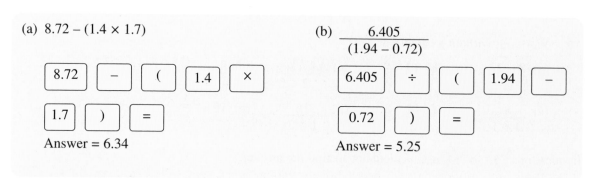

(a) $8.72 - (1.4 \times 1.7)$

| 8.72 | − | (| 1.4 | × |

| 1.7 |) | = |

Answer = 6.34

(b) $\dfrac{6.405}{(1.94 - 0.72)}$

| 6.405 | ÷ | (| 1.94 | − |

| 0.72 |) | = |

Answer = 5.25

Exercise 3E

1 Work out what answer you would get when the buttons below are pressed.

(a) | (| 8 | + | 7 |) | ÷ | 3 | = |

(b) | 1 | 8 | − | (| 5 | × | 2 |) | = |

(c) | 1 | 2 | ÷ | (| 6 | − | 3 |) | = |

(d) | 9 | ÷ | (| 6 | ÷ | 2 |) | = |

2 Write down the sequence of buttons you would press to work out the following calculations.

(a) $17 - (4.2 \times 3)$

(b) $\dfrac{28}{2.41 + 4.59}$

Work out

3 $18.41 - (7.2 \times 1.3)$

4 $11.01 + (2.45 \div 7)$

5 $(2.38 + 5.6) \div 1.4$

6 $9.6 + (11.2 \div 4)$

7 $(8.73 \div 3) - 1.4$

8 $11.7 - (2.6 \times 2.7)$

9 $7.41 - \left(\dfrac{6.44}{1.4}\right)$

10 $\left(\dfrac{11.39}{1.7}\right) - 2.63$

11 $\dfrac{28.65}{(1.7 + 0.21)}$

12 $(1.56 + 4.32) \div 2.45$

13 $3.2 \times (1.9 - 0.74)$

14 $4.956 \div (1.3 - 0.71)$

15 $(7.77 \div 1.4) \times 1.49$

16 $(2.67 + 1.2 + 5) \times 1.1$

17 $23 - (9.2 \times 1.85)$

18 $\dfrac{(8.41 + 0.704)}{1.47}$

19 $\dfrac{132.43}{8.2 \times 0.95}$

20 $\dfrac{43.87 - 8.17}{17}$

21   Find three pairs of equivalent expressions

A $\dfrac{24}{3} - 2$ B $\dfrac{24 - 2}{3}$ C $24 - 2 \div 3$ D $(24 - 2) \div 3$

E $24 - \dfrac{2}{3}$ F $\dfrac{24}{3 - 2}$ G $24 \div (3 - 2)$

22   Write down the sequence of buttons you would press to evaluate the following.

(a) $\dfrac{9 - 3}{4 + 8}$ (b) $\dfrac{30}{8 - 3} + 4 \times 7$

Work out

23 $(1.75 + 0.6) \times (8.93 - 4.03)$

24 $\dfrac{14.24}{8.17 - 3.72}$

25 $\dfrac{17.5 + 3.62}{0.62 + 4.18}$

26 $\dfrac{6.16 \times 4}{11.5 - 7.65}$

27 $\dfrac{17}{8} + \dfrac{13}{4}$

28 $\dfrac{17.6}{2.2} + \dfrac{13.5}{1.5}$

29 $\dfrac{13.86}{3.15} - \dfrac{5.94}{2.7}$

30 $\dfrac{24.65 + 6.55}{6.5 \times 3}$

CHECK YOURSELF ON SECTIONS 1.3 AND 1.4

1   Multiplying by a 2 or 3 digit number

Work out.

(a) 35×18 (b) 63×27 (c) 316×42

2   Dividing by a 2 digit number

(a) Work out $391 \div 17$

(b) How many 15 seater coaches will be needed for a group of 356 people?

3   Order of operations

Work out, without a calculator.

(a) $17 - 3 \times 4$ (b) $82 + 10 \div 2$ (c) $32 \div (12 - 8)$

(d) $(3 + 8) \times (9 - 4)$ (e) $25 \div (15 \div 3)$ (f) $5 + 5 \times 5$

4   Using a calculator

Evaluate the following.

(a) 22.5×4.4 (b) $28.5 - 4.2 \times 3$ (c) $6.31 + \dfrac{3.68}{1.6}$

(d) $\dfrac{4.93}{2.9} - 0.63$ (e) $61.65 \div (8.27 - 1.42)$

1.5   Sequences

In section 1.5 you will learn how to:

- find the next term in a sequence

- find and use a rule for a sequence

- solve problems involving harder sequences

Here is sequence 3 7 11 15 19

- A number sequence is a set of numbers in a given order

- Each number in a sequence is called a *term*.

Here are three sequences. Try to find the next term in each one.

(a) 5, 8, 12, 17, ?   (b) $\frac{1}{2}$, 1, 2, 4, ?   (c) 15, 14, 16, 13, 17, ?

Exercise 1M

1   The numbers in boxes make a sequence. Find the next term.

(a) | 9 | 7 | 5 | 3 | [ ] |

(b) | 4 | 9 | 14 | 19 | [ ] |

(c) | 2 | 9 | 16 | 23 | [ ] |

(d) | 2 | 3 | 5 | 8 | 12 | [ ] |

In Questions 2 to 17 write down the sequence and find the next term.

2   21, 17, 13, 9   3   60, 54, 48, 42

4   1, 2, 4, 8, 16   5 $\frac{1}{2}$, 1, $1\frac{1}{2}$, 2

6   3, $4\frac{1}{2}$, 6, $7\frac{1}{2}$ 7   60, 59, 57, 54, 50

8   5, 7, 10, 14   9   3, 30, 300, 3000

10   1.7, 1.9, 2.1, 2.3   11   1, 3, 9, 27

12   8, 4, 0, –4, –8   13   7, 5, 3, 1, –1

14   1, 2, 4, 7, 11   15   –2, –1, 0, 1

16   200, 100, 50, 25   17   11, 10, 8, 5, 1

Exercise 1E

1   Write down each sequence and find the next term.

(a)   2, 5, 8, 11   (b)   2, 8, 14, 20   (c)   –2, 0, 2, 4

(d)   0.9, 1, 1.1, 1.2   (e)   22, 17, 12, 7   (f)   0.2, 0.5, 0.8

32

In questions 2 to 7 you may have to add, subtract, multiply or divide to find the next term.

2   21, 15, 9

3   0.2, 2, 20, 200

4   0.8, 1, 1.2

5   80, 40, 20, 10

6   11, 8, 5, 2

7   10000, 1000, 100

8   Write down the sequence and find the missing number.

(a) | 3 | 6 | 12 | 24 | |

(b) | 4 | | 10 | 13 | 16 |

(c) | 32 | 16 | 8 | 4 | |

(d) | | 6 | 3 | 0 | –3 |

The next four questions are more difficult. Find the next term.

9   1, 2, 6, 24, 120

10   2×4^2, 3×5^2, 4×6^2

11   $\frac{1}{3}$, $\frac{2}{5}$, $\frac{3}{7}$, $\frac{4}{9}$

12   2, 2, 4, 12, 48, 240

13   Golf balls can be stacked in a 'solid' pyramid.
The picture shows the view from above a pyramid
with **1** ball at the top, **4** balls on the next
layer and **9** balls on the next layer after that.
How many balls will be on the next layer?

Sequence rules

- For the sequence 10, 13, 16, 19, 22, ... the first term is 10 and the term-to-term rule is 'add 3'.

  For the sequence 3, 6, 12, 24, 48, ... the term-to-term rule is 'double' or 'multiply by 2'.

Exercise 2M

1   The first term of a sequence is 20 and the term-to-term rule is 'add 5'. Write down the first five terms of the sequence.

2   You are given the first term and the rule of several sequences.
    Write down the first five terms of each sequence.

	First term	Rule
(a)	8	add 2
(b)	100	subtract 4
(c)	10	double
(d)	64	divide by 2

3   Write down the rule for each of these sequences.

    (a) 3, 10, 17, 24

    (b) 100, 89, 78, 67

    (c) 0.7, 0.9, 1.1, 1.3

    (d) 1, 2, 4, 8, 16

4   The rule for the number sequences below is
                              'double and add 1'

    Find the missing numbers

    (a) $2 \rightarrow 5 \rightarrow 11 \rightarrow 23 \rightarrow \boxed{}$

    (b) $\boxed{} \rightarrow 7 \rightarrow 15 \rightarrow 31$

    (c) $\boxed{} \rightarrow 51 \rightarrow \boxed{} \rightarrow \boxed{}$

5   The rule for the number sequences below is
                              'multiply by 3 and take away 2'

    Find the missing numbers

    (a) $2 \rightarrow 4 \rightarrow 10 \rightarrow \boxed{}$

    (b) $\boxed{} \rightarrow 7 \rightarrow 19 \rightarrow 55$

    (c) $1 \rightarrow \boxed{} \rightarrow \boxed{} \rightarrow \boxed{}$

6   Write down the rule for each of these sequences.

    (a) $2, 2\frac{1}{2}, 3, 3\frac{1}{2}, 4, \ldots$

    (b) 5, 10, 20, 40, 80, ...

    (c) 1.5, 1.6, 1.7, 1.8, ...

    (d) 81, 27, 9, 3, 1, ...

7　In the sequences of squares the number of matches is shown.

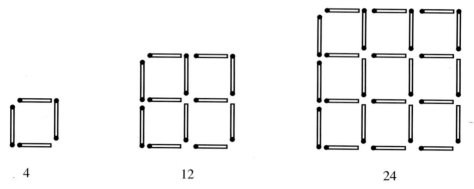

4　　　　　　　　　12　　　　　　　　　24

(a) Draw the next square in the sequence and write down the number of matches in the square.

(b) Copy and complete the number pattern below.

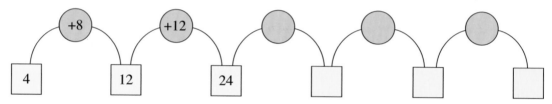

8　The first number in a sequence is 5. Write down a possible rule so that all the terms in the sequence are odd numbers.

9　The rule for a sequence is 'add 3'. The first three terms of the sequence are negative numbers. Find what numbers the first term of the sequence could be.

Exercise 2E

1　In this question the rule for several *different* sequences is 'add 5'.

(a) Find a sequence for which all the terms are divisible by 5.

(b) Find a sequence for which none of the terms is a whole number.

(c) Can you find a sequence with the 'add 5' rule in which all the terms are odd numbers?

2　In a *linear* sequence the terms go up or go down in equal steps. For example 7, 10, 13, 16, … or 20, 18, 16, 14, ….

Fill in the missing numbers in these linear sequences

(a) 2, ☐, 8, ☐, ☐, 17

(b) 10, ☐, 18, ☐, 26, 30, ☐

(c) ☐, 37, ☐, ☐, 28, 25

3 Find the first five terms of each sequence.

(a)
> The 2nd term is 9
> The rule is 'add 5'

(b)
> The 4th term is 11
> The rule is 'take away 3'

(c)
> The 3rd term is 12
> The rule is 'multiply by 2'

(d)
> The 2nd term is 10
> The rule is 'multiply by 10'

4 (a) Copy this pattern and write down the next three lines. Do not use a calculator!

$1 \times 999 = 999$
$2 \times 999 = 1998$
$3 \times 999 = 2997$
$4 \times 999 = 3996$

(b) Copy this pattern and write down the next two lines.

$3 \times 5 = 15$
$33 \times 5 = 165$
$333 \times 5 = 1665$
$3333 \times 5 = 16665$

(c) Copy and complete $333\,333\,333 \times 5 =$

5 (a) Look at the pattern below and then continue it for a further three rows.

$2^2 + 2 + 3 = 9$
$3^2 + 3 + 4 = 16$
$4^2 + 4 + 5 = 25$

.   .   .   .
.   .   .   .
.   .   .   .

(b) Write down the line which starts

$12^2 + \ldots$

6 (a) Copy this pattern and write down the next line.

$1 \times 9 = 9$
$21 \times 9 = 189$
$321 \times 9 = 2889$
$4321 \times 9 = 38\,889$
$54321 \times 9 = 488\,889$

(b) Complete this line $87\,654\,321 \times 9 =$

7 (a) Copy this pattern and write down the next line.

$$1 + 9 \times \quad 0 = \quad 1$$
$$2 + 9 \times \quad 1 = \quad 11$$
$$3 + 9 \times \quad 12 = \quad 111$$
$$4 + 9 \times \quad 123 = 1111$$

 (b) Find the missing numbers

$$\boxed{} + 9 \times \boxed{} = 1111111$$

8 (a) Copy this pattern and write down the next line.

$$3 \times 4 = 3 + 3 \times 3$$
$$4 \times 5 = 4 + 4 \times 4$$
$$5 \times 6 = 5 + 5 \times 5$$

 (b) Copy and complete

$$10 \times 11 =$$
$$11 \times 12 =$$

9 The odd numbers can be added in groups to give an interesting sequence.

$$1 \qquad\qquad\qquad = \quad 1 \quad = \quad 1^3 \quad (1 \times 1 \times 1)$$
$$3 + 5 \qquad\qquad = \quad 8 \quad = \quad 2^3 \quad (2 \times 2 \times 2)$$
$$7 + 9 + 11 \quad = \quad 27 \quad = \quad 3^3 \quad (3 \times 3 \times 3)$$

The numbers 1, 8, 27 are called *cube* numbers. Another cube number is 5^3 (we say '5 cubed')

$$5^3 = 5 \times 5 \times 5 = 125$$

Write down the next three rows of the sequence to see if the sum of each row always gives a cube number.

10 A famous sequence in mathematics is Pascal's triangle.

 (a) Look carefully at how the triangle is made.
Write down the next row. It starts: 1 7 ...

 (b) Look at the diagonal marked A.
Predict the next three numbers in
the sequence 1, 3, 6, 10, 15, ...

 (c) Work out the *sum* of the numbers
in each row of Pascal's triangle.
What do you notice?

 (d) Without writing down all the
numbers, work out the sum of the
numbers in the 10th row of the
triangle.

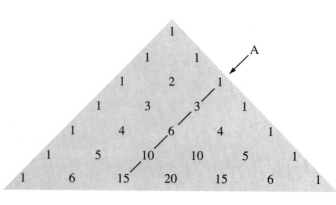

CHECK YOURSELF ON SECTION 1.5

1   Finding the next term in a sequence

Write down each sequence and find the next term.

(a) 1, 5, 9, 13

(b) −4, −1, 2, 5

(c) 61, 55, 49, 43

(d) $\frac{1}{2}$, 1, 2, 4

(e) 0.7, 0.9, 1.1

2   Using a rule for a sequence

The rule for the sequences below is '*double and add 3*'.

Find the missing numbers

(a) 1 → 5 → 13 → ☐

(b) 2 → ☐ → ☐ → 37

(c) ☐ → 15 → 33 → ☐

3   Solving problems involving harder sequences

Write down each sequence and find the next term.

(a) 27, 9, 3, 1

(b) 1 × 2², 2 × 3², 3 × 4²

(c) 1, 3, 7, 15

(d) 2, 3, 1, 4, 0, 5, −1

(e) Draw the next diagram in each sequence

(i)

(ii)

1.6   Perimeter and area

In section 1.6 you will learn how to:

- find perimeters
- find areas involving rectangles
- find areas involving triangles

Perimeter

The perimeter of a shape is the distance around its edges. It is a length and is measured in units of length such as metres or centimetres.

Exercise 1M

1   Find the perimeter of each shape.

(a)
15 cm
7 cm   7 cm
15 cm

(b)
6 cm
10 cm   8 cm

(c)
13 cm
18 cm   18 cm
13 cm

2   The shapes below are drawn on 1 cm squared paper.

Find the perimeter of each shape.

(a)
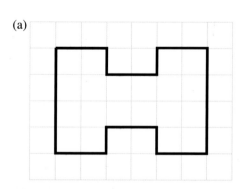

(b)
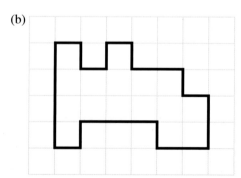

3 Measure the sides of these shapes and work out the perimeter of each one.

(a)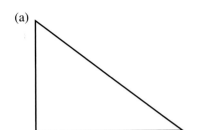

(b)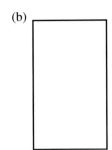

(c)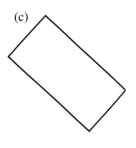

4 Find the perimeter of these pictures.

(a)

(b)

(c)

5 Find the perimeter of each rectangle.

(a)
6 cm
8 cm

(b) 5 cm
12 cm

(c)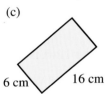
6 cm   16 cm

(d) 17 cm
4 cm

6 Find the perimeter of each shape.

(a) rectangle 9 cm by 5 cm   (b) square with each side 14 cm

(c) rectangle 8.5 cm by 3.5 cm   (d) equilateral triangle of side 6 cm

7 What is the **total** perimeter of these 2 **squares**?

3 cm

7 cm

Exercise 1E

1 Copy and complete this table showing the measurements of rectangles.

length	9 cm	8 cm	6 cm	8 cm	6.7 cm	
width	7 cm	3 cm			2.9 cm	4.5 cm
perimeter			26 cm	34 cm		37 cm

2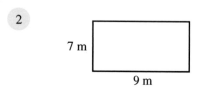

7 m

9 m

(a) Find the perimeter of this garden.

(b) Ed wants to put fence panels around the entire edge of the garden. Each fence panel is 2 m long. How many fence panels will Ed need? The panels can be cut if necessary.

The shapes in questions 3 to 10 consist of rectangles joined together. Find the missing lengths and then work out the perimeter of each shape. The lengths are in cm.

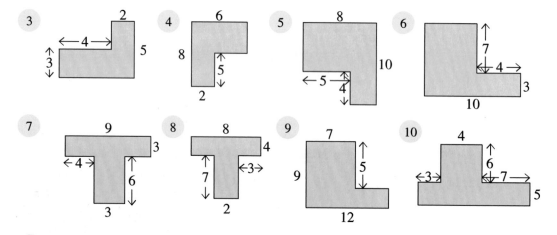

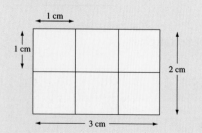

11 The perimeter of a rectangular lawn is 50 m.

The shortest side is 8 m. How long is the longest side?

12 A picture frame has its length twice its height. The total length of wood used in the frame is 108 cm. Work out the length of the frame.

Area

The area of a shape is the amount of surface it covers. It is measured in squares, usually square metres (m^2) or square centimetres (cm^2)

Rectangles

1 cm

1 cm

2 cm

3 cm

The area of this rectangle is 6 cm^2 (each square has an area of 1 cm^2).

length × *width* = 3 × 2 = 6 cm^2

area of rectangle = length × width

Find the area of the shape.

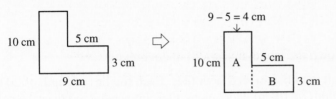

$$9 - 5 = 4 \text{ cm}$$

area A = 10 × 4 = 40

area B = 5 × 3 = 15

total area = 40 + 15

= 55 cm²

Exercise 2M

1   Find the area of each rectangle

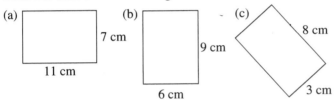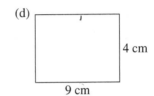

(a) 7 cm, 11 cm (b) 9 cm, 6 cm (c) 8 cm, 3 cm (d) 4 cm, 9 cm

2   Measure the length and width of these rectangles and then work out the area of each one

(a)    (b)

3   Find each blue area below (the lengths are in cm)

(a) 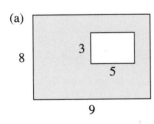   (b)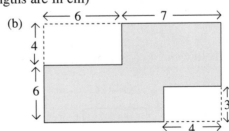

4   Find the area of each square below

(a) 4 cm   (b) 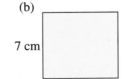 7 cm   (c) 6 cm   (d) 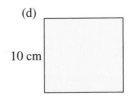 10 cm

5   25 cm²   How long is each side of this square?

6   2 m   1.5 m

(a) Write down the length and width in cm only.

(b) This wall is to be covered with tiles. Each tile has a length of 20 cm and a width of 10 cm. How many tiles are needed to cover the entire wall?

Exercise 2E

1   Find the area of each shape. The lengths are in cm.

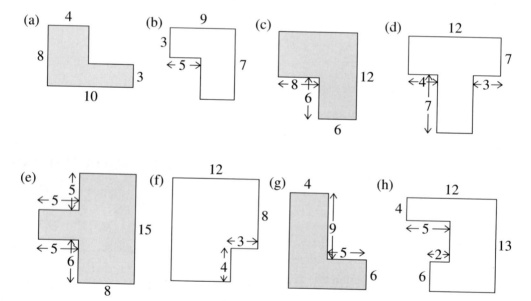

2   In the rectangles below, the area is written inside the shape. Calculate the length of the side marked x.

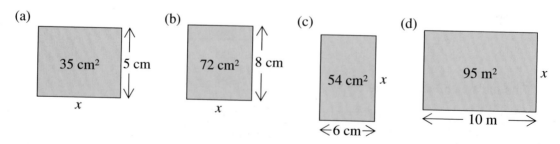

3   A square has an area of 64 cm². How long is each side of this square?

4   A square has an area of 49 cm². Find the perimeter of this square.

5   A lawn is surrounded by a path which is 1m wide.

Calculate the area of the path.

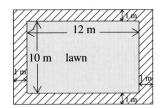

6

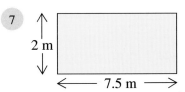

Calculate the area of the pink shaded cross.

7

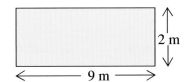

Shahanya wants to paint the two walls shown above. Each tin of paint will cover 11 m². How many tins of paint will she need?

Triangles

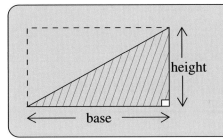

area of rectangle = base × height

area of triangle = $\frac{1}{2}$ (area of rectangle)

area of triangle = $\frac{1}{2}$ (base × height)

Find the area of each triangle.

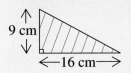

area = $\frac{1}{2}$ (16 × 9) = 72 cm²

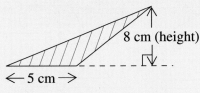

area = $\frac{1}{2}$ (5 × 8) = 20 cm²

44

Exercise 3M

1 Find the area of each triangle. Lengths are in cm.

(a)

(b)

(c)

(d)

(e)

(f)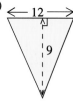

(g)

(h)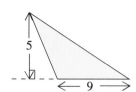

2 Find the area of each triangle below:

(a) base = 8 m, height = 10 m

(b) base = 12 cm, height = 7 cm

(c) base = 20 mm, height = 8 mm

(d) base = 50 m, height = 15 m

3 Find the area of each triangle. Lengths are in cm.

(a)

(b)

(c)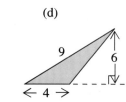

(d)

4 Copy and complete this table showing the measurements of triangles.

base	6 cm	8 cm	14 cm		7 cm
height	4 cm			30 cm	
area		36 cm²	140 cm²	90 cm²	105 cm²

5 Find the total area of each shape. Lengths are in cm.

(a)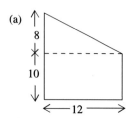

(b)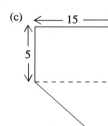

(c)

Exercise 3E

1 Find the total area of each shape. Lengths are in cm.

(a)
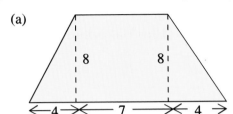

(b)
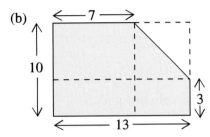

(c)
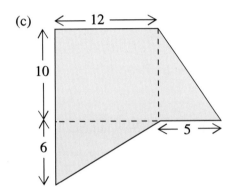

(d)
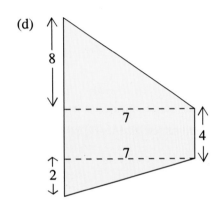

2 Each of the shapes here has an area of 2 cm².

(a) On square dotty paper draw three more
    shapes with area 2 cm².

(b) Draw three shapes with area 3 cm².

(c) Draw one shape with area 4 cm² *and*
    perimeter 10 cm.

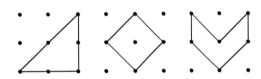

3

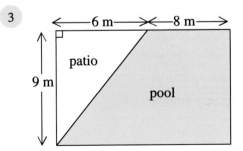

Calculate the area of the pool.

46

4 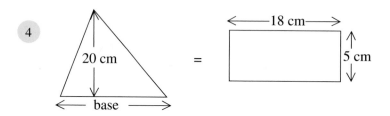 = The area of the triangle is equal to the area of the rectangle. How long is the base of the triangle?

5 Find the area, coloured pink.

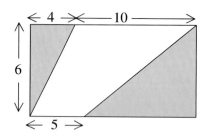

Investigation – area and perimeter

You need squared paper. Each side of the rectangles below must be a whole number.

Part A

Draw four different rectangles which all have a *perimeter* of 24 cm.

Part B

Draw three different rectangles which all have an *area* of 24 cm².

Part C

 Draw at least four rectangles which have a perimeter of 20 cm.

(1) Work out the area of each rectangle.

(2) Which of your rectangles has the largest area?

Part D

 The perimeter of a new rectangle is 32 cm.

(1) *Predict* what the sides of the rectangle will be so that it has the largest possible area.

(2) Check by drawing different rectangles to see if your prediction was correct.

Part E

A rectangle has a perimeter of 100 cm. What are the length and width if the rectangle is to have the largest possible area? What is the largest possible area?

CHECK YOURSELF ON SECTION 1.6

1   Finding perimeters

Find the perimeter of each shape

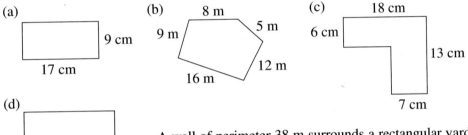

(a)   9 cm   17 cm

(b)   8 m   9 m   5 m   12 m   16 m

(c)   18 cm   6 cm   13 cm   7 cm

(d)   12 m

A wall of perimeter 38 m surrounds a rectangular yard of length 12 m. What is the width of the yard?

2   Finding areas involving rectangles

Find the area of each shape

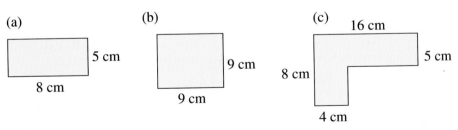

(a)   5 cm   8 cm

(b)   9 cm   9 cm

(c)   16 cm   5 cm   8 cm   4 cm

(d)   A rectangular room has an area of 42 m². If the width of the room is 6 m, what is its length?

3 Finding areas involving triangles

Find the area of each shape

(a)

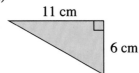

11 cm

6 cm

(b)

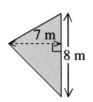

7 m

8 m

(c)

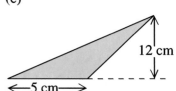

12 cm

←5 cm→

(d)

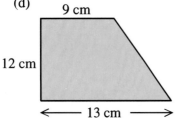

9 cm

12 cm

13 cm

(e) A triangle has an area of 80 m². If the base
of the triangle is 8 m, what is its height?

UNIT 1 MIXED REVIEW

Part one

Copy and complete by writing the missing digits in the boxes

1 (a)

```
    □ 3 □
+   1 □ 2
─────────
    4 0 8
```

(b)

```
    3 □ 9
+ □ 0 □
─────────
  5 6 3
```

(c)

```
    □ 8 □
+ 1 □ 8
─────────
  7 6 3
```

(d)

```
    3 □ 9
+ □ 5 □
─────────
  7 0 5
```

(e)

```
    □ 4 □
+ 1 □ 8
─────────
  4 1 4
```

(f)

```
    5 □ 9
+ □ 9 □
─────────
  8 5 3
```

2 (a) □ 0 – 4 □ = 7

(b) 4 □ – □ 8 = 8

(c) □ 6 + 5 □ = 138

(d)

```
  □ 1 □
- 2 □ 3
─────────
  6 3
```

(e)

```
  6 □ 1
- □ 7 □
─────────
  4 1 3
```

(f)

```
  4 □ 4
- □ 2 □
─────────
  3 4 5
```

3 (a)

```
    □ 7
×     2
─────────
  1 3 □
```

(b)

```
    □ 6
×     4
─────────
  3 4 □
```

(c)

```
    □ 7
×     6
─────────
  3 4 □
```

(d)

$$
\begin{array}{r}
\boxed{}\ 9 \\
\times \qquad 3 \\
\hline
1\ 1\ \boxed{}
\end{array}
$$

(e)

$$
\begin{array}{r}
\boxed{}\ \boxed{}\ 9 \\
\times \qquad\qquad 6 \\
\hline
1\ 4\ 3\ \boxed{}
\end{array}
$$

(f)

$$
\begin{array}{r}
\boxed{}\ \boxed{}\ 3 \\
\times \qquad\qquad 4 \\
\hline
2\ 1\ 3\ \boxed{}
\end{array}
$$

4 (a)

$$
3\overline{)1\ \boxed{}\ 9}
$$ quotient 5 3

(b)

$$
4\overline{)2\ \boxed{}\ 8}
$$ quotient 5 7

(c)

$$
6\overline{)5\ \boxed{}\ 4}
$$ quotient 9 4

(d)

$$
7\overline{)4\ 5\ \boxed{}}
$$ quotient 6 5

(e)

$$
7\overline{)\boxed{}\ 4\ 1}
$$ quotient 6 3

(f)

$$
9\overline{)4\ \boxed{}\ 6}
$$ quotient 5 4

5 Copy and complete the cross number.

Clues across
1. $57 \div 3$
3. $2 \times 3 \times 4$
5. $(17 - 8) \times 2$
6. $448 \div 8$
7. $49 + 35$
8. $87 - 18$
10. $(10 \times 10) - 10$
11. $47 + 47$

Clues down
1. $203 - 86$
2. $7 \times 2 \times 7$
3. $(1000 \div 4) + 4$
4. $7 \times 7 - 3$
7. $445 \div 5$
8. $3 \times 4 \times 5$
9. 11×4

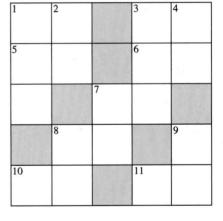

Part two

1 Find the area of each shape. The lengths are in cm.

(a)

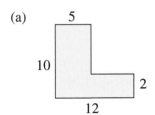

(b)

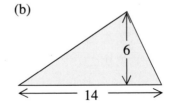

2 Copy and complete the multiplication squares

	8		
5 35			40
	8	18	
		54	48
63			

	9		
7 15		18	
	63		28
10			
		40	20
	72	48	

3 There are 32 biscuits in a packet and there are 7 packets. How many biscuits are there?

4 Copy and complete by finding the missing number.

(a) $5 \times \square - 6 = 24$ (b) $30 - 4 \times \square = 2$

(c) $36 \div \square + 7 = 11$ (d) $(12 - \square) \times 4 = 20$

(e) $32 - (12 - \square) = 28$ (f) $13 - \square \div 2 = 7$

Evaluate, using a calculator

5 $0.37 + 9.75 - 0.6$

6 19.5×3.2

7 $11 - 3.2 \times 2$

8 $4.5 + \dfrac{4.48}{1.4}$

9 $\dfrac{8.94 + 3.66}{3.6}$

10 $\dfrac{7.008 + 1.44}{1.32}$

11 $\dfrac{11.39}{1.7} - 2.63$

12 $3.2 + \dfrac{4.704}{3.36}$

13 $\dfrac{28.1 + 0.55}{1.6 + 0.31}$

14 $25 - (8.2 \times 1.75)$

15 $4.956 \div (1.5 - 0.91)$

16 $\dfrac{14.24}{9.17 - 4.72}$

17 Write down the rule for each sequence.
(Reminder. For the sequence 5, 8, 11, 14,…the rule is 'add 3')

(a) 2, 7, 12, 17   (b) 1, 2, 4, 8, 16   (c) 45, 39, 33, 27

(d) 0.6, 0.8, 1   (e) 1, 3, 9, 27   (f) 1, 3, 7, 15, 31

18 Find the area of each shape. Lengths are in cm

(a)

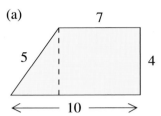

(b)

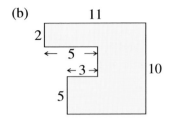

19 Find the perimeter of each shape in question 18 .

20 You are looking for a mystery number.

Use the clues to find it.

● the sum of the digits is 10

● the number reads the same forwards as backwards

● the number is less than 2000

● the number has no zeros

● the number has four digits

21 A balloon seller takes 23 seconds
to blow up each balloon.
How long does it take to blow
up two hundred and forty-five
balloons?

Puzzles and Problems 1

1. Arrange the digits 1, 2, 3 and 4, one into each box,
so that the answer is as large as possible. You may use a calculator.

□□
× □□
‾‾‾‾‾‾‾

or

□□□
× □
‾‾‾‾‾‾‾

2. Arrange the digits 1, 2, 3, 4 and 5, one into each box, so that the answer
is as large as possible.

□□□
× □□
‾‾‾‾‾‾‾

or

□□□□
× □
‾‾‾‾‾‾‾

3. What is the largest number which can be found with a single
multiplication using each of the digits 1, 2, 3, 4, 5 and 6 once only?

4. Here are some black and white beads in a pattern

(a) What colour is the 20th bead?

(b) What colour is the 71st bead?

(c) What position in the line is the 12th black bead?

(d) What position in the line is the 12th white bead?

5. What is the largest possible number of people in a room if
no two people have a birthday in the same month?

6. Two different numbers on this section of a till receipt are
obscured by food stains. What are the two numbers?

tapes at £ .99 : £87.89

7. The letters A, B, C, D, E appear once in every row, every
column and each main diagonal of the square. Copy the
square and fill in the missing letters

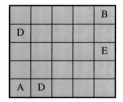

8. King Henry has 9 coins which look identical but in fact one of
them is an underweight fake. Describe how he could discover
the fake using just *two* weighings on an ordinary balance.

A long time ago!   1

The Four Colour Theorem

If you need to colour the areas on a map (in geography, history, etc), it should be possible to use no more than 4 colours. At no boundary between the two areas must the same colour be used for both areas.

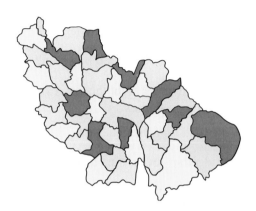

You may have two areas of the same colour meeting at a single point if necessary. A gentleman called August Ferdinand Möbius first wrote about this problem in the nineteenth century.

Exercise

Make a rough copy of each map below and try to colour each section using 4 colours only. The colour in one section must not be the same as that in any section next to it.

1

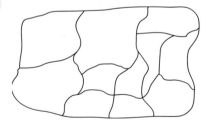

2

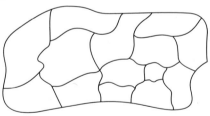

3

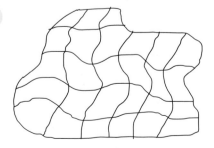

4   Have you managed with 4 colours only so far? Now draw your own map and see if no more than 4 colours are needed to fill it in.

At last! This theorem was finally proved to be correct late in the twentieth century by using a computer programme.

Mental Arithmetic Practice 1

There are two sets of mental arithmetic questions in this section. Ideally a teacher will read out each question twice, with pupils' books closed. Each test of 20 questions should take about 20 minutes.

Test 1

1. What is thirty multiplied by ten?

2. What is forty-two divided by seven?

3. Write the number eight thousand and forty-three in figures.

4. Write 0.25 as a fraction.

5. Add together seven, nine and fifteen.

6. What number should you subtract from seventy-three to get the answer nineteen?

7. How many thirds make up three whole ones?

8. How many centimetres are equal to eighty millimetres?

9. What is four point eight multiplied by ten?

10. What is four squared?

11. If seventy per cent of the children in a class are girls, what percentage of the class are boys?

12. Write a factor of 16 which is greater than 5.

13. The side of a square is six metres. What is the area of the square?

14. Write down any multiple of seven.

15. At midnight the temperature is minus four degrees celsius. By midday the temperature rises eighteen degrees. What is the temperature at midday?

16. Write down the number that is halfway between twelve and eighteen?

17. A train leaves Derby at eight ten. It arrives at Birmingham fifty-five minutes later. At what time does it arrive at Birmingham?

18. Ten per cent of a number is twenty-eight. What is the number?

19. What is the obtuse angle between clock hands showing four o'clock?

20. How much change from five pounds would you get after spending three pounds and forty-two pence?

Test 2

1. What is eight multiplied by seven?

2. Write the number five thousand and twenty-seven in figures.

3. Write the number that is sixteen less than two hundred.

4. What is double sixteen?

5. Add together eight, fifteen and seven.

6. Write three-quarters as a decimal.

7. How many twenty pence coins make two pounds and eighty pence?

8. Change fifteen centimetres into millimetres.

9. Round three hundred and sixty-six to the nearest ten.

10. What is three hundred and forty divided by one hundred?

11. One quarter of a number is seven. What is the number?

12 What number is nine squared?

13 If twenty-three per cent of the people in a cinema wear glasses, what percentage of the people do not wear glasses?

14 What number is halfway between four and eleven?

15 What is three-fifths of one hundred?

16 The temperature in Newcastle was minus three degrees. The temperature in Madrid was nineteen degrees warmer. What was the temperature in Madrid?

17 Write three tenths as a decimal number.

18 Ali buys a pen for £1.25 and a drink for 53p. How much change will Ali receive from a five pound note?

19 Two angles in a triangle are seventy-four degrees and sixty degrees. How large is the third angle?

20 A television programme starts at twenty minutes to six and lasts forty-five minutes. At what time does the programme finish?

2.1   Averages and range

In section 2.1 you will learn how to:

- find the mean, median and mode

- find the range

- compare 2 sets of data using averages and range

The mean
All the data is added and the total is divided by the number of items.

The median
When the data is arranged in order of size, the median is the one in the middle.
If there are two 'middle' numbers, the median is in the middle of these two numbers.

The mode
The number which occurs most often.
A set of data may have more than one mode.

The range
The difference between the largest value and the smallest value.
The range is a measure of how *spread* out the data is. The range is *not* an average.

The shoe sizes of 8 people were: 8, 4, 6, 10, 7, 6, 6, 9

(a) mean shoe size $= \dfrac{8 + 4 + 6 + 10 + 7 + 6 + 6 + 9}{8} = \dfrac{56}{8} = 7$

(b) arrange the shoe sizes in order: 4 6 6 6 7 8 9 10

the median is the $\frac{1}{2}$-way number

$\text{median} = \dfrac{6 + 7}{2} = 6.5$

(c) mode = 6 because there are more 6s than any other number

(d) range = highest number – lowest number = 10 – 4 = 6

Exercise 1M

1 For each set of numbers, find the mode

   (a) 8, 6, 3, 3, 5, 5, 6, 3, 9   (b) 7, 4, 8, 4, 3, 7, 2

2 For each set of numbers, find the mean

   (a) 8, 4, 3, 7, 7, 7   (b) 3, 9, 2, 8, 3   (c) 8, 2, 9, 3, 8, 5, 6, 8, 7, 4

3 For each set of numbers, find the median

   (a) 5, 3, 6, 2, 2   (b) 1, 2, 3, 4   (c) 7, 14, 13, 8, 7, 18, 17, 5, 14, 11

4 For each set of numbers, find the range

   (a) 6, 9, 5, 3, 12, 13, 6   (b) 8, 4, 12, 17, 9, 23, 8, 17, 17, 3, 19

5 In four different shops the price of a
   pound of apples is 89p, 67p, 76p and 84p.
   What is the mean price of the apples?

6 In eight mental arithmetic tests, Carl
   scores 13, 15, 9, 14, 15, 10, 13 and 15.
   What was Carl's mean mark?

7 Carys and Nina play cricket. During one month they score the runs shown below.

   (a) Find the mean score for Carys.   (b) Find the mean score for Nina.

Carys			
28	15	41	38
18	3	13	51
39	14		

Nina			
2	23	9	74
46	12	34	16

   (c) Who has the higher mean score and by how much?

8 Harry played a computer game nine times. His scores are below.

   43000   37800   46500   48150   33800
   39170   45700   49060   46350

   Find his median score.

9   The children in class 7C list how many pets they have.

2	6	3	2	0	1	8	2	1	3	5	2	2
0	3	2	0	1	8	4	2	5	6	1	6	3

    (a) Which number of pets is the mode?

    (b) Write down the range for these numbers.

10   The total height of 4 children is 660 cm.

    Find the mean height of the children.

11   Nine dogs weigh 207 kg in total. Find the mean average weight of the dogs.

12   Lynne caught twelve fish.
    Their masses were:

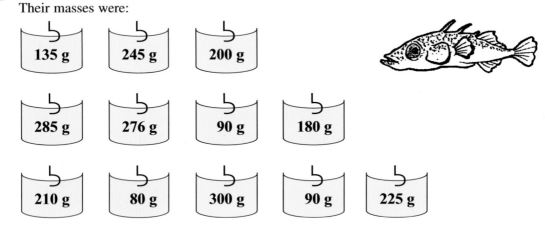

135 g   245 g   200 g

285 g   276 g   90 g   180 g

210 g   80 g   300 g   90 g   225 g

    (a) Find the modal mass (the mode).

    (b) Find the median mass.

    (c) Find the range.

    (d) Find the mean mass.

Exercise 1E

1   (a) Calculate the mean of the numbers 8, 5, 3, 8, 7, 5, 6

    (b) Calculate the new mean when the lowest number is removed.

2   In a science test the marks for the boys were 13, 16, 9, 13, 18, 15
    and the marks for the girls were 12, 16, 19, 17.

    (a) Find the mean mark for the boys.

    (b) Find the mean mark for the girls.

    (c) Find the mean mark for the whole class.

3 The range for nine numbers on a card is 56. One number
   is covered by a piece of blu-tac. What could that number be?

55	22	13
38	61	10
24	44	

4 (a) Copy and complete: 'For the set of numbers 7, 7, 8, 10, 11, 12, 12, 13, there are ⬚
       modes. The modes are ⬚ and ⬚.'

   (b) Find the mode or modes for this set of numbers 2, 3, 3, 3, 5, 5, 7, 8, 8, 8, 10, 10, 11, 11,
       12, 12, 12, 14, 15.

5 Rena throws a dice ten times and wins 50p if the median score is more than 4. The dice
   shows 5, 6, 5, 2, 1, 4, 6, 3, 6, 2. Find the median score.
   Does she win 50p?

6 The temperature in seven towns across the UK were
   recorded at 03:00.

Grantham	−1°	Taunton	0°
Aberdare	1°	Burnley	−5°
Loughborough	−2°	Portrush	−4°
Perth	−7°		

   What was the median temperature?

7 Colin has 5 cards. The mean of the five cards is 7. The
   range of the five cards is 8. What numbers are on the
   two other cards?

   | 7 | 7 | 7 | ⬚ | ⬚ |

8 There were 5 people living in a house. The *median* age
   of the people was 21 and the range of their ages was 3.

   Write each sentence below and write next to it whether it is
   True, Possible or *False*.

   (a) Every person was either 20 or 21 years old.

   (b) The oldest person in the house was 24 years old.

   (c) The mean age of the people was less than 21 years.

9 Meg has 4 cards. The mean of the four cards is 5.
   What number is on the final card?

   | 3 | 6 | 8 | ⬚ |

10 (a) Sid has 3 cards. Find the mean. | 5 | | 2 | | 11 |

  (b) Sid takes another card and the mean goes up by 2. | 5 | | 2 | | 11 | | |
  What number is on the new card?

11 Cath has 5 cards. There are two modes which are 11 and 16.
The total on all five cards is 69.

  (a) Write down the number on each card. (b) Write down the median.

12 Will has 4 cards. The mean for three of the cards is 7.
When the fourth card is included, the mean for all four cards is 6.
Write down the number on the fourth card.

13 Think of five numbers which have a mean of 6 and a median of 4. Ask a friend to check your answer.

14 Make a list of 9 numbers (not all the same!) so that the mode, the median and the mean are all the same value (for example: the set of numbers 5, 6, 7, 7, 10 have mode, median and mean equal to 7). Ask a friend to check your list.

Shoe sizes

The Freeman family: 11   5   5   10   6
The Davidson family: 4   8   5   4   9   10

For the Freeman family: find an average, eg. mode = 5
                        find the range, i.e. 11 − 5 = 6
For the Davidson family: find an average, e.g. mode = 4
                        find the range, i.e. 10 − 4 = 6

Compare the shoe sizes of the Freeman family and the Davidson family.

Answer

The mode (modal shoe size) for the Freeman family is greater than the mode for the Davidson family but the range for the Freeman family is the same as the range for the Davidson family (i.e. they have the same spread).

Comparing sets of data

To compare 2 sets of data, always write at least 2 things:

1 Compare an average (i.e. mean, median or mode).

2 Compare the range of each set of data (this shows how spread out the data is).

Exercise 2M

1. Data A: 2   3   7   8   9

   Data B: 2   3   4   5   6

   Copy and complete the statements below to compare Data A and Data B:

   Data A: median = _____ range = _____

   Data B: median = _____ range = _____

   'The median for Data A is (greater / smaller) than the median for Data B and the range of Data A is (greater/smaller) than the range of Data B (i.e. Data A is (more/less) spread out).'

2. Data C: 6   8   4   13   9   2

   Data D: 12   5   14   11   4   8

   Copy and complete the statements below to compare Data C and Data D:

   Data C: mean = _____ range = _____

   Data D: mean = _____ range = _____

   'The mean for Data C is . . . . than the mean for Data D but the range of Data C is . . . . than the range of Data D (i.e. Data C is . . . . spread out).'

3. Some children in Year 7 were asked how many portions of fruit and vegetables they ate each day. The following were recorded:

   Class 7C: mean = 2.3   range = 7

   Class 7D: mean = 2.1   range = 6

   Copy and complete the sentence below to compare portions eaten by children in class 7C and class 7D.

   'The mean portion for class 7C is . . . . than the mean portions for class 7D and the range of portions for class 7C is . . . . than the range of portions for class 7D.'

4. 12 pupils in year 7 and 12 pupils in year 11 were asked how many hours of TV they watched each day. The results are recorded below:

Year 7	6	7	4	4	2	6	4	5	7	1	3	3
Year 11	2	1	1	5	3	5	6	8	4	3	1	2

   (a) Work out the median and range for year 7.

   (b) Work out the median and range for year 11.

   (c) Write a sentence to compare the number of hours of TV watched each day by pupils in year 7 and year 11.

5 20 children were asked how many baths or showers they had each week (10 children from Year 8 and 10 children from Year 9). The results are below:

(a) Work out the mean and range for year 8.

(b) Work out the mean and range for year 9.

(c) Write a sentence to compare the number of baths or showers taken by children in year 8 and year 9.

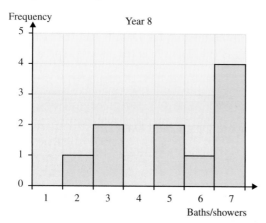
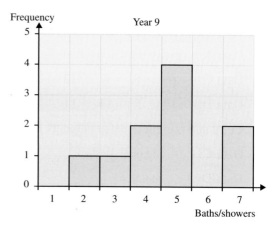

Exercise 2E

1 18 children were asked how often they ate meat each week (10 children from Year 9 and 8 children from Year 11). The results are below:

(a) Work out the mean and range for Year 9.

(b) Work out the mean and range for Year 11.

(c) Write a sentence to compare the number of times meat is eaten each week by children in Year 9 and Year 11.

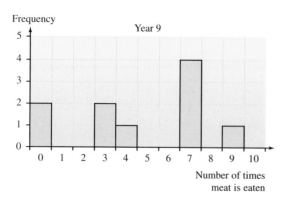
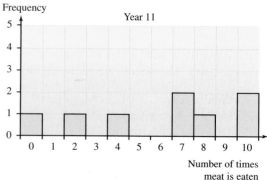

2   The heights (in metres) of the players in two rugby teams are shown below:

Catcott: 1.85, 1.95, 1.66, 1.98, 1.88, 1.91, 1.81, 2, 1.82,
         1.93, 1.88, 1.81, 1.89, 1.95, 1.86

Tipperton: 1.87, 1.99, 1.93, 1.85, 1.94, 1.86, 1.87, 1.96,
         1.92, 1.93, 1.85, 1.99, 1.97, 1.89, 1.96

(a) Find the median height for Catcott.

(b) Find the range for Catcott.

(c) Find the median height for Tipperton.

(d) Find the range for Tipperton.

(e) Which team generally has taller players?
     Give reasons for your answers.

3

Helen and Nadia record their best ten times for a swimming race. The times (in seconds) are shown below:

Helen: 75, 70, 69, 70, 74, 69, 73, 69, 67, 74

Nadia: 78, 81, 80, 76, 80, 79, 69, 79, 80, 78

(a) Find the mean time for Helen.

(b) Find the range for Helen.

(c) Find the mean time for Nadia.

(d) Find the range for Nadia.

(e) Who is generally quicker? Give reasons for your answers.

4   I can dial a computer helpline at either ALC or COMPH. For my last five calls to each company, this is how long I had to wait.

ALC	7 min	8 min	5 min	7 min	8 min
COMPH	2 min	14 min	8 min	1 min	5 min

Find the mean and the range for the waiting time for each company. Using the mean and the range, decide which company gives the better service. Explain why.

Investigation – averages and range

Part A. Look at the class register and ask the first half of the pupils for their height or weight or number of pencils/pens they have or anything of your choice.

Part B. Find the mean, median, mode and range of the data listed in Part A.

Part C. Ask the other half of the pupils for the same data.

Part D. Find the mean, median, mode and range of the data listed in Part C.

Part E. Compare the two sets of data using the averages and range.

CHECK YOURSELF ON SECTION 2.1

1 Finding the mean, median and mode

Consider 9, 13, 8, 3, 15, 4, 8, 12

(a) Find the mean (b) Find the median (c) Find the mode

2 Finding the range

Sonia has the following exam marks:

83, 69, 72, 48, 73, 58, 85, 61, 76

Write down the range for her marks.

3 Comparing 2 sets of data using averages and range

The Warriors and the Sabres are two basketball teams. The ages (in years) of the players in each team are listed below:

The Warriors: 24   22   17   28   22   19   31   27   21   27
The Sabres: 28   24   18   20   19   30   27   19   24   18

Use the mean and range to write a sentence to compare the ages of the players for the Warriors and the Sabres.

2.2 Fractions

In section 2.2 you will learn how to:

- find equivalent fractions

- find a fraction of a number

- add and subtract fractions

Equivalent fractions

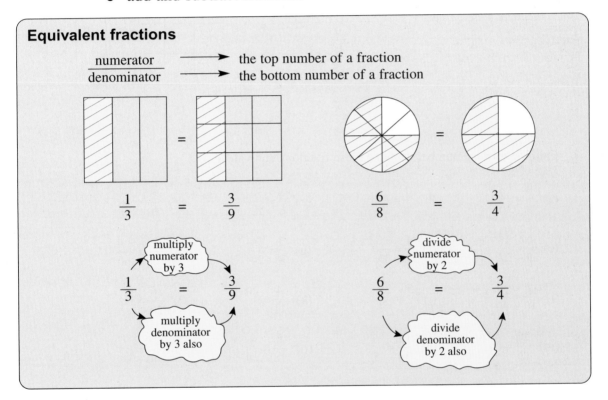

$$\frac{\text{numerator}}{\text{denominator}} \longrightarrow \text{the top number of a fraction}$$
$$\phantom{\frac{\text{numerator}}{\text{denominator}}} \longrightarrow \text{the bottom number of a fraction}$$

$$\frac{1}{3} = \frac{3}{9} \qquad \frac{6}{8} = \frac{3}{4}$$

$$\frac{1}{3} = \frac{3}{9}$$
multiply numerator by 3
multiply denominator by 3 also

$$\frac{6}{8} = \frac{3}{4}$$
divide numerator by 2
divide denominator by 2 also

When the numerator and denominator are changed into smaller numbers, we say the fraction is *cancelled down*.

(a) Cancel $\frac{9}{21}$

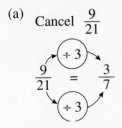

$$\frac{9}{21} = \frac{3}{7}$$
÷ 3
÷ 3

(b) Cancel $\frac{10}{15}$

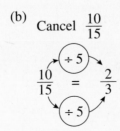

$$\frac{10}{15} = \frac{2}{3}$$
÷ 5
÷ 5

(c) Find the missing number to make these fractions equivalent.

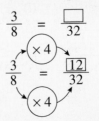

$$\frac{3}{8} = \frac{\square}{32}$$

$$\frac{3}{8} = \frac{\boxed{12}}{32}$$
× 4
× 4

66

Exercise 1M

1   Copy each diagram below then shade them in to show that the given fractions are equivalent.

(a)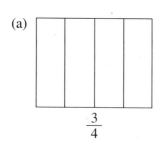

$\dfrac{3}{4}$

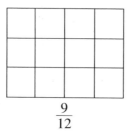

$\dfrac{9}{12}$

(b)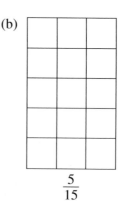

$\dfrac{5}{15}$

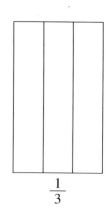

$\dfrac{1}{3}$

2   Find the missing number to make these fractions equivalent.

(a) $\dfrac{3}{4} = \dfrac{\square}{16}$

(b) $\dfrac{1}{5} = \dfrac{\square}{20}$

(c) $\dfrac{5}{6} = \dfrac{\square}{12}$

(d) $\dfrac{8}{10} = \dfrac{\square}{5}$

(e) $\dfrac{5}{9} = \dfrac{\square}{27}$

(f) $\dfrac{4}{7} = \dfrac{\square}{35}$

(g) $\dfrac{3}{8} = \dfrac{\square}{24}$

(h) $\dfrac{12}{20} = \dfrac{\square}{60}$

(i) $\dfrac{7}{10} = \dfrac{\square}{30}$

(j) $\dfrac{5}{8} = \dfrac{25}{\square}$

(k) $\dfrac{4}{11} = \dfrac{20}{\square}$

(l) $\dfrac{16}{20} = \dfrac{48}{\square}$

(m) $\dfrac{20}{25} = \dfrac{4}{\square}$

(n) $\dfrac{18}{30} = \dfrac{\square}{5}$

(o) $\dfrac{8}{18} = \dfrac{4}{\square}$

(p) $\dfrac{28}{40} = \dfrac{7}{\square}$

3   Cancel down each fraction to its simplest terms.

(a) $\dfrac{6}{10}$

(b) $\dfrac{10}{30}$

(c) $\dfrac{9}{15}$

(d) $\dfrac{7}{35}$

(e) $\dfrac{24}{30}$

(f) $\dfrac{28}{36}$

(g) $\dfrac{20}{30}$

(h) $\dfrac{14}{21}$

(i) $\dfrac{12}{18}$

(j) $\dfrac{27}{45}$

(k) $\dfrac{35}{45}$

(l) $\dfrac{20}{24}$

(m) $\dfrac{40}{50}$

(n) $\dfrac{18}{63}$

(o) $\dfrac{33}{77}$

(p) $\dfrac{45}{60}$

(q) $\dfrac{54}{81}$

(r) $\dfrac{18}{72}$

(s) $\dfrac{56}{72}$

(t) $\dfrac{32}{48}$

(u) $\dfrac{75}{100}$

(v) $\dfrac{36}{63}$

(w) $\dfrac{36}{96}$

(x) $\dfrac{72}{108}$

(y) $\dfrac{75}{135}$

4 In each part of this question, one fraction is not equivalent to the others. Write down the fraction which is the odd one out.

(a) $\dfrac{4}{6}, \dfrac{6}{10}, \dfrac{12}{18}, \dfrac{2}{3}, \dfrac{10}{15}$

(b) $\dfrac{9}{24}, \dfrac{15}{40}, \dfrac{3}{8}, \dfrac{5}{9}, \dfrac{12}{32}$

(c) $\dfrac{15}{18}, \dfrac{35}{42}, \dfrac{50}{60}, \dfrac{40}{48}, \dfrac{32}{40}$

(d) $\dfrac{16}{28}, \dfrac{36}{63}, \dfrac{44}{77}, \dfrac{20}{45}, \dfrac{28}{49}$

Exercise 1E

Example: In the table given below, pick out all the letters above the fractions which are equivalent to one half $\left(\dfrac{1}{2}\right)$.

C	Q	E	A	Y	P	R	N	H	F	letters
$\dfrac{5}{10}$	$\dfrac{3}{4}$	$\dfrac{2}{4}$	$\dfrac{21}{42}$	$\dfrac{1}{5}$	$\dfrac{5}{12}$	$\dfrac{6}{12}$	$\dfrac{3}{6}$	$\dfrac{4}{7}$	$\dfrac{5}{10}$	fractions

The letters are C, E, A, R, N, F

because... $\dfrac{5}{10}, \dfrac{2}{4}, \dfrac{21}{42}, \dfrac{6}{12}, \dfrac{3}{6}, \dfrac{5}{10}$ are all the same as $\dfrac{1}{2}$.

Now rearrange the letters to make the name of a country.

C, E, A, R, N, F $\longrightarrow$ FRANCE

In the questions below, find the fractions in the table which are equivalent to the given fraction. Rearrange the letters to make a word using the clue.

1 $\left(\dfrac{1}{10}, \text{drink}\right)$

R	E	F	E	F	T	O	W	C	A
$\dfrac{2}{20}$	$\dfrac{5}{60}$	$\dfrac{9}{108}$	$\dfrac{5}{50}$	$\dfrac{12}{96}$	$\dfrac{3}{30}$	$\dfrac{4}{20}$	$\dfrac{10}{100}$	$\dfrac{6}{50}$	$\dfrac{7}{70}$

2 $\left(\dfrac{2}{3}, \text{country}\right)$

A	N	E	R	S	B	I	Z	Q	L
$\dfrac{4}{6}$	$\dfrac{9}{12}$	$\dfrac{14}{22}$	$\dfrac{60}{90}$	$\dfrac{16}{25}$	$\dfrac{8}{12}$	$\dfrac{22}{33}$	$\dfrac{20}{30}$	$\dfrac{32}{49}$	$\dfrac{12}{18}$

3 $\left(\dfrac{3}{5}, \text{sport}\right)$

T	G	U	F	O	Y	R	A	B	L
$\dfrac{18}{36}$	$\dfrac{36}{60}$	$\dfrac{27}{45}$	$\dfrac{30}{40}$	$\dfrac{20}{25}$	$\dfrac{12}{20}$	$\dfrac{9}{15}$	$\dfrac{12}{18}$	$\dfrac{6}{10}$	$\dfrac{18}{21}$

4 $\left(\dfrac{1}{3}, \text{city}\right)$

L	P	A	U	R	I	D	N	S	B
$\dfrac{3}{9}$	$\dfrac{2}{8}$	$\dfrac{5}{7}$	$\dfrac{4}{12}$	$\dfrac{7}{20}$	$\dfrac{6}{18}$	$\dfrac{8}{24}$	$\dfrac{10}{30}$	$\dfrac{3}{5}$	$\dfrac{5}{15}$

5 $\left(\dfrac{5}{9}, \text{clothing}\right)$

T	M	S	R	K	C	E	H	O	I
$\dfrac{100}{180}$	$\dfrac{21}{70}$	$\dfrac{20}{36}$	$\dfrac{35}{63}$	$\dfrac{18}{21}$	$\dfrac{40}{70}$	$\dfrac{24}{45}$	$\dfrac{45}{81}$	$\dfrac{140}{160}$	$\dfrac{15}{27}$

6 $\left(\dfrac{3}{4}, \text{fruit}\right)$

B	O	P	A	E	I	H	C	R	T
$\dfrac{6}{7}$	$\dfrac{12}{16}$	$\dfrac{33}{44}$	$\dfrac{6}{8}$	$\dfrac{6}{9}$	$\dfrac{30}{40}$	$\dfrac{18}{25}$	$\dfrac{15}{20}$	$\dfrac{36}{48}$	$\dfrac{9}{12}$

7   Now make up your own question like question 6 and test it on a friend.

8   Ask your teacher for card. Cut out 24 cards as shown. On each pair of cards write down two equivalent fractions.

Now play a game with 2, 3 or 4 players using these equivalent fraction cards.

How to play:

- Shuffle the cards, place them face down in a pattern of 6 rows by 4 columns.

- Decide who will go first.

- Each turn requires a player to turn over a pair of cards.

- If the pair of cards are equivalent such as $\frac{1}{5}$ and $\frac{2}{10}$ the player keeps the pair. If the cards are not equivalent turn the cards face down again.

- Try to remember which cards are where!

- If you find a pair you get another go, the player with the most pairs when no cards are left is the winner.

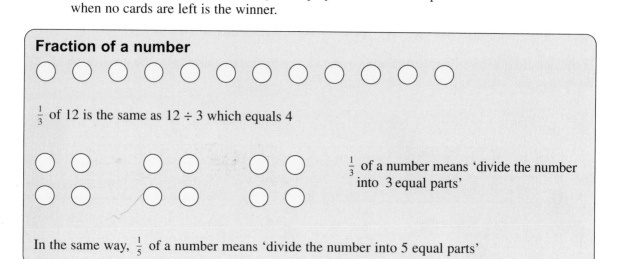

Fraction of a number

○ ○ ○ ○ ○ ○ ○ ○ ○ ○ ○ ○

$\frac{1}{3}$ of 12 is the same as $12 \div 3$ which equals 4

○ ○   ○ ○   ○ ○ $\frac{1}{3}$ of a number means 'divide the number into 3 equal parts'

○ ○   ○ ○   ○ ○

In the same way, $\frac{1}{5}$ of a number means 'divide the number into 5 equal parts'

Exercise 2M

1   Work out

(a) $\frac{1}{3}$ of 15   (b) $\frac{1}{2}$ of 18   (c) $\frac{1}{6}$ of 24   (d) $\frac{1}{10}$ of 80

(e) $\frac{1}{4}$ of 28   (f) $\frac{1}{7}$ of 42   (g) $\frac{1}{8}$ of 72   (h) $\frac{1}{20}$ of 100

2   Jack has saved £21. He spends $\frac{1}{3}$ of his money.

   (a) How much money does he spend?

   (b) How much money does he have left?

3   Tania has 30 old toys. She gives away $\frac{1}{6}$ of these toys.

   (a) How many toys does she give away?

   (b) How many toys does she have left?

4   Work out

   (a) $\frac{1}{4}$ of 12 cm   (b) $\frac{1}{6}$ of £18   (c) $\frac{1}{3}$ of 36 cm

   (d) $\frac{1}{2}$ of 56 litres   (e) $\frac{1}{5}$ of £45   (f) $\frac{1}{6}$ of £48

   (g) $\frac{1}{10}$ of 250 kg   (h) $\frac{1}{8}$ of 56 cm   (i) $\frac{1}{9}$ of 81 cm

   (j) $\frac{1}{20}$ of 340 kg   (k) $\frac{1}{12}$ of 180 kg   (l) $\frac{1}{15}$ of 300 m

   (m) $\frac{1}{100}$ of 7000 litres   (n) $\frac{1}{50}$ of £4000   (o) $\frac{1}{30}$ of 270 kg

5   1 hour = 60 minutes

   Find

   (a) $\frac{1}{3}$ of an hour   (b) $\frac{1}{10}$ of an hour   (c) $\frac{1}{15}$ of an hour

6   Find each missing number below

   (a) $\frac{1}{\Box}$ of 27 = 9   (b) $\frac{1}{\Box}$ of 40 = 8   (c) $\frac{1}{\Box}$ of 38 = 19

(d) $\frac{1}{\square}$ of 16 = 4   (e) $\frac{1}{\square}$ of 50 = 5   (f) $\frac{1}{\square}$ of 36 = 9

(g) $\frac{1}{\square}$ of 64 = 8   (h) $\frac{1}{\square}$ of 120 = 40   (i) $\frac{1}{\square}$ of 60 = 12

Work out $\frac{3}{5}$ of £80

Find $\frac{1}{5}$ of 80 first, so 80 ÷ 5 = 16

$\frac{1}{5}$ of 80 = 16, so $\frac{3}{5}$ of 80 = 16 × 3 = 48

So $\frac{3}{5}$ of £80 = £48

Exercise 2E

1 Work out   (a) $\frac{1}{5}$ of 35   (b) $\frac{4}{5}$ of 35

2 Work out   (a) $\frac{1}{8}$ of 72   (b) $\frac{3}{8}$ of 72

3 Work out

(a) $\frac{3}{4}$ of 20   (b) $\frac{5}{8}$ of 24   (c) $\frac{7}{10}$ of 90   (d) $\frac{2}{5}$ of 55

(e) $\frac{5}{6}$ of 42   (f) $\frac{4}{9}$ of 18   (g) $\frac{2}{3}$ of 48   (h) $\frac{5}{7}$ of 56

4 Mario has an order for 60 pizzas. If $\frac{5}{12}$ of his pizzas must be vegetarian, how many will be non-vegetarian?

5 A petrol tank in a car holds 56 litres when full. How much petrol is in the tank when it is $\frac{3}{8}$ full?

6 Full marks in a science test were 80. How many marks did Hannah get if she got $\frac{9}{10}$ of full marks?

7   Here are calculations with letters. Put the answers in order of size, smallest first. Write down the letters to make a word.

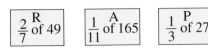

$\frac{2}{7}$ of 49 R $\frac{1}{11}$ of 165 A $\frac{1}{3}$ of 27 P

$\frac{4}{9}$ of 45 M $\frac{3}{4}$ of 16 Y $\frac{5}{6}$ of 300 D $\frac{5}{8}$ of 96 I

8   Work out

(a) $\frac{2}{3}$ of 45 kg

(b) $\frac{4}{5}$ of 90 cm

(c) $\frac{5}{9}$ of £108

(d) $\frac{4}{7}$ of £63

(e) $\frac{5}{8}$ of 240 kg

(f) $\frac{3}{20}$ of 160 m

(g) $\frac{5}{12}$ of 48 cm

(h) $\frac{8}{9}$ of 54 m

(i) $\frac{37}{100}$ of £400

9   A table is bought for £217 and sold at a car bootsale for $\frac{3}{7}$ of the original price. How much was the table sold for?

10 Find each missing number below.

(a) $\frac{\square}{\square}$ of 30 = 18

(b) $\frac{\square}{3}$ of 15 = 10

(c) $\frac{3}{\square}$ of 40 = 12

(d) $\frac{3}{\square}$ of 28 = 21

(e) $\frac{4}{5}$ of $\square$ = 16

(f) $\frac{7}{10}$ of $\square$ = 28

11 Draw a copy of the rectangle.
    (a) Shade in $\frac{1}{3}$ of the squares.

(b) Draw crosses in $\frac{1}{5}$ of the unshaded squares.

    (c) How many squares are neither shaded nor have crosses in them?

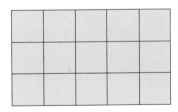

Adding and subtracting fractions

Fractions can be added or subtracted when they have the same denominator.

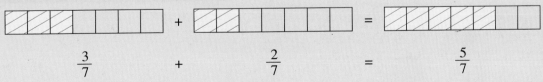

$\frac{3}{7}$ + $\frac{2}{7}$ = $\frac{5}{7}$

Only add the numerators, *not* the denominators

If fractions do not have the same denominator, change them into *equivalent fractions* which do have the same denominator before adding or subtracting.

(a) $\dfrac{1}{6} + \dfrac{1}{3}$

$= \dfrac{1}{6} + \dfrac{2}{6}$

$= \dfrac{3}{6} = \dfrac{1}{2}$

(b) $\dfrac{7}{8} - \dfrac{3}{4}$

$= \dfrac{7}{8} - \dfrac{6}{8}$

$= \dfrac{1}{8}$

(c) $\dfrac{2}{5} + \dfrac{3}{7}$

$= \dfrac{14}{35} + \dfrac{15}{35}$

$= \dfrac{29}{35}$

Cancel final answer if you can

Exercise 3M

Work out

1. $\dfrac{1}{7} + \dfrac{3}{7}$

2. $\dfrac{1}{4} + \dfrac{2}{4}$

3. $\dfrac{2}{8} + \dfrac{3}{8}$

4. $\dfrac{4}{5} - \dfrac{3}{5}$

5. $\dfrac{8}{9} - \dfrac{6}{9}$

6. $\dfrac{7}{10} + \dfrac{2}{10}$

7. $\dfrac{2}{9} + \dfrac{3}{9}$

8. $\dfrac{1}{25} + \dfrac{2}{25}$

9. $\dfrac{5}{7} - \dfrac{2}{7}$

10. $\dfrac{3}{8} + \dfrac{3}{8}$

11. Harry gave $\dfrac{2}{7}$ of his money to his son and $\dfrac{4}{7}$ of his money to his daughter. What fraction of his money did he give away in total?

12. Marie photographs $\dfrac{4}{9}$ of a herd of elephants and Wes photographs another $\dfrac{1}{9}$ of the herd.

What total fraction of the herd of elephants was photographed?

13. Copy and complete each box below

(a) $\dfrac{2}{3} = \dfrac{\square}{9}$ so $\dfrac{1}{9} + \dfrac{2}{3} = \dfrac{1}{9} + \dfrac{\square}{9} = \dfrac{\square}{9}$

(b) $\dfrac{1}{2} = \dfrac{\square}{8}$ so $\dfrac{7}{8} - \dfrac{1}{2} = \dfrac{7}{8} - \dfrac{\square}{8} = \dfrac{\square}{8}$

(c) $\dfrac{7}{10} = \dfrac{\square}{20}$ so $\dfrac{7}{10} - \dfrac{9}{20} = \dfrac{\square}{20} - \dfrac{9}{20} = \dfrac{\square}{20} = \dfrac{\square}{4}$

In questions 14 to 29 , change one of the fractions to an equivalent fraction first before adding or subtracting.

14 $\frac{2}{5} + \frac{3}{10}$

15 $\frac{1}{4} - \frac{1}{8}$

16 $\frac{3}{4} - \frac{1}{2}$

17 $\frac{3}{8} - \frac{1}{4}$

18 $\frac{5}{8} + \frac{1}{4}$

19 $\frac{1}{4} + \frac{1}{2}$

20 $\frac{1}{16} + \frac{1}{2}$

21 $\frac{5}{8} - \frac{1}{2}$

22 $\frac{4}{5} + \frac{1}{10}$

23 $\frac{3}{8} + \frac{1}{2}$

24 $\frac{7}{20} - \frac{1}{10}$

25 $\frac{1}{6} + \frac{1}{3}$

26 $\frac{5}{9} - \frac{7}{18}$

27 $\frac{27}{50} - \frac{3}{10}$

28 $\frac{5}{12} + \frac{1}{3}$

29 $\frac{19}{40} - \frac{3}{8}$

Exercise 3E

1
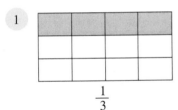
$\frac{1}{3}$
$+$
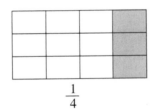
$\frac{1}{4}$
$=$
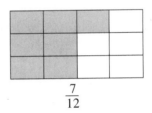
$\frac{7}{12}$

Draw similar diagrams to show that $\frac{2}{3} + \frac{1}{4} = \frac{11}{12}$.

2 Copy and complete each box below.

(a) $\frac{1}{2} + \frac{1}{5}$

$= \frac{\Box}{10} + \frac{\Box}{10}$

$= \frac{\Box}{10}$

(b) $\frac{2}{3} + \frac{1}{4}$

$= \frac{\Box}{12} + \frac{\Box}{12}$

$= \frac{\Box}{12}$

(c) $\frac{7}{8} - \frac{2}{3}$

$= \frac{\Box}{24} - \frac{\Box}{24}$

$= \frac{\Box}{24}$

In questions 3 to 14 , work out the answers and cancel if necessary.

3 $\frac{3}{5} + \frac{1}{4}$

4 $\frac{1}{6} + \frac{3}{4}$

5 $\frac{3}{4} - \frac{1}{3}$

6 $\frac{2}{3} - \frac{4}{7}$

7 $\frac{3}{8} + \frac{2}{5}$

8 $\frac{5}{6} - \frac{5}{8}$

9 $\frac{9}{10} - \frac{7}{9}$

10 $\frac{3}{5} + \frac{3}{8}$

11 $\dfrac{11}{12} - \dfrac{1}{5}$

12 $\dfrac{5}{7} + \dfrac{2}{9}$

13 $\dfrac{4}{9} + \dfrac{1}{5}$

14 $\dfrac{7}{10} - \dfrac{2}{3}$

15 Work out

(a) $\dfrac{1}{2} + \dfrac{1}{3} + \dfrac{1}{12}$

(b) $\dfrac{3}{5} + \dfrac{1}{4} - \dfrac{7}{10}$

(c) $\dfrac{5}{6} + \dfrac{1}{10} - \dfrac{4}{5}$

16

Ruby goes shopping. She spends $\dfrac{1}{3}$ of her money on shoes and $\dfrac{1}{5}$ of her money on shirts.

(a) What fraction of her money has she spent in total?

(b) What fraction of her money does she have left?

17 Find the perimeter of this rectangle.

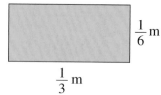

$\dfrac{1}{6}$ m

$\dfrac{1}{3}$ m

=

18 The fraction sum $\dfrac{1}{3} + \dfrac{4}{6}$ is made from four different digits and the sum is 1

Find other fraction sums using four different digits so that the sum is 1

2.3   Fractions, decimals, percentages

In section 2.3 you will learn how to:

● convert between fractions, decimals and percentages

Changing fractions to decimals

You should know that:

$\dfrac{1}{10} = 0.1$ $\dfrac{2}{10} = 0.2$ $\dfrac{3}{100} = 0.03$ $\dfrac{1}{4} = 0.25$ $\dfrac{1}{2} = 0.5$ $\dfrac{3}{4} = 0.75$

Convert denominator to 10, 100, etc.

$$\frac{1}{5} = \frac{2}{10} = 0.2 \qquad\qquad \frac{1}{25} = \frac{4}{100} = 0.04 \qquad\qquad \frac{9}{20} = \frac{45}{100} = 0.45$$

Cancelling fractions can help.

$$\frac{12}{16} = \frac{3}{4} = 0.75 \qquad\qquad\qquad \frac{60}{240} = \frac{1}{4} = 0.25$$

Exercise 1M

Convert these fractions into decimals.

1 $\dfrac{7}{10}$ 2 $\dfrac{39}{100}$ 3 $\dfrac{1}{2}$ 4 $\dfrac{7}{100}$ 5 $\dfrac{9}{10}$

6 $\dfrac{13}{100}$ 7 $\dfrac{1}{4}$ 8 $\dfrac{1}{100}$ 9 $\dfrac{41}{100}$ 10 $\dfrac{3}{4}$

Copy and complete the boxes.

11 $\dfrac{7}{20} = \dfrac{35}{100} = 0 \cdot \square\square$ 12 $\dfrac{3}{20} = \dfrac{\square}{100} = 0 \cdot \square\square$

13 $\dfrac{4}{5} = \dfrac{\square}{10} = 0 \cdot \square$ 14 $\dfrac{3}{12} = \dfrac{\square}{4} = 0 \cdot \square\square$

15 $\dfrac{3}{5} = \dfrac{\square}{10} = 0 \cdot \square$ 16 $\dfrac{4}{25} = \dfrac{\square}{100} = 0 \cdot \square\square$

Convert these fractions into decimals.

17 $\dfrac{11}{20}$ 18 $\dfrac{2}{5}$ 19 $\dfrac{7}{25}$ 20 $\dfrac{27}{36}$ 21 $\dfrac{17}{20}$

22 $\dfrac{23}{25}$ 23 $\dfrac{19}{25}$ 24 $\dfrac{150}{200}$ 25 $\dfrac{120}{200}$ 26 $\dfrac{18}{72}$

27 Copy and complete the table.

Fraction	$\frac{2}{5}$		$\frac{71}{100}$		$\frac{1}{50}$		$\frac{9}{20}$
Decimal		0.03		0.45		0.53	

Exercise 1E

Convert the fractions to decimals and then write the numbers in order of size, smallest first.

1   $\frac{8}{20}$, 0.3, $\frac{9}{25}$ 2 $\frac{3}{4}$, $\frac{3}{5}$, 0.7

3   $\frac{12}{16}$, 0.7, $\frac{4}{5}$ 4 $\frac{1}{5}$, 0.15, $\frac{1}{20}$

Convert these fractions into decimals.

5   $\frac{19}{1000}$ 6 $\frac{1}{125}$ 7 $\frac{17}{125}$ 8 $\frac{54}{72}$ 9 $\frac{150}{2000}$

10   $\frac{7}{250}$ 11 $\frac{19}{76}$ 12 $\frac{89}{500}$ 13 $\frac{36}{3000}$ 14 $\frac{173}{10000}$

Changing decimals into fractions

$0.6 = \frac{6}{10} = \frac{3}{5}$ $0.27 = \frac{27}{100}$

$0.65 = \frac{65}{100} = \frac{13}{20}$ $0.04 = \frac{4}{100} = \frac{1}{25}$

cancel down the fractions if possible

Exercise 2M

Change these decimals into fractions.

1   0.3   2   0.7   3   0.01   4   0.09   5   0.13

6   0.51   7   0.69   8   0.9   9   0.23   10   0.37

11   0.89   12   2.3   13   4.73   14   5.01   15   6.7

Copy and complete.

16   $0.4 = \frac{\square}{10} = \frac{\square}{5}$ 17 $0.05 = \frac{\square}{100} = \frac{\square}{\square}$ 18 $0.08 = \frac{8}{\square} = \frac{\square}{25}$

19   $0.12 = \frac{\square}{100} = \frac{\square}{\square}$ 20 $0.37 = \frac{\square}{\square}$

Exercise 2E

1. Carol and Oscar each have a bar of chocolate. Carol has eaten 0.85 of her bar and Oscar has eaten $\frac{17}{20}$ of his bar.

   Who has eaten the most chocolate?

Change these decimals into fractions (cancel down fractions when possible).

2 0.8	3 0.05	4 0.08	5 0.25	6 0.24
7 0.02	8 0.4	9 0.32	10 0.15	11 0.18
12 0.75	13 3.2	14 4.5	15 0.56	16 6.04
17 7.12	18 3.75	19 8.6	20 2.95	21 4.36

Changing fractions and percentages

(a) Percentage to fraction
('per cent' means 'out of 100')

$$60\% = \frac{60}{100} = \frac{3}{5}$$

$$24\% = \frac{24}{100} = \frac{6}{25}$$

$$2\% = \frac{2}{100} = \frac{1}{50}$$

(b) Fraction to percentage
(make the denominator equal to 100)

$$\frac{4}{5} = \frac{80}{100} = 80\%$$

$$\frac{3}{20} = \frac{15}{100} = 15\%$$

$$3\frac{1}{2} = \frac{350}{100} = 350\%$$

- Learn the following:

$$\frac{1}{4} = 25\% \qquad \frac{1}{8} = 12\frac{1}{2}\% \qquad \frac{1}{3} = 33\frac{1}{3}\% \qquad \frac{2}{3} = 66\frac{2}{3}\%$$

Exercise 3M

1. Change these percentages into fractions. Cancel down answers where possible.

   (a) 40%   (b) 7%   (c) 22%   (d) 80%   (e) 5%

   (f) 89%   (g) 10%   (h) 28%   (i) 4%   (j) 35%

2   Copy and complete the following.

(a) $\dfrac{2}{5} = \dfrac{40}{100} = \square\%$

(b) $\dfrac{9}{20} = \dfrac{45}{100} = \square\%$

(c) $\dfrac{3}{25} = \dfrac{\square}{100} = \square\%$

(d) $\dfrac{11}{20} = \dfrac{\square}{100} = \square\%$

(e) $\dfrac{9}{10} = \dfrac{\square}{100} = \square\%$

(f) $\dfrac{19}{50} = \dfrac{\square}{100} = \square\%$

3   Here are some test marks. Change them to percentages.

(a) $\dfrac{17}{20}$

(b) $\dfrac{13}{25}$

(c) $\dfrac{46}{50}$

4

During one season, Lewis won 70% of his races. What *fraction* of his races did he win?

5   Megan spent 36% of her money on the first day of her holiday. What *fraction* of her money did she spend?

6   Write down each fraction with its equivalent percentage.

(a) $\dfrac{1}{3}$

(b) $\dfrac{3}{4}$

(c) $\dfrac{2}{3}$

(d) $\dfrac{1}{8}$

7   Write down which fractions are greater than the given percentage

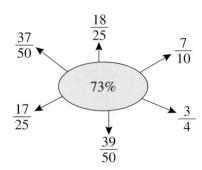

8   Rosa was absent from school for $\frac{1}{25}$ of the Autumn term. What *percentage* of the Autumn term was she absent for?

9   One in five people in Henton own a laptop computer. What *percentage* of people in Henton own a laptop?

Changing decimals, fractions and percentages

Exercise 3E

1   Copy and complete to change the following decimals into percentages.

(a) $0.37 = \dfrac{\square}{100} = \square\%$

(b) $0.17 = \dfrac{\square}{100} = \square\%$

(c) $0.03 = \dfrac{\square}{100} = \square\%$

(d) $0.4 = \dfrac{4}{10} = \dfrac{\square}{100} = \square\%$

2   Change these percentages into decimals.

(a) 29%

(b) 52%

(c) 80%

(d) 6%

(e) 3%

(f) 13%

(g) 130%

(h) 240%

3   Copy and complete the table.

	fraction	decimal	percentage
(a)		0.3	
(b)			55%
(c)			12%
(d)	$\frac{1}{20}$		
(e)		0.48	

4   Jack scores 12 out of 25 in a Science test and Marie scores 46%. Who got the higher mark and by how much?

5   Christy ate 0.4 of an extra large pizza and Rob ate $\frac{9}{20}$ of the pizza. What percentage of the pizza was not eaten?

6 Each fraction, decimal or percentage has an equivalent in the list with letters.
Find the letters to make a sentence.

(a) $\boxed{50\%, \frac{1}{4}, 10\%, 0.2, 0.11}$ $\boxed{17\%, 11\%}$ $\boxed{0.75, 99\%, \frac{1}{10}}$ $\boxed{20\%, \frac{1}{4}, \frac{1}{8}, 0.7}$

(b) $\boxed{\frac{7}{10}, 0.8, 45\%, \frac{17}{100}, 0.5, \frac{1}{4}, \frac{10}{25}, 0.11}$ $\boxed{\frac{3}{6}, \frac{4}{16}, 0.05, 80\%}$ $\boxed{\frac{22}{200}, 0.8, 75\%, 11\%, \frac{8}{10}}$

(c) $\boxed{17\%}$ $\boxed{45\%, 0.25, 75\%}$ $\boxed{0.11, \frac{99}{100}, \frac{4}{10}, \frac{41}{50}, \frac{400}{500}}$ $\boxed{\frac{3}{20}, \frac{2}{16}, \frac{99}{100}, \frac{1}{3}, 0.4, 0.8, \frac{10}{20}, 11\%}$

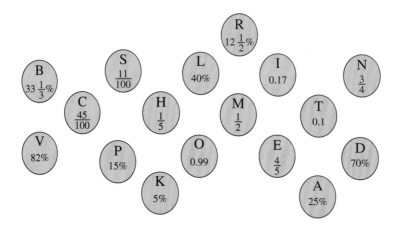

Investigation – Escape

In the town of Decford a prison has 10 cells. All the cells have one prisoner in them and all the cell doors are locked.

- A jailer walks from cell 1 to cell 10 and unlocks each door.

- The jailer returns to the start and locks every second door.

- The jailer returns to the start and changes the state of every third door (ie. cells 3, 6, 9). '*Changes the state of a door*' means '*lock if unlocked*' or '*unlock if locked*'.

- The jailer repeats the process for every fourth door then fifth door, sixth, seventh, eighth, ninth and finally tenth.

  (a) How many prisoners can now escape through an unlocked door? Write down the cell numbers of those prisoners who can escape.

  (b) The prison in the city of Centford has 100 cells. A jailer repeats the above process from changing the state of every door then every second door, etc. to changing the state of every 100th door. How many prisoners can now escape through an unlocked door? Write down the cell numbers of those prisoners who can escape. Can you explain *why* these cell doors are unlocked at the end?

CHECK YOURSELF ON SECTIONS 2.2 AND 2.3

1   Finding equivalent fractions

Find the missing number to make these fractions equivalent.

(a) $\dfrac{1}{6} = \dfrac{\square}{42}$

(b) $\dfrac{7}{9} = \dfrac{28}{\square}$

(c) $\dfrac{32}{48} = \dfrac{2}{\square}$

(d) $\dfrac{5}{7} = \dfrac{30}{\square}$

(e) Write down which fractions are equivalent to $\dfrac{7}{8}$.

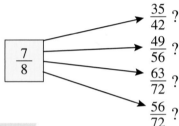

2   Finding a fraction of a number

Work out

(a) $\dfrac{1}{6}$ of 24

(b) $\dfrac{5}{6}$ of 24

(c) $\dfrac{3}{5}$ of 70

(d) $\dfrac{2}{7}$ of 56

3   Adding and Subtracting fractions

Work out

(a) $\dfrac{8}{9} - \dfrac{1}{9}$

(b) $\dfrac{2}{5} + \dfrac{3}{7}$

(c) $\dfrac{3}{4} - \dfrac{2}{3}$

(d) $\dfrac{3}{4} + \dfrac{1}{16}$

4   Converting between fractions, decimals and percentages

There are four groups of equivalent fractions, decimals and percentages below. Write down each group (beware: there are two odd ones out). For example $\frac{1}{2}$, 0.5, 50% would be a group.

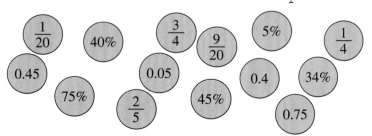

2.4 Angles

In section 2.4 you will learn how to:

- label angles
- measure and draw angles with a protractor
- estimate angles
- identify acute, obtuse and reflex angles
- calculate angles on a straight line and at a point
- calculate angles in a triangle

Labelling angles

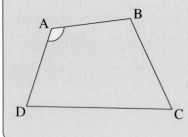

This is called angle DAB or angle BAD. We write this as DÂB or BÂD. Angles are labelled with capital letters and the middle letter wears a 'hat' to indicate an angle.

Exercise 1M

Name the shaded angles below:

1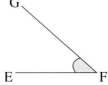

2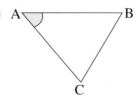

3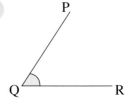

4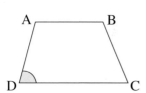

5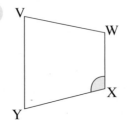

6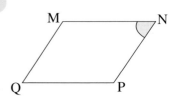

Write down the size of each angle stated below:

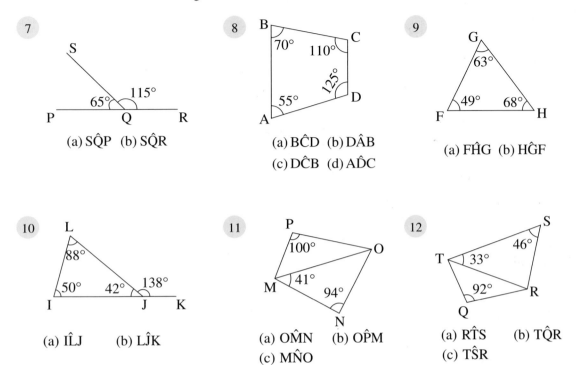

7

S

65° 115°

P Q R

(a) SQ̂P (b) SQ̂R

8

B
70° 110° C
125°
55°
A D

(a) BĈD (b) DÂB
(c) DĈB (d) AD̂C

9

G
63°
49° 68°
F H

(a) FĤG (b) HĜF

10

L
88°
50° 42° 138°
I J K

(a) IL̂J   (b) LĴK

11

P
100° O
41°
M
94°
N

(a) OM̂N   (b) OP̂M
(c) MN̂O

12

S
46°
T 33°
92°
Q R

(a) RT̂S   (b) TQ̂R
(c) TŜR

Exercise 1E

Give the measurement of each angle listed.
Remember to read the correct scale. Some questions are done for you, to remind you of this.

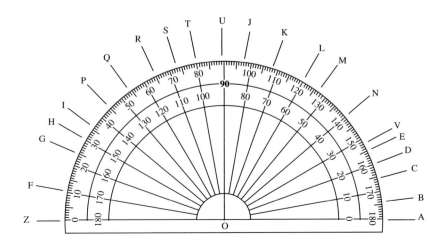

1	AÔD = 20°	2	AÔN =	3	AÔL = 60°	4	AÔK =
5	ZÔF =	6	ZÔP = 45°	7	ZÔR =	8	ZÔT = 80°
9	ZÔI =	10	ZÔG =	11	AÔC =	12	AÔV =
13	AÔQ = 126°	14	AÔP =	15	AÔF =	16	AÔB =
17	ZÔH =	18	ZÔB =	19	ZÔC =	20	ZÔD =
21	AÔG =	22	AÔH =	23	AÔI =	24	AÔM =
25	AÔR =	26	ZÔE =	27	ZÔJ =	28	ZÔK =
29	ZÔL =	30	ZÔM =	31	AÔE =	32	AÔJ =
33	AÔU =	34	AÔS =	35	ZÔN =	36	ZÔQ =
37	ZÔS =	38	ZÔU =	39	ZÔV =	40	AÔT =

Exercise 2M

Use a protractor to measure the angles indicated.

1
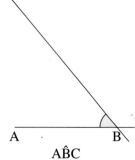
AB̂C

2
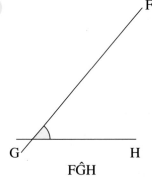
FĜH

3
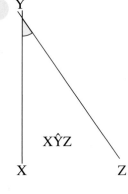
XŶZ

4
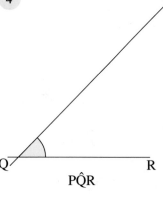
PQ̂R

5

DF̂E

6
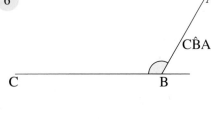
CB̂A

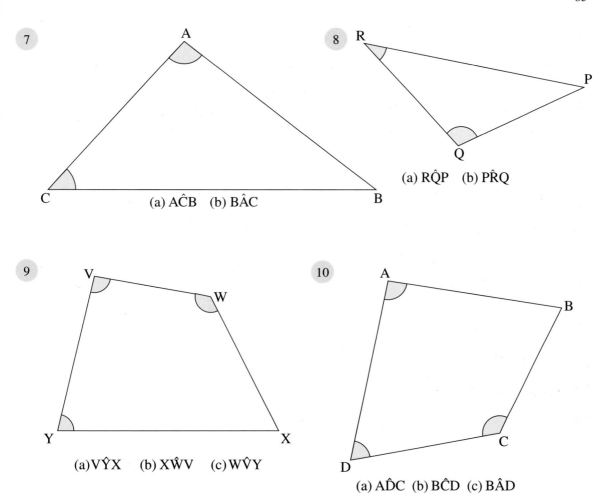

7   (a) AĈB   (b) BÂC

8   (a) RQ̂P   (b) PR̂Q

9   (a) VŶX   (b) XŴV   (c) WV̂Y

10   (a) AD̂C   (b) BĈD   (c) BÂD

Drawing angles with a protractor

Exercise 2E

Use a protractor to draw the following angles accurately.

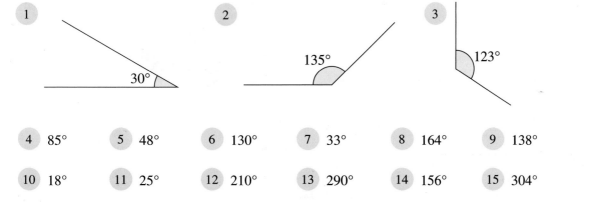

1   30°

2   135°

3   123°

4   85°   5   48°   6   130°   7   33°   8   164°   9   138°

10   18°   11   25°   12   210°   13   290°   14   156°   15   304°

Estimating angles

Exercise 3M

State whether these angles are correctly or incorrectly labelled. Do *not* measure the angles.
Estimate! Where the angles are clearly incorrect, write down an estimate for the correct angle.

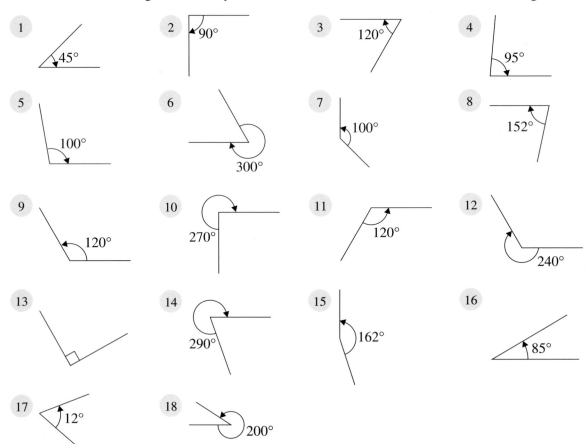

19 Find a partner. One person draws an angle then both of you estimate the size of the angle. Now use a protractor to measure the angle. The person with the closest estimate scores one point.

Score a bonus point if your estimate is exactly the correct size. Draw as many angles as time allows. Who has the best eye for estimating?

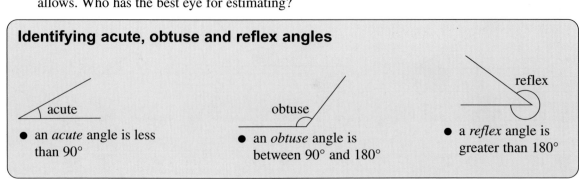

Identifying acute, obtuse and reflex angles

acute

obtuse

reflex

- an *acute* angle is less than 90°
- an *obtuse* angle is between 90° and 180°
- a *reflex* angle is greater than 180°

Exercise 3E

For each angle shown in Exercise 3M, state whether the angle marked is acute, obtuse, reflex or a right angle.

Calculating angles on a straight line and at a point

- **Angles on a straight line**

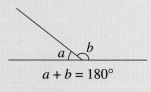

$$a + b = 180°$$

The angles on a straight line add up to 180°

- **Angles at a point**

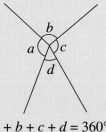

$$a + b + c + d = 360°$$

The angles at a point add up to 360°

- **Vertically opposite angles**

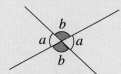

The opposite angles are equal when two lines intersect

(a)

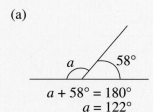

$$a + 58° = 180°$$
$$a = 122°$$

(b)

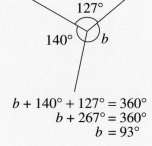

$$b + 140° + 127° = 360°$$
$$b + 267° = 360°$$
$$b = 93°$$

(c)

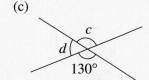

$c = 130°$ (vertically opposite angles)

$d + 130° = 180°$ (angles on a straight line)

$d = 50°$

Exercise 4M

Find the angles marked with letters.

1

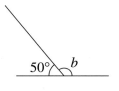

2

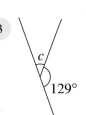

3

4

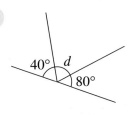

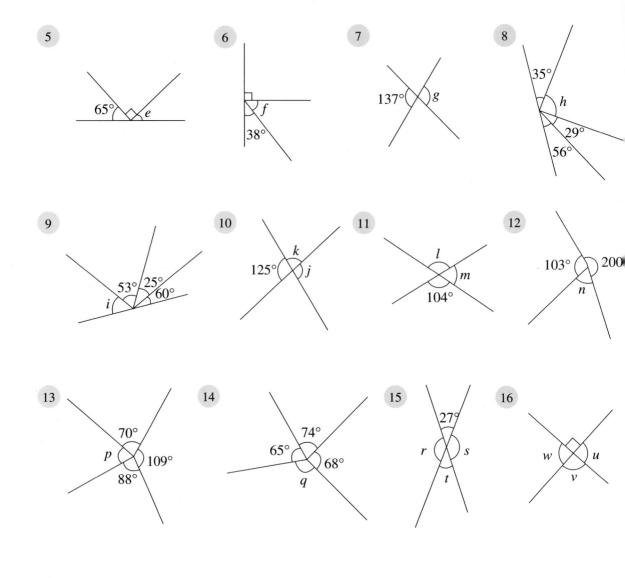

5 65° e

6 f 38°

7 137° g

8 35° h 29° 56°

9 53° 25° 60° i

10 125° k j

11 l m 104°

12 103° 200 n

13 70° p 109° 88°

14 74° 65° 68° q

15 27° r s t

16 w u v

Exercise 4E

Find the angles marked with letters.

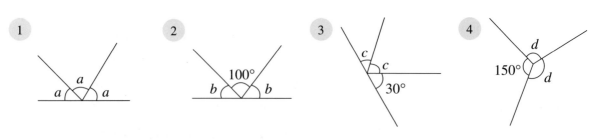

1 a a a

2 100° b b

3 c c 30°

4 d 150° d

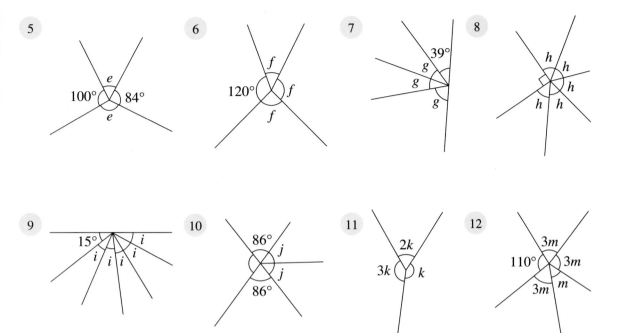

5 $100°$ e e $84°$

6 $120°$ f f f

7 $39°$ g g g

8 h h h h h

Calculating angles in a triangle

Draw a triangle of any shape on a piece of card and cut it out accurately. Now tear off the three corners as shown.

When the angles a, b and c are placed together they form a straight line.

We see that:

The angles in a triangle add up to 180°

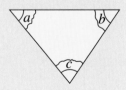

9 $15°$ i i i i

10 $86°$ j j $86°$

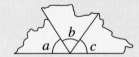

11 $2k$ $3k$ k

12 $3m$ $110°$ $3m$ $3m$ m

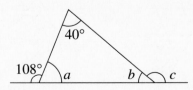

Find the angles marked with letters.

$a = 72°$ (angles on a straight line)

$b + 72° + 40° = 180°$ (angles in a triangle)

$b = 68°$

$c = 112°$ (angles on a straight line)

Exercise 5M

Find the angles marked with letters.

1

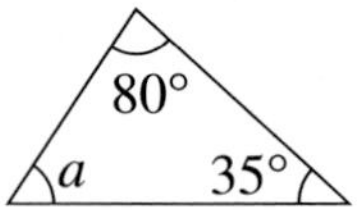

80°
a   35°

2

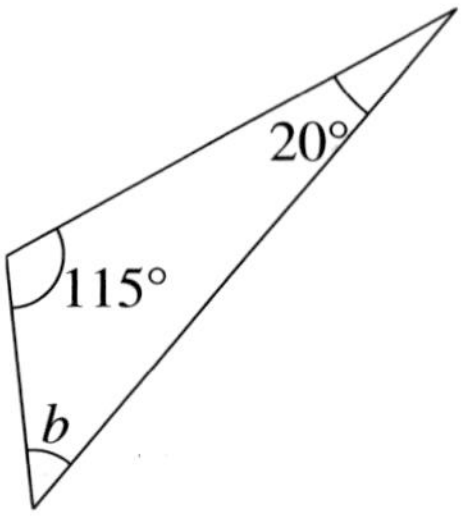

20°
115°
b

3

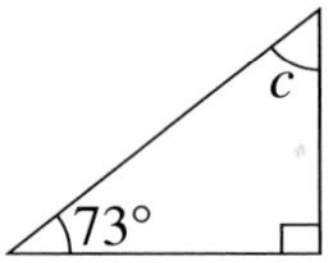

c
73°

4

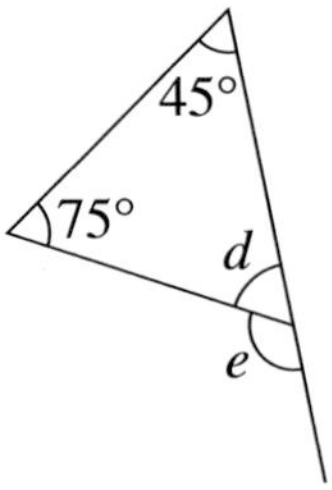

45°
75°
d
e

5

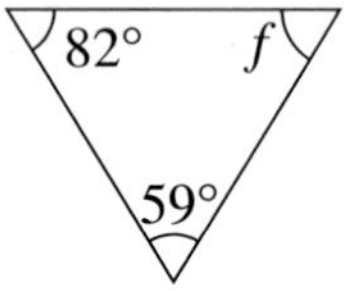

82°   f
59°

6

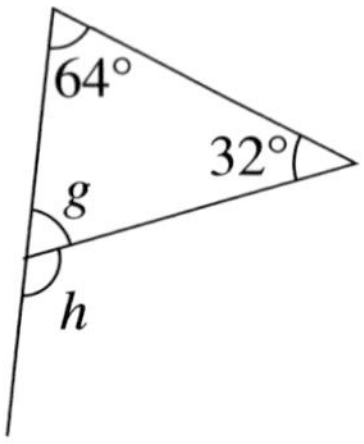

64°
32°
g
h

7

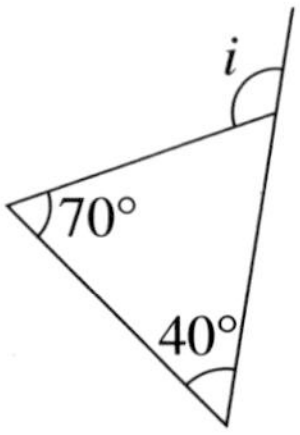

i
70°
40°

8

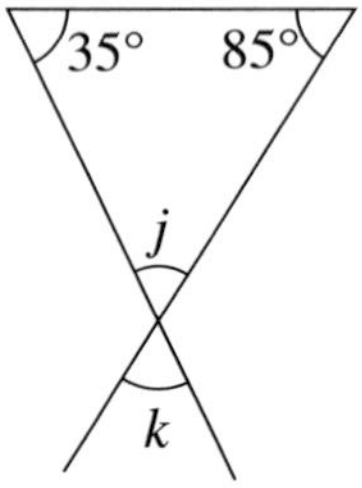

35°   85°
j
k

9

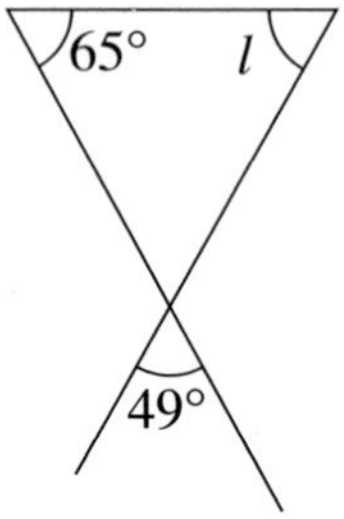

65°   l
49°

10

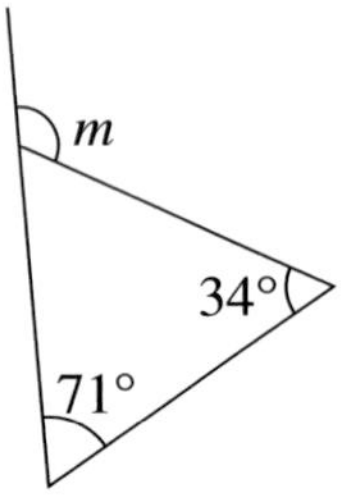

m
34°
71°

11

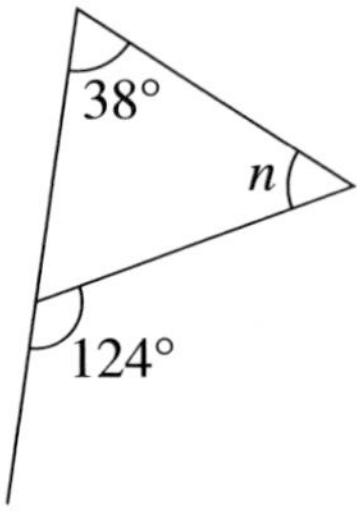

38°
n
124°

12

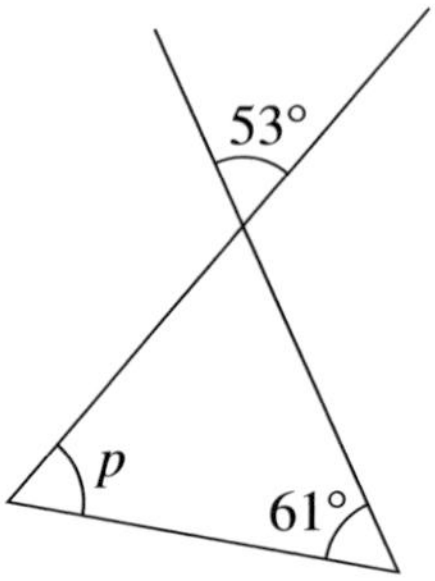

53°
p
61°

13

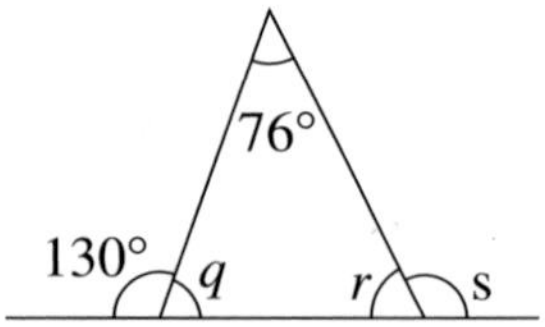

76°
130° q   r s

14

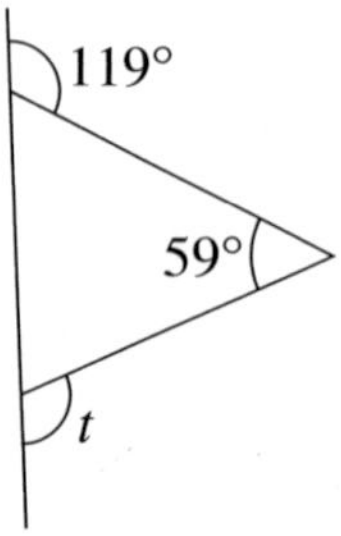

119°
59°
t

15

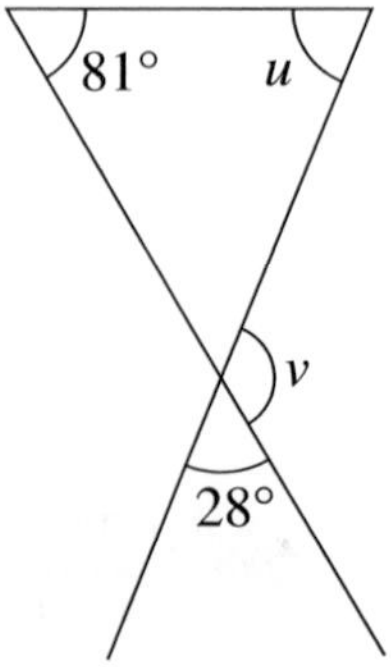

81°   u
v
28°

16

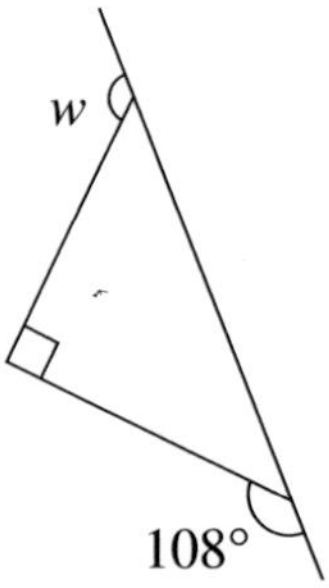

w
108°

Isosceles and equilateral triangles

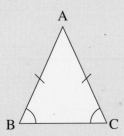

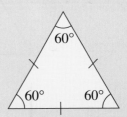

An *isosceles* triangle has two equal sides and two equal angles.

The sides AB and AC are equal (marked with a dash) so angles B̂ and Ĉ are also equal.

An *equilateral* triangle has three equal sides and three equal angles (all 60°).

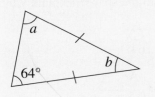

Find the angles marked with letters.

$a = 64°$ (isosceles triangle)

$b + 64° + 64° = 180°$ (angles in a triangle)

$b = 52°$

Exercise 5E

Find the angles marked with letters.

1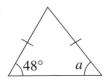

2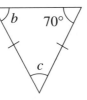

3

4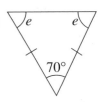

5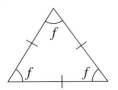

6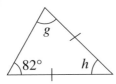

7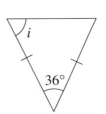

8

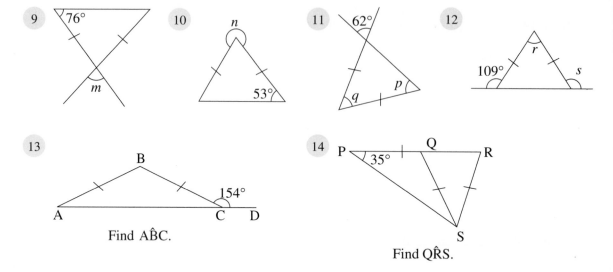

9 $76°$ m

10 n $53°$

11 $62°$ q p

12 r $109°$ s

13

B

$154°$

A   C   D

Find AB̂C.

14 P $35°$ Q R

S

Find QR̂S.

15 Julie has laid a patio with triangular slabs as shown below. She has one space to fill (yellow below). She has 3 slabs remaining. Which slab will fit perfectly into the space? Explain why.

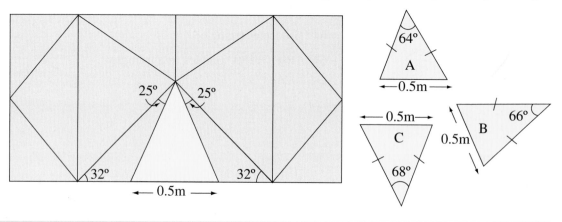

$25°$ $25°$

$32°$ $32°$

← 0.5m →

$64°$

A

←0.5m→

←0.5m→ $66°$

C   B

0.5m

$68°$

CHECK YOURSELF ON SECTION 2.4

1   Labelling angles

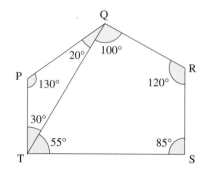

Q

$20°$ $100°$

P

$130°$ $120°$ R

$30°$

$55°$ $85°$

T   S

Write down the size of each angle stated below:

(a) RŜT

(b) PT̂Q

(c) RQ̂T

2   Measuring and drawing angles with a protractor

Use a protractor to measure the two angles below.

(a)   (b)

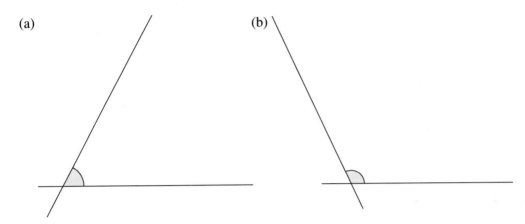

Use a protractor to draw angles of (c) 73° (d) 135°

3   Estimating angles

Estimate the size of each angle below (do *not* use a protractor).

(a)   (b)   (c)

4   Identifying acute, obtuse and reflex angles

State whether each statement below is true or false.

(a)   (b)   (c)

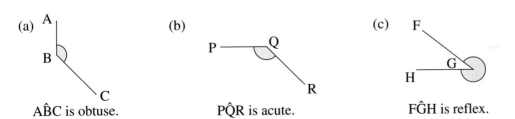

A$\hat{\text{B}}$C is obtuse.   P$\hat{\text{Q}}$R is acute.   F$\hat{\text{G}}$H is reflex.

5   Calculating angles on a straight line and at a point

(a)

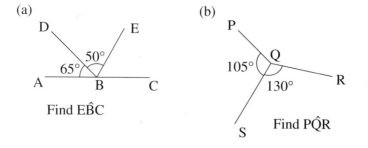

Find EB̂C

(b)

Find PQ̂R

(c)

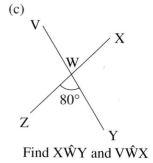

Find XŴY and VŴX

6   Calculating angles in a triangle

(a)

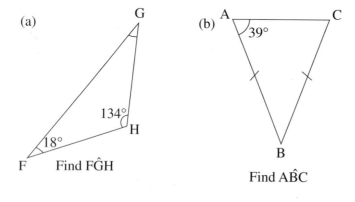

Find FĜH

(b)

Find AB̂C

(c)

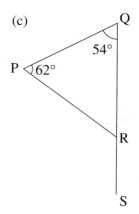

Find PR̂Q and PR̂S

2.5   Rules of Algebra

In section 2.5 you will learn how to:

- use letters for numbers
- collect like terms
- substitute numbers into a formula
- tackle balance puzzles

Using letters for numbers

Many problems can be solved by using letters instead of numbers. This is called using *algebra*.

> Remember: the *letters stand for numbers*

- Suppose there are N cows in a field. If the farmer puts 3 more cows in the field, there will be
  $N + 3$ cows in the field.

- $N + 3$ is an expression. An expression is usually a mixture of letters, numbers and signs. An expression has no '=' sign.

- Suppose there are y people on a bus. At a bus stop n people get off the bus. There are now $y - n$ people on the bus.

- $y - n$ is an expression.

- If I start with a number N and treble it, I will have $N \times 3$. In algebra the '$\times$' sign is left out and the number is written before the letter so I will have $3N$.

- If I start with a number x then double it and add 4, I will have $2x + 4$.

- $2x + 4$ is an expression.

Exercise 1M

In questions 1 to 10 write down the expression.

1 I start with a number N then add 3.

2 I start with a number d then take away 9.

3 I start with a number x then double it.

4 I start with a number y then add 25.

5 I start with a number k, double it then subtract 8.

6 I start with a number M, treble it then take away 4.

7 I start with a number p and multiply it by 25.

8 I start with a number w, double it then add 15.

9 I start with a number q, multiply it by 10 then subtract 8.

10 I start with a number b, multiply it by 3 then add 8.

96

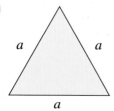

The perimeter p of the triangle is
$$p = x + x + x$$
This is written as $p = 3x$

Complete the statement below for the perimeter p of this square
$$p = \ldots \ldots$$

Use algebra to find the perimeter p of each shape in questions 12 to 17.

12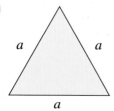

13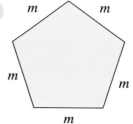

14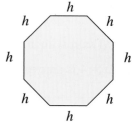

15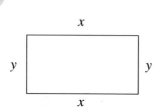

16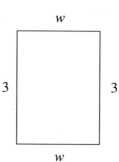

17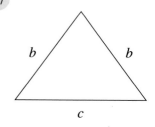

Exercise 1E

In questions 1 to 10 write down the expression.

1 I start with b, add c and then take away m.

2 I start with x, double it and then add y.

3 I start with Q, add 8 and then take away p.

4 I start with s, treble it and then take away w.

5. I add together a, b and c then subtract 8.

6. I start with $4x$, take away y and then add 5.

7. I subtract f from g and then add n.

8. I start with $2y$, add $3w$ and then take away x.

9. I start with m multiply by 6 and then add $3n$.

10. I subtract $3p$ from $5q$ and then add $4m$.

11. A sweet weighs x grams. How many grams do five sweets weigh?

12. A piece of rope is 20m long. A prisoner ties on an extra piece of rope of length y metres. How long is the entire piece of rope now?

13. A piece of wood is w cm long. I cut off a piece 9 cm long. What is the length of the remaining piece of wood?

14. Carl has m CD's. Shalina has 3 times as many CD's. How many CD's does Shalina have?

15. On Tuesday there are x people in a cinema. On Saturday there are four times as many people plus another 45. How many people were in the cinema on Saturday?

16. Tania spends £n on magazines. Chris spends £4 more than Tania. How much money does Chris spend?

17. Draw and label a triangle whose perimeter p is given by the formula $p = 2x + 5$.

18. Draw and label a rectangle whose perimeter p is given by the formula $p = 2a + 2b$.

Collecting like terms

The expression $4a + 3a$ can be *simplified* to $7a$.

a means $1a$ so $6a - a = 6a - 1a = 5a$

$5x$ and $3x$ are called *like* terms

$5x$ and $3y$ are called *unlike* terms

The sum or difference of two terms can only be simplified if the terms are *like* terms.

We can collect like terms.

(a) $5 + n + 2 + 4n = 5n + 7$ ← collect in alphabetical order, with letter terms written before any numbers on their own

(b) $y + 3 + y + 4 + w = w + 2y + 7$ ←

(c) $4x - 4$ cannot be simplified (no like terms)

(d) $5y + x - 5y = x$ ← do not write $0y$ do not write $1x$

(e) Simplify $6x + 4y + 2x - 2y$

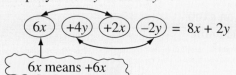

$6x$ $+4y$ $+2x$ $-2y$ $= 8x + 2y$

$6x$ means $+6x$

(f) Simplify $6m + 3x - m + 6 - 3x$

$6m$ $+3x$ $-m$ $+6$ $-3x$ $= 5m + 6$

Exercise 2M

Simplify the following expressions where possible. If you cannot simplify write down the expression given.

1 $3a + 5a$	2 $6x - 2x$	3 $4a + 3b$	4 $6c - 4d$
5 $3d + d$	6 $3x + 2$	7 $7y + 2y$	8 $5h - 3h$
9 $8w - 5w$	10 $6y - 5y$	11 $7x + y$	12 $8m + m$
13 $16y - 9y$	14 $6m + 5n$	15 $4x + 6$	16 $5b + 8b$
17 $20t - 8t$	18 $7p - 6p$	19 $10n + 15n$	20 $6a - 5$
21 $8x + 2$	22 $14h + 16h$	23 $9 - 7x$	24 $8b - 4$
25 $7a + 6$	26 $5c + c$	27 $12y - 12$	28 $12y - y$

Exercise 2E

Simplify the following expressions as far as possible by collecting like terms.

1 $3a + 5b + 3a + 2b$

2 $2x + 4y + 7x + 3y$

3 $8x + 4y - 5x - 2y$

4 $7m + 5n - 4m + 3n$

5 $6a + 5 + a + 4$

6 $8a + 3b - 6a + 4b$

7 $5x + 9 - 2x - 7$

8 $7p + 9q + 2p - 4q$

9 $7x + 8 + x - 6$

10 $a + 14b + 5a - 4b$

11 $6m + 8 + 6m - 7$

12 $3h + 20 - h + 5$

13 $5m + 2n + 4n + 7m$

14 $8p + 6q - 3q - 2p$

15 $6x + 10 - 6 + 3x$

16 $7x + 3y + x + 6$

17 $8a + 3b - 4a + 4c$

18 $5w + 8 - 3w + w$

19 $8 + 4a + 7 - 2a$

20 $4y + 8 - 5 - 3y$

21 $5c - c + 6a + 8c$

22 $5p + 6q + 4p - 4q$

23 $7m + 9n - 7n + 4$

24 $6x + 8 - x + 9x$

25 Write down an expression for the perimeter of each shape below. Collect like terms where possible.

(a)

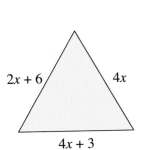

$2x + 6$ $4x$

$4x + 3$

(b)

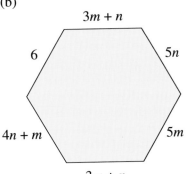

$3m + n$

6 $5n$

$4n + m$ $5m$

$3m + n$

(c)

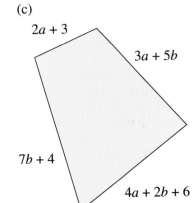

$2a + 3$

$3a + 5b$

$7b + 4$

$4a + 2b + 6$

26 Which two expressions below are *equivalent* (this means they give the same answer when the like terms are collected).

(a) $5x + 3 - 2x + 6y + x$ (b) $3y + 4x + 3y + 6 - 2$ (c) $7 + 4y + 4x + 2y - 3$

More rules

$a + b = b + a$

$a \times b = b \times a$ ($a \times b$ is written as ab so $ab = ba$)

$a \times a = a^2$

$\dfrac{a}{b} = a \div b$

Exercise 3M

1. Think of a pair of values for a and b to show that $a + b = b + a$

2. Think of a pair of values for m and n to show that $mn = nm$

3. (a) Write down any pairs of expressions from below that are equal to each other.

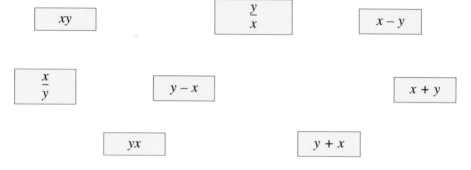

$$xy \qquad \frac{y}{x} \qquad x - y$$

$$\frac{x}{y} \qquad y - x \qquad x + y$$

$$yx \qquad y + x$$

   (b) For each chosen pair from part (a), write down a pair of values for x and y which show that you are correct.

4. (a) Write down any pairs of expressions from below that are equal to each other.

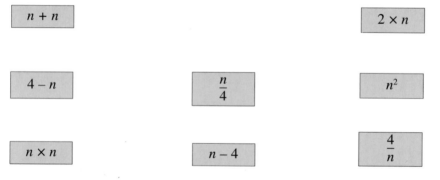

$$n + n \qquad 2 \times n$$

$$4 - n \qquad \frac{n}{4} \qquad n^2$$

$$n \times n \qquad n - 4 \qquad \frac{4}{n}$$

   (b) For each chosen pair from part (a), write down a value for n which shows that you are correct.

5. (a) Choose values for m, n and p to show that $mnp = mpn = pmn$.

   (b) Repeat part (a) with a different set of values for m, n and p.

6. The diagram shows a rectangle attached to a square. Write down an expression for the total area of the shape.

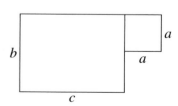

Exercise 3E

In questions 1 to 12 write down each statement and say whether it is 'true' or 'false' for all values of the symbols used.

> If you are not sure, try different values for the letter

1   $x + x + x = 3x$

2   $xw = wx$

3   $m \times m = 2m$

4   $m + n = n + m$

5   $y \times y = y^2$

6   $a - b = b - a$

7   $a \times 5 = 5a$

8   $\dfrac{x}{2} = \dfrac{2}{x}$

9   $a \times a \times a = 3a$

10   $a \div 3 = 3 \div a$

11   $\dfrac{1}{2}$ of $b = \dfrac{b}{2}$

12   $a^2 = 2a$

13   Copy and complete

(a) If $x + y = 80$ then $x = 80 - \square$

(b) If $p - q = 30$ then $p = \square + \square$

(c) If $a \times b = 20$ then $a = \dfrac{\square}{\square}$

(d) If $m + n = 50$ then $n = \square - \square$

(e) If $wx = 100$ then $x = \dfrac{\square}{\square}$

(f) If $mn = e$, then $n = \dfrac{\square}{\square}$

14   Simplify the following expressions.

(a) $\dfrac{m}{m}$

(b) $\dfrac{4a}{4}$

(c) $\dfrac{n^2}{n}$

(d) $\dfrac{6x}{x}$

Investigation – Number walls

Here we have three bricks with a number written inside each one.

A wall is built by putting more bricks on top to form a sort of pyramid.

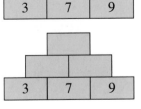

The number in each of the new bricks is found by adding together the numbers in the two bricks below like this:

PART A

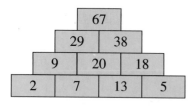

Here is another wall.

1 If you rearrange the numbers at the bottom, does it affect the total at the top?

2 What is the largest total at the top that you can get using the same numbers?

3 What is the smallest total?

4 *How* do you get the largest total?

PART B

1 What happens to the total at the top if the bottom numbers are

(a) the same? (eg. 5, 5, 5, 5)

(b) consecutive? (eg. 2, 3, 4, 5)

2 Write down any patterns or rules that you notice.

PART C

1 What happens if you use different numbers at random (eg. 7,3,5,11)

2 Given 4 numbers at the bottom, can you find a way to predict the top number without finding all the bricks in between?

PART D

Can you find a rule with 3 bricks at the bottom, or 4 bricks?

Can algebra help? (Hint: see diagram)

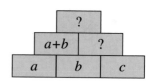

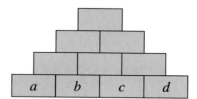

Substituting into a formula

(a) The perimeter p of this shape is given by the formula

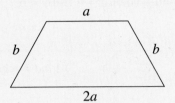

$$p = 3a + 2b$$

Find p when $a = 5$ and $b = 4$

$$p = 3a + 2b$$

$$p = (3 \times 5) + (2 \times 4)$$

$$p = 15 + 8$$

$$p = 23$$

(b) $h = 4(x + 3)$ Find h when $x = 7$

(Remember: always work out brackets first)

$$h = 4(x + 3)$$

$$h = 4(7 + 3) \quad \text{do brackets first}$$

$$h = 4 \times 10$$

$$h = 40$$

Exercise 4M

1 The perimeter p of this triangle is given by the formula $p = 3x$

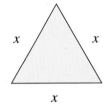

Find p when $x = 6$

2 The perimeter p of a pentagon is given by the formula $p = 5y$

Find p when $y = 8$

3 The perimeter p of a four-sided shape (quadrilateral) is given by the formula $p = a + b + c + d$.

Find p when $a = 9$, $b = 6$, $c = 14$ and $d = 17$

4 The cost in pounds, C, for hiring a video camera is given by the formula $C = 4d + 15$ where d is the number of days of hire.

Find C when $d = 8$

5 The cost in pounds, C, for hiring a car is given by the formula $C = 2n + 25$ where n is the number of miles travelled.

Find C when $n = 150$

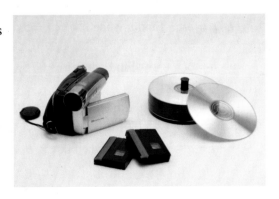

104

6 The perimeter p of a rectangle with sides x and y is given by the formula $p = 2(x + y)$.

Find p when $x = 8$ and $y = 6$

7

A formula for the perimeter p of this kite is
$$p = 2a + 36$$

Find p when (a) $a = 7$ (b) $a = 43$ (c) $a = 3.5$

8 A formula to work out the speed v of an object is $v = u + at$.

Find v when $u = 5$, $a = 10$ and $t = 7$

Exercise 4E

A formula is given in each question. Find the value of the letter required in each case.

1 $a = 3b + 5$ Find a when $b = 4$

2 $p = 4n - 9$ Find p when $n = 6$

3 $y = 5x - 3$ Find y when $x = 8$

4 $m = 16 - n$ Find m when $n = 7$

5 $h = 18 - 2g$ Find h when $g = 6$

6 $w = 4(p + 5)$ Find w when $p = 3$

7 $p = 7(q - 4)$ Find p when $q = 8$

8 $y = \dfrac{m}{4}$ Find y when $m = 36$

9 $a = \dfrac{b}{3}$ Find a when $b = 21$

10 $c = \dfrac{d}{3} + 9$ Find c when $d = 12$

11 $y = \dfrac{x}{10} - 6$ Find y when $x = 80$

12 $m = n^2$ Find m when $n = 5$

13 $p = qr$ Find p when $q = 6$, $r = 5$

14 $y = ab - 8$ Find y when $a = 8$, $b = 3$

15 $h = 6(x + y)$ Find h when $x = 7$, $y = 5$

16 $k = a(a + b)$ Find k when $a = 8$, $b = 2$

17 $x = m(9 - n)$ Find x when $m = 10$, $n = 4$

18 $c = 3fg$ Find c when $f = 2$, $g = 9$

19 $y = a^2 - b^2$ Find y when $a = 8$, $b = 3$

20 $n = \dfrac{x}{y} + x$ Find n when $x = 12$, $y = 4$

Balance puzzles

On the balance ○ and △ represent weights

Find ○ if △ = 5 for this balance puzzle

Clearly for these scales to balance exactly, then ○ =10

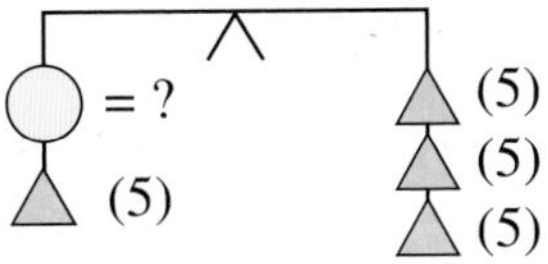

Exercise 5M

Copy each diagram and find the value of the required symbol.

1 Find □ if △ = 4.

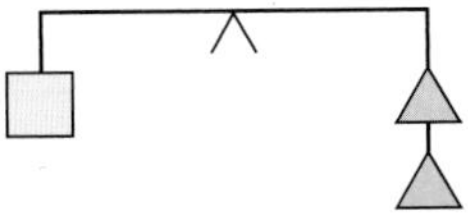

2 Find ○ if △ = 10.

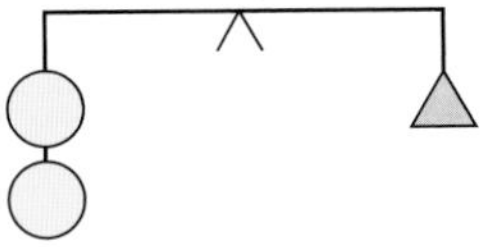

3 Find ○ if □ = 4.

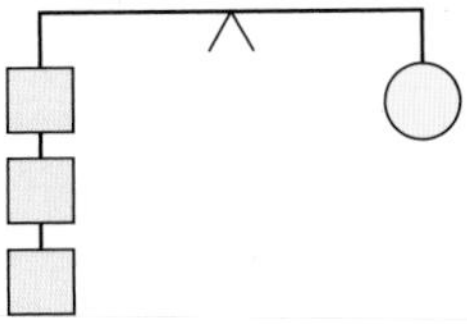

4 Find □ if △ = 12.

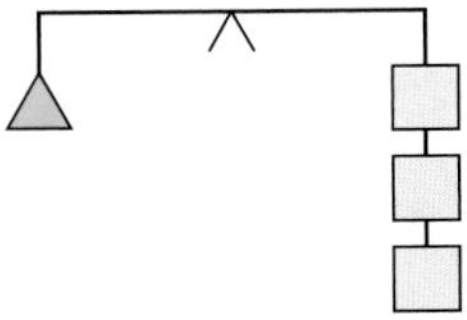

5 Find △ if □ = 0.2.

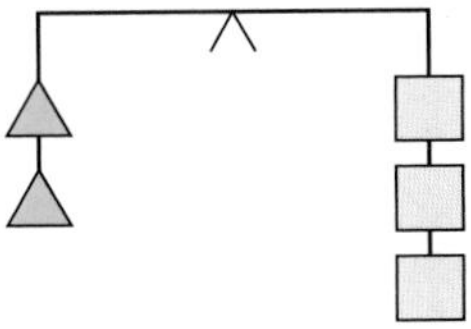

6 Find △ if □ = 6.

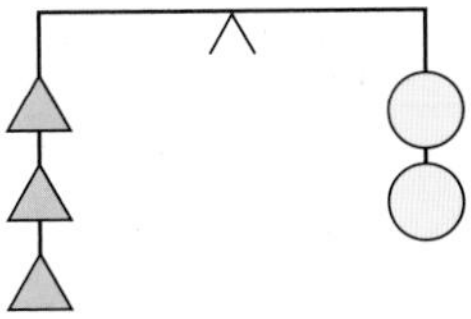

7 Find □ if ○ = 8.

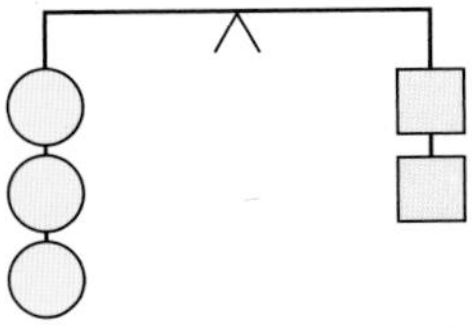

8 Find △ if □ = 15.

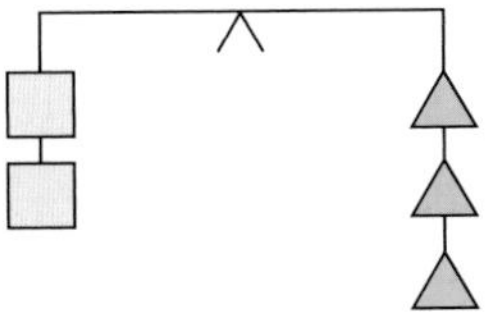

9 Find △ if ○ = 14.

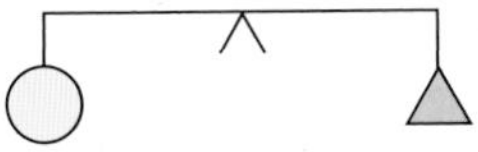

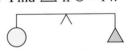

10 Find □ if ○ = 8.

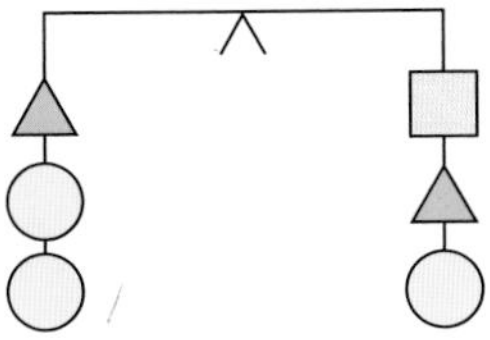

11 Find ○ if △ = 6.

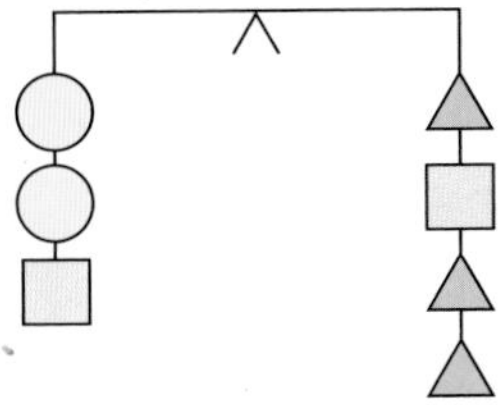

12 Find ○ if □ = 5.

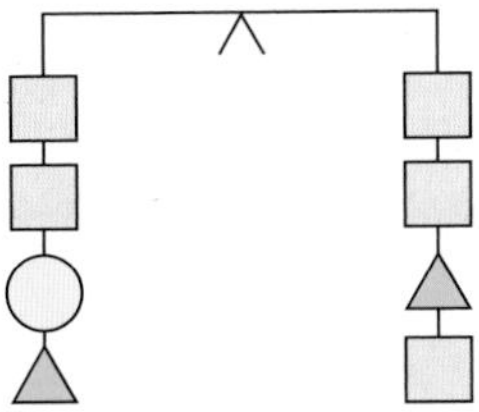

106

Exercise 5E

Copy each diagram and find the value of the unknown symbols.

1 ○ = 10, find △ and □.

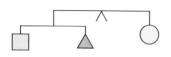

2 △ = 8, find ○ and □.

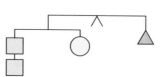

3 □ = 14, find ○ and △.

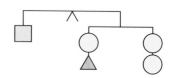

4 □ = 6, find ○ and △.

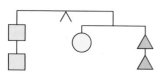

5 ○ = 8, find □ and △.

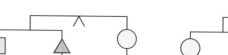

6 □ = 4, find ○ and △.

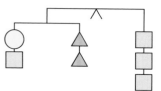

7 △ = 4, find ○ and □.

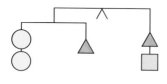

8 ○ = 10, find △ and □.

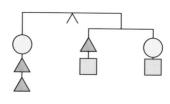

9 △ = 5, find ○ and □.

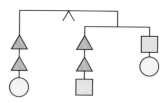

10 □ = 3, find ○ and △.

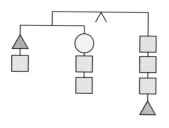

11 □ = 6, find △ and ○.

12 ○ = 5, find □ and △.

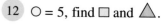
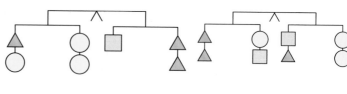

13 △ = 4, find ○ and □.

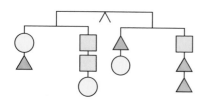

14 ○ = 8, find □ and △.

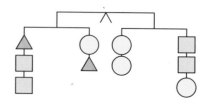

15 □ = 4, find ○ and △.

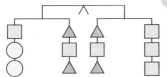

16 ○ = 3, find

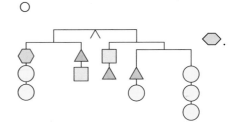

CHECK YOURSELF ON SECTION 2.5

1   Using letters for numbers

(a) I start with a number x then multiply it by 4.
    Write down an expression for what I now have.

(b) Joe has n mints. He gives six mints to his sister.
    Write down an expression for how many mints Joe now has.

(c) 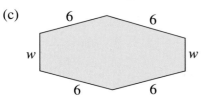   Write down an expression for the perimeter of
                                 this shape.

2   Collecting like terms

Simplify the following expressions as far as possible.

(a) $4m + 3n - 2m + 6n$ (b) $8y - y$ (c) $8p + 6 + 3p - 7p$ (d) $6a + 4b - 2b - 4a$

3   Substituting numbers into a formula

(a) The cost in pounds, C, for hiring a van is given by the
    formula $C = 3n + 45$, where n is the number of miles travelled.
    Find C when $n = 200$.

(b) $w = 6m - 3$ Find w when $m = 6$.

(c) $y = 3(7 - x)$ Find y when $x = 5$.

4 Tackling balance puzzles

(a) Find ☐ if ○ = 12.

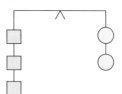

(b) Find ☐ and ○ if △ = 6.

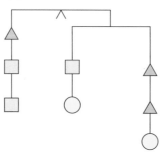

UNIT 2   MIXED REVIEW

Part one

1   Cancel down these fractions

(a) $\dfrac{15}{20}$ 　　　　(b) $\dfrac{24}{28}$ 　　　　(c) $\dfrac{36}{38}$ 　　　　(d) $\dfrac{75}{200}$

2   Work out

(a) $\dfrac{3}{5}+\dfrac{1}{5}$ 　　　(b) $\dfrac{3}{8}$ of 24 　　　(c) $\dfrac{3}{4}-\dfrac{1}{2}$

3   Answer true or false:

(a) $20\% = \dfrac{1}{5}$ 　　(b) $\dfrac{1}{5}+\dfrac{1}{5}=\dfrac{2}{10}$ 　　(c) $\dfrac{16}{20}=\dfrac{8}{10}$

4   Write down an expression for the perimeter of each shape.

(a)

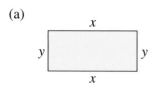

(b)

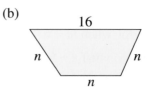

5   Draw a shape with a perimeter of $m + 2n$.

6 Simplify:

(a) $5w + w + 3y + 2w$ (b) $6p + 2q - p + 4q$ (c) $3m + 5 - m - 3$

7 Two objects x and y are placed on scales. x is found to be more than 12 g and y is less than 8 g. Arrange the objects x, y and a 9.5 g weight in order, lightest first.

8 What is 90% as a fraction?

9 What fraction of the whole line is AB?

A ⊢⊣⊢⊣⊢⊣⊢⊣ B ⊢⊣

10 What fraction is 0.75?

11 Write down the value of the angles marked with letters.

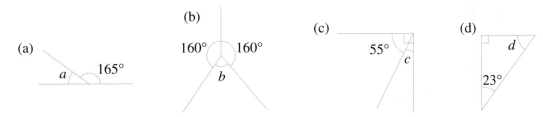

(a)   165° a

(b)   160°   160° b

(c)   55° c

(d) d 23°

12 (a) Find the mean of the numbers   6, 3, 4, 8, 9

(b) Find the median of the numbers   8, 6, 8, 4, 1, 7, 5

(c) Find the mode of the numbers   8, 6, 7, 5, 7, 6, 5, 7

(d) Find the range of the numbers   5, 3, 9, 17, 13, 4

13 In which of the following diagrams is $\frac{5}{8}$ of the shape shaded green?

A

B

C

D

14 Find the size of AD̂B.

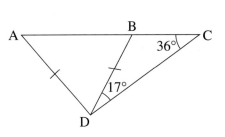

15 Kelly has 5 cards.

The mean of the five cards is 8.

The range of the five cards is 6.

 8   8   8   ☐   ☐

What numbers are on the other two cards?

Part Two

1 Copy and complete this table showing equivalent fractions, decimals and percentages.

fraction	decimal	percentage
		16%
	0.7	
$\frac{1}{4}$		

2 Write down an expression for each of the following:

(a) I start with n, double it and then subtract 8.

(b) I start with p, treble it and then add r.

3 Which is larger?

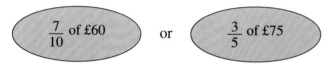

$\frac{7}{10}$ of £60   or $\frac{3}{5}$ of £75

4 Which angles below are obtuse?

5 Tariq has six cards.

The mean of the six cards is 8.

7	4	12	9	10	

What number is on the final card?

6 Use a ruler and protractor to draw this triangle accurately. Measure the length marked x.

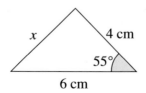

x 4 cm

55°

6 cm

7 Here is a diagram of a designer's logo for 'speedo' training shoes:

(a) Make an accurate drawing of the logo using a ruler, pencil and protractor.

(b) Measure the length AB on your drawing.

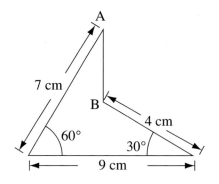

8 In number walls each brick is made by adding the two bricks underneath it.

Fill in the missing expression on these walls

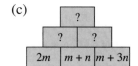

(a)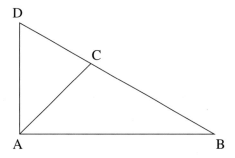

(b)

(c)

9 The cost in pounds C, of hiring a cement mixer is given by the formula C = 18n + 53, where n is the number of days the cement mixer is hired for.

Find C when the cement mixer is hired for 3 days.

10 In the diagram opposite ... →

(a) Measure angle $A\hat{B}D$ using a protractor.

(b) Measure angle $A\hat{C}B$ using a protractor.

(c) What is the length of the line DB in centimetres?

(d) What is the length of the line AB in millimetres?

(e) How many triangles can be seen in the diagram?

(f) What do all the angles in any triangle add up to?

11 Work out

(a) $\dfrac{2}{9} + \dfrac{2}{9}$

(b) $\dfrac{1}{4} + \dfrac{2}{5}$

(c) $\dfrac{5}{8} - \dfrac{3}{10}$

12 There are 72 houses in the village of Cowsley. There are 98 houses in the village of Sefton. Last Halloween $\frac{3}{8}$ of the houses in Cowsley put out pumpkins and $\frac{2}{7}$ of the houses in Sefton put out pumpkins. Which village had more houses with pumpkins?

13 Solve the following balance puzzle, writing your answer $x = \ldots$

14 Ten children in Year 7 and ten children in Year 9 were asked how many hours of exercise they did each week. The results are recorded below:

Year 7: 5, 6, 9, 2, 0, 8, 1, 2, 5, 2

Year 9: 8, 5, 1, 8, 9, 4, 7, 4, 6, 8

(a) Work out the mean and range for Year 7.

(b) Work out the mean and range for Year 9.

(c) Write a sentence to compare the hours of exercise taken by children in Year 7 and Year 9.

15 Here are six algebra cards.

(a) Add the expressions on card B and card E.

(b) Which two cards always have the same value?

(c) Which card has the largest value when $n = 3$?

(d) Add the expressions on all six cards.

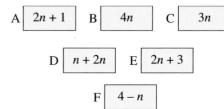

Puzzles and Problems 2

Hidden words

(a) Start in the top left box.

(b) Work out the answer to the calculation in the box.

(c) Find the answer in the top corner of another box.

(d) Write down the letter in that box.

(e) Repeat steps (b), (c) and (d) until you arrive back at the top left box.
What is the message.

1

100	61	62	70	11	71
X	A	D	N	I	F
9 + 12	100 – 11	4 × 15	32 ÷ 8	100 – 45	37 + 22
25	52	90	89	21	9
O	I	O	N	T	E
63 + 8	2 × 7 × 5	60 – 23	45 + 17	14 + 51	88 ÷ 8
91	60	4	37	17	55
N	R	G	R	E	S
38 + 25	60 – 29	49 + 51	3 + 4 + 5	5 × 9	100 ÷ 4
45	65	59	31	63	12
H	H	F	U	N	S
48 + 42	22 – 5	28 + 33	82 + 9	37 + 15	9 ÷ 1

2

90	29	68	91	50	48
X	A	Q	L	R	B
90 – 82	(2 × 15) + 4	70 – 3	3 × 13	60 – 17	25 – 16
1	46	17	28	34	5
A	O	T	E	N	U
30 × 3	10 + 2 – 7	65 – 43	98 – 81	18 ÷ 18	27 – 11
16	41	40	77	33	23
A	P	E	N	A	O
47 – 29	75 – 27	16 + 34	71 – 42	16 + 75	91 – 50
22	43	18	39	8	9
H	E	R	T	Y	A
5 × 8	10 + 11 + 12	41 – 13	65 – 42	66 – 20	94 – 17

3

41	60	81	45	54	9
X	A	E	A	R	E
4×7	$31 - (5 \times 5)$	$26 \div 2$	7×9	6×7	7×7
28	**63**	**6**	**49**	**10**	**17**
A	T	L	E	Y	L
$55 + 45$	$81 - 42$	$3 \times 3 \times 3$	$200 - 145$	$70 - 18$	$13 + 15 + 17$
0	**13**	**100**	**39**	**92**	**77**
A	N	N	O	C	P
$73 + 19$	$20 - (4 + 7)$	$100 \div 10$	$29 + 25$	5×12	$13 \div 13$
52	**27**	**55**	**30**	**33**	**42**
O	C	D	N	U	?
$9 + 10 + 11$	$99 \div 3$	$0 \div 7$	9×9	$68 \div 4$	$27 + 14$

4

100	19	84	6	81	56
X	I	E	L	S	W
12×7	9×9	$90 \div 15$	12×8	8×7	$72 \div 8$
96	**144**	**121**	**97**	**116**	**25**
V	D	F	W	T	S
$8 + 9 + 41$	$10 \times 2 \times 5$	$84 \div 7$	7×5	$43 - 10 - 7$	$102 - 5$
40	**91**	**101**	**58**	**22**	**5**
O	R	D	I	L	U
$20 \div 4$	$71 - 49$	$6 + 7 + 44$	$32 - 7$	$3 \times 4 \times 12$	$67 + 49$
12	**35**	**26**	**9**	**85**	**1**
T	A	O	O	H	S
$38 + 47$	$17 \div 17$	11×11	$49 + 42$	$58 - 39$	$2 \times 2 \times 5 \times 2$

5

337	121	356	1	100	180
X	R	S	S	F	E
17×5	$5 \times (31 - 22)$	$7 + 77 + 777$	$1011 \div 3$	$(28 - 19) \times 9$	$17 + 18 + 19$
58	**108**	**472**	**23**	**85**	**321**
I	S	E	T	M	E
$4557 \div 7$	$80 - 37$	$8 \times 5 - 39$	$90 - 17 - 38$	$237 - 189$	11×11
35	**266**	**99**	**45**	**210**	**43**
R	W	G	S	A	P
$5 \times 6 \times 7$	$10000 \div 100$	59×7	$900 \div 5$	$813 - 547$	$100 - (7 \times 6)$
48	**81**	**54**	**651**	**861**	**745**
O	L	A	D	T	I
$3204 \div 9$	$745 \div 1$	$(9 \times 8) - 49$	$1 + 20 + 300$	$3 \times 3 \times 6 \times 2$	$800 - 328$

A long time ago!   2

Napier's rods

An early calculator was invented by John Napier in the sixteenth century. It was made of rods which were marked as shown below. Each rod shows the 'times table' for the number at the top.

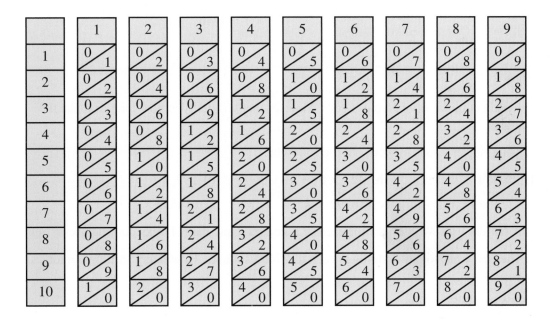

	1	2	3	4	5	6	7	8	9
1	0/1	0/2	0/3	0/4	0/5	0/6	0/7	0/8	0/9
2	0/2	0/4	0/6	0/8	1/0	1/2	1/4	1/6	1/8
3	0/3	0/6	0/9	1/2	1/5	1/8	2/1	2/4	2/7
4	0/4	0/8	1/2	1/6	2/0	2/4	2/8	3/2	3/6
5	0/5	1/0	1/5	2/0	2/5	3/0	3/5	4/0	4/5
6	0/6	1/2	1/8	2/4	3/0	3/6	4/2	4/8	5/4
7	0/7	1/4	2/1	2/8	3/5	4/2	4/9	5/6	6/3
8	0/8	1/6	2/4	3/2	4/0	4/8	5/6	6/4	7/2
9	0/9	1/8	2/7	3/6	4/5	5/4	6/3	7/2	8/1
10	1/0	2/0	3/0	4/0	5/0	6/0	7/0	8/0	9/0

To multiply two numbers together eg. 678 × 7, place the rods together with 6, 7 and 8 at the top. Place next to the blue rod with the numbers 1 to 9.

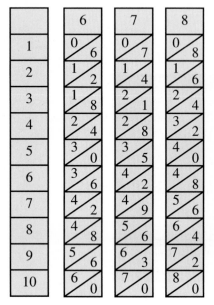

We are multiplying by 7 so look at row 7. Add the numbers diagonally moving from right to left.

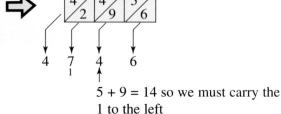

5 + 9 = 14 so we must carry the 1 to the left

$$678 \times 7 = 4746$$

Exercise

1   Draw and cut out a set of Napier's rods. Your teacher will tell you how long to make the rectangles.

2   Use your Napier's rods to work out the following:

   (a) 368×4 (b) 427×6 (c) 592×7

   (d) 4276×9 (e) 56392×4 (f) 684539×7

   (g) A builder uses 4965 bricks for each of 8 houses. How many bricks does he use in total?

   (h) The Army has to pay 3 shillings each to 27483 soldiers. How many shillings in total is this?

3   **RESEARCH:** Find out:

   (a) When were Napier's rods most widely used?

   (b) In which kinds of jobs were they used?

   (c) How can Napier's rods be used to multiply by 2-digit numbers?

   (d) Can Napier's rods be used for division?

Mental Arithmetic Practice 2

Here are two sets of mental arithmetic questions. Ideally a teacher will read out each question twice, with pupils' books closed. Each test of 20 questions should take about 20 minutes.

Test 1

1. What is thirty multiplied by ten?

2. The side of a square is seven metres. What is the area of the square?

3. What number is eleven more than sixty-nine?

4. Change twenty metres into centimetres.

5. What is one quarter of sixty-four?

6. If I buy a notepad for forty-five pence and a rubber for twenty-two pence, how much change do I get from one pound?

7. How many five pence coins make two pounds?

8. What is twenty per cent of twenty pounds?

9. What is three quarters of forty-four euros?

10. The perimeter of a square is twenty centimetres. What is the area of the square?

11. What number is squared to make forty-nine?

12. What decimal number is fifty-five divided by one hundred?

13. How many faces has a cube?

14. How many minutes is it from nine forty-five till noon?

15. What is the angle between the hands of a clock at two o'clock?

16. What is the perimeter of a rectangle which measures thirteen metres by six metres?

17. Write down one half of three hundred and thirty.

18. What is one fifth of two hundred?

19. Two angles in a triangle add up to ninety-four degrees. What is the size of the third angle?

20. A lottery prize of twenty million pounds is shared equally between forty people. How much does each winner receive?

Test 2

1. Write three hundredths as a decimal number

2. How many thirds are there in two whole ones?

3. Work out twenty per cent of fifty-five pounds.

4. If you have four thousand pence, how much do you have in pounds?

5. Answer true or false: 'Ten per cent of two thousand pounds is twenty pounds.'

6. What is the next prime number after seven?

7. Write down all the factors of eight.

8. Subtract twenty centimetres from two metres, giving your answer in metres as a decimal number.

9. What is ten multiplied by nought point nought seven?

10. Write three quarters as a decimal.

11 Add together seven, seventeen and twenty-seven.

12 Forty-two per cent of the pupils at a school are boys. What percentage are girls?

13 The temperature is four degrees celsius at noon. Six hours later the temperature has fallen twenty degrees. What is the new temperature?

14 Write in figures the number four hundred and two thousand and twelve.

15 How many sixes are there in fifty-four?

16 What five coins make forty-five pence?

17 A train leaves London at eleven thirty a.m and arrives in Paris at two p.m. How long does the journey take?

18 What is the sum of six, sixteen and sixty?

19 Find the change from a five pound note when you spend two pounds sixty-nine pence.

20 Write down the next number in the sequence: one, two, four, eight.

UNIT 3

3.1 Coordinates

In this section you will learn how to:

- use coordinates with positive and negative numbers
- solve problems involving shapes

- To get to the point P on this grid we go **across** 1 and **up** 3 from the bottom corner.

  The position of P is (1, 3).

  The numbers 1 and 3 are called the **coordinates** of P.

  The coordinates of Q are (4, 2).

  The *origin* is at (0, 0).

  We call the first coordinate the *x*-coordinate and the second coordinate the *y*-coordinate.

  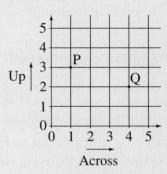

- The *across* coordinate is always *first* and the *up* coordinate is *second*.

  Remember: 'Along the corridor and up the stairs'.

- Notice also that the *lines* are numbered, *not* the squares.

Exercise 1M

1 Write down the coordinates of all the points marked like this:
A(5, 1) B(1, 4)
Don't forget the brackets.

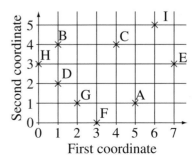

2 The map below shows a remote Scottish island used for training by the S.A.S. Write down the coordinates of the following places:

(a) Rocket launcher
(b) H.Q.
(c) Hospital A
(d) Rifle range
(e) Officers' mess
(f) Radar control

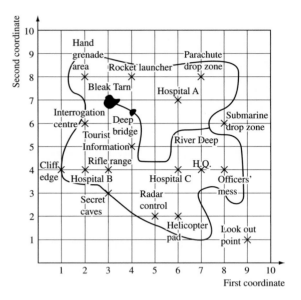

3 Make a list of the places which are at the following points:

(a) (2, 8) (b) (7, 8) (c) (3, 3)
(d) (6, 4) (e) (2, 6) (f) (6, 2)
(g) (2, 4) (h) (9, 1)

4 Make up your own map and mark points of interest.

Negative coordinates

The x axis can be extended to the left and the y axis can be extended downwards to include the negative numbers $-1, -2, -3$ etc.

The word 'BACON' can be found using the letters in the following order:
$(2, -2), (2, 3), (-2, -3), (-2, -1), (-1, 2)$

Similarly the coordinates of the points which spell out the word 'CAN' are
$(-2, -3), (2, 3), (-1, 2)$

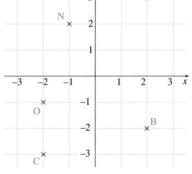

Exercise 1E

Copy the crossword grid and complete it using the clues on the next page.
The letters are found using coordinates on the grid on the next page.

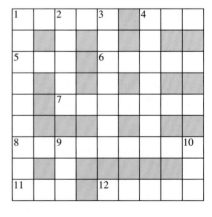

Across

1. (−3, 4) (−4, −2) (−3, 4) (1, 3) (3, −3)

4. (5, 5) (−4, −2) (3, −3)

5. Internet provider

6. (−4, −2) (−3, −4) (3, −3) (−4, −2) (5, −5)

7. (2, −2) (3, −3) (−2, 5) (−4, 1) (−3, −4) (2, −2) (1, 3)

8. (3, −3) (1, 3) (−3, 4) (−3, −4) (4, 4) (0, 1) (−4, −2) (0, 1) (2, −2)

11. German for 'THE'.

12. (−4, 1) (−4, −2) (−2, −2) (5, 2) (0, 1)

Down

1. (−3, 4) (5, −5) (−4, −2) (−2, 2) (2, −2) (1, 3) (3, −3) (1, 3) (2, 5)

2. (−3, 4) (−2, 5) (5, −5) (5, 2) (2, −2)

3. Useful for books

4. Used in mathematics

9. (−3, 4) (−4, −2) (3, −3)

10. (2, −2) (−4, −2) (0, 1)

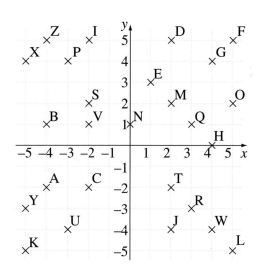

Coordinate pictures

Plot the points below and join them up in order

(a) (3, 3), (1, 3), (0, 4), (3, 5), (4, 6), (6, 6), (7, 4), (7, 3), (8, 2), (5, 1), (4, 2), (1, 3)

(b) (5, 5), (5, 4), (6, 2), (7, 3)

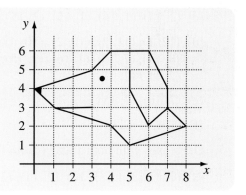

Exercise 2M

Plot the points given and join them up in order.
Write on the grid what the picture is.

1   Draw *x* and *y* axes with values from 0 to 14.

   (a) (6, 13), (1, 3), (2, 1), (12, 1), (8, 9), (6, 5), (4, 5), (8, 13), (6, 13), (8, 13), (13, 3), (12, 1).

   (b) (1, 3), (9, 3), (7, 7), (6, 5), (8, 5).
      Now colour in the shape.

122

2 Draw *x* and *y* axes with values from 0 to 10.

  (a) (3, 2), (4, 2), (5, 3), (3, 5), (3, 6), (2, 7), (1, 6), (1, 8), (2, 9),
      (3, 9), (5, 7), (4, 6), (4, 5), (6, 4), (8, 4), (8, 5), (6, 7), (5, 7).

  (b) (7, 4), (9, 2), (8, 1), (7, 3), (5, 3).

  (c) (1, 6), (2, 8), (2, 9), (2, 7).

  (d) Draw a dot at (3, 8).
      Colour in the shape.

3 Draw *x* and *y* axes with values from 0 to 16

  (a) (4, 7), (6, 5), (7, 5), (8, 3), (9, 5), (11, 5), (12, 7),
      (15, 9), (15, 10), (12, 11), (9, 11), (8, 14), (7, 11),
      (6, 11), (4, 9), (1, 11), (3, 8), (1, 5), (4, 7).

  (b) (15, 12), (16, 12), (16, 13), (15, 13), (15, 12).

  (c) (14, 14), (13, 14), (13, 15), (14, 15), (14, 14).

  (d) (12, 8), (13, 8).

  (e) Draw a dot at (13, 10). Colour in the shape.

4 Draw axes with both *x* and *y* from 0 to 17.

  (a) (5, 1), (6, 6), (6, 3), (7, 2), (6, 2), (5, 1).

  (b) (8, 11), (8, 8), (10, 10), (11, 12), (11, 15).

  (c) (2, 14), (1, 14), (1, 15), (2, 15).

  (d) (12, 1), (11, 2), (10, 2), (10, 4), (9, 6), (8, 7), (7, 10), (8, 11), (9, 13), (11, 15), (10, 17),
      (8, 17), (7, 16), (4, 16), (2, 15), (2, 14), (3, 13), (5, 13), (6, 12), (4, 7), (4, 2), (3, 2),
      (2, 1), (12, 1).

  (e) (7, 16), (7, 15).

  (f) (5, 13), (6, 13).

5 Draw axes with both *x* and *y* from 0 to 11.

  (a) (7, 1), (3, 1), (1, 10), (2, 11), (3, 10), (4, 11), (5, 10), (6, 11), (7, 10), (8, 6), (8, 5),
      (9, $4\frac{1}{2}$), (9, 4), (8, 4), (9, 3), (5, 3), (5, 2), (7, 1).

  (b) (5, 5), (4, 6), (5, 7), (6, 6), (7, 7), (8, 6), (7, 5), (6, 6), (5, 5).

  (c) (5, 2), (6, 2), (6, $1\frac{1}{2}$).

  (d) (7, 5), (8, 5).

  (e) (7, 4), (8, 4).

  (f) (3, 7), (2, $6\frac{1}{2}$), (3, 6).

  (g) Put dots at (5, 6) and (7, 6).

6 Draw axes with both x and y from 0 to 18.

(a) (0, 3), (1, 4), (2, 6), (4, 8), (6, 8), (8, 9), (12, 9), (13, 11), (12, 12), (12, 14), (14, 12), (15, 12), (17, 14), (17, 12), (16, 11), (17, 10), (17, 9), (16, 9), (15, 8), (14, 9), (13, 9).

(b) (16, 9), (16, 7), (14, 5), (14, 1), (15, 1), (15, 6), (13, 4), (13, 1), (12, 1), (12, 4), (11, 5), (9, 5), (9, $6\frac{1}{2}$), (9, 4), (8, 3), (8, 1), (7, 1), (7, 4), (6, 6), (6, 4), (5, 3), (5, 1), (6, 1), (6, 3), (7, 4), (6, 6), (6, 7), (3, 2), (1, 2), (0, 3).

7 Design your own coordinates picture.

Complete the shape

Two sides of a rectangle are drawn

Find   (a) the coordinates of the fourth vertex of the rectangle

(b) the coordinates of the centre of the rectangle.

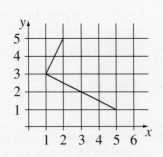

The complete rectangle is shown.

(a) Fourth vertex is at (6, 3)

(b) Centre of rectangle is at ($3\frac{1}{2}$, 3)

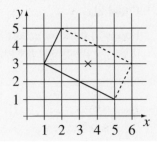

Exercise 2E

1 The graph shows several incomplete quadrilaterals.
Copy the diagram and complete the shapes.

(a) Write down the coordinates of the fourth vertex of each shape.

(b) Write down the coordinates of the centre of each shape.

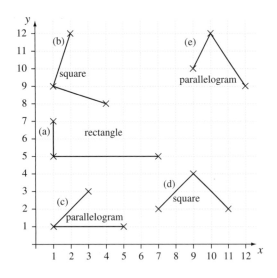

2 Copy the graph shown.

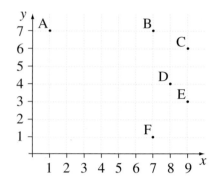

(a) A, B and F are three corners of a square. Write down the coordinates of the other corner.

(b) B, C and D are three corners of another square. Write down the coordinates of the other corner.

(c) D, E and F are three corners of a rectangle. Write down the coordinates of the other corner.

3 Draw a grid with values from 0 to 10. Plot the three points given and then find the coordinates of the point which makes a square when the points are joined up.

(a) (1, 2), (1, 5), (4, 5)

(b) (5, 6), (7, 3), (10, 5)

(c) (0, 9), (1, 6), (4, 7)

4 You are given the vertices but not the sides of two parallelograms P and Q.

For each parallelogram find *three* possible positions for the fourth vertex.

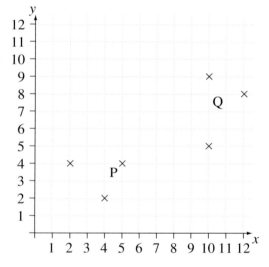

5 Copy the graph shown.

(a) A, B and C are three corners of a square. Write down the coordinates of the other corner.

(b) C, A and D are three corners of another square. Write down the coordinates of the other corner.

(c) B, D and E are three corners of a rectangle. Write down the coordinates of the other corner.

(d) C, F and G are three vertices of a parallelogram. Write down the coordinates of the other vertex.

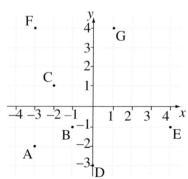

6 The crosses mark two vertices of an isosceles triangle A.

Find as many points as you can, with whole number coordinates, for the third vertex of the triangle.

[There are, in fact, 12 possible points for the third vertex. Find as many as you can.]

7 The diagram shows one side of an isosceles triangle B.

(a) Find *six* possible points, with whole number coordinates, for the third vertex of the triangle.

(b) Explain how you could find the coordinates of several more positions for the third vertex.

3.2 Long multiplication and division 2

In section 3.2 you will:

- practise long multiplication and long division

- solve word problems

Reminder. See section 1.3

42 × 37

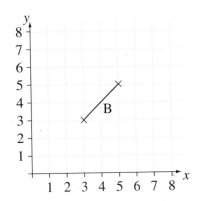

1161 ÷ 27

$$\begin{array}{r} 4\,3 \\ 27\overline{)1161} \\ -108\!\downarrow \\ \hline 81 \\ -81 \\ \hline 0 \end{array}$$

(27×4)

(27×3)

Exercise 1M

1. Copy and complete

(a)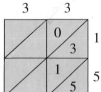

(b)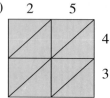

(c)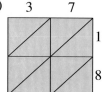

2. Work out

(a) 36×29

(b) 54×21

(c) 312×24

(d) 207×32

(e) 27×27

(f) 241×32

3. Copy and complete

(a)
$$
\begin{array}{r}
3\,2 \\
11{\overline{)\,3\ 5\ 2}} \\
-\ \square\ \square \downarrow \qquad (3 \times 11) \\
\hline
2\ 2 \\
\square\square \qquad (2 \times 11)
\end{array}
$$

(b)
$$
\begin{array}{r}
5\ 3 \text{ remainder } \square \\
13{\overline{)\,6\ 9\ 1}} \\
-\ \square\ \square \downarrow \qquad (5 \times 13) \\
\hline
4\ 1 \\
\square\square \qquad (3 \times 13) \\
\hline
\square
\end{array}
$$

Work out

4. $480 \div 15$

5. $714 \div 21$

6. $962 \div 26$

7. Copy and complete

(a) $32 \times 17 = \square\square\square$

(b) $11 \times \square\square\square = 3575$

(c) $\square\square \times 17 = 408$

(d) $22 \times 55 = \square\square\square\square$

8. Work out the total cost of 45 pens at 22p each. Give your answer in pounds.

9. A box of 15 golf balls costs 975 pence. How much does each ball cost?

10. There are 23 rooms in a school and each room has 33 chairs. How many chairs are there altogether?

Exercise 1E

Work out and give the remainder where necessary.

1. $267 \div 12$

2. $409 \div 11$

3. $637 \div 15$

4. $714 \div 23$

5. $819 \div 25$

6. $561 \div 37$

7   A shop owner buys 52 tins of paint at 84p each. How much does he spend altogether?

8   Eggs are packed twelve to a box. How many boxes are needed for 444 eggs?

9   Bambi the cat eats one tin of cat food every day. How much will it cost to feed Bambi for 31 days if each tin costs 45p?

10 In this multiplication the missing digits are 2, 3, 4, 5. Find the missing numbers

$$\begin{array}{r} \square\square \\ \times\ \square\square \\ \hline 1\ 2\ 4\ 2 \end{array}$$

11 How many 23-seater coaches will be needed for a school trip for a party of 278?

12 Joe wants to buy as many 34p stamps as possible. He has £5 to spend. How many can he buy and how much change is left?

13 It costs £972 to hire a boat for a day. A trip is organised for 36 people. How much does each person pay?

14 Tins of spaghetti are packed 24 to a box. How many boxes are needed for 868 tins?

15 On average a school needs 87 exercise books a week. How many books are needed for 38 weeks?

16 A prize of 470 chocolate bars is shared equally between 18 winners. How many bars does each winner get and how many are left over?

17 Each class of a school has 31 pupils plus one teacher and there are 15 classes in the school. The school hall can take 26 rows of chairs with 18 chairs in a row. Is that enough chairs for all the pupils and teachers?

18 When Philip was digging a hole in his garden he struck oil! The oil came out at a rate of £17 for every minute of the day and night. How much does Philip receive in a 24-hour day?

3.3 Decimals 1

In section 3.3 you will learn how to:

- measure shapes using decimals
- use place value with decimals
- write numbers in order of size
- add and subtract decimal numbers

Decimal point

Decimals are a way of expressing fractions. The decimal point separates the whole number from the fractions

The length of this pencil is 5 cm and 4 tenths of a cm.

As a decimal we write this as 5.4 cm.

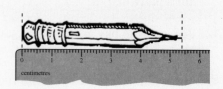

For more accurate measuring we might need hundredths or even thousandths of a cm.

The number 427.35 is $427\frac{35}{100}$.

We can write it like this.

$$\begin{array}{cccccc} \text{hundreds} & \text{tens} & \text{units} & & \text{tenths} & \text{hundredths} \\ 4 & 2 & 7 & . & 3 & 5 \end{array}$$

Exercise 1M

1.  Write down the length of this feather.

2. Use a ruler to measure the length of each object or animal.

   (a)

   (b)

   (c)

   (d)

   (e)

3 Write these numbers as decimals.

(a) $3\frac{1}{10}$ (b) $7\frac{9}{10}$ (c) $5\frac{4}{10}$ (d) $11\frac{3}{10}$ (e) $211\frac{7}{10}$

4 Write the numbers shown by each of the arrows.

5 Use the number line above to work out the following

(a) $0.4 + 0.1$ (b) $1.2 + 0.3$ (c) $2 + 0.7$ (d) $3 - 0.7$

(e) $0.1 + 0.2 + 0.3$ (f) $2.3 - 0.4$ (g) $3.1 - 2$ (h) $0.4 + 3.1$

6 Give the value of the underlined figure.

(a) $5.\underline{7}$ (b) $\underline{1}7.4$ (c) $1\underline{5}.23$ (d) $8.4\underline{6}$

(e) $0.7\underline{1}$ (f) $3.2\underline{4}$ (g) $0.\underline{3}2$ (h) $1\underline{4}.2$

(i) $\underline{3}6.04$ (j) $3.0\underline{7}$ (k) $\underline{4}11.5$ (l) $8.3\underline{6}$

7 Give the next two terms in each sequence

(a) 0.2 0.3 0.4 0.5

(b) 0.1 0.3 0.5 0.7

(c) 0.4 0.8 1.2

(d) 0.3 0.5 0.7 0.9

(e) 1.3 1.2 1.1

8 Write the answer only

(a) $1.5 + 0.4$ (b) $1.3 - 0.3$ (c) $2.4 + 0.5$ (d) $4 - 0.4$

(e) $3.6 + 1.2$ (f) $8 - 1.2$ (g) $1.8 - 1.4$ (h) $4.5 - 0.6$

(i) $1.5 + 1.9$ (j) $1.7 - 0.9$ (k) $4.1 + 9$ (l) $0.2 + 0.8$

9 The number 3.745 is 'three point seven four five', *not* 'three point seven hundred and forty-five'. £1.67 is spoken as 'one pound sixty-seven'. £2.05 is spoken as 'two pounds and five pence'.

Write the following in words.

(a) 7.52 (b) 6.237 (c) 11.04 (d) 60.65

(e) £5.65   (f) £3.05   (g) 6.324 (h) £0.50

Exercise 1E

In questions 1 to 16 answer True (T) False (F).

1   0.7 is less than 0.71   2   0.61 is more than 0.16.

3   0.08 is more than 0.008   4   0.5 is equal to 0.500

5   0.613 is less than 0.631   6   7.0 is equal to 0.7.

7   6.2 is less than 6.02   8   0.09 is more than 0.1.

9   2.42 is equal to 2.420   10   0.63 is less than 0.36

11   0.01 is more than 0.001   12   0.78 is less than 0.793

13   8 is equal to 8.00   14   0.4 is more than 0.35

15   0.07 is less than 0.1   16   0.1 is equal to $\dfrac{1}{10}$.

17   Here is a pattern of numbers based on 3. ⟶

three thousand	3000
three hundred	300
thirty	30
three	3
nought point three	0.3
nought point nought three	0.03

Write a similar pattern based on 7 and extend it from 70 000 000 down to 0.0007. Write the numbers in figures and in words

18   What does the digit 7 in 3.271 represent? And the 2? And the 1?

19   What does the digit 3 in 5.386 represent? And the 6? And the 8?

20   Write the decimal number equivalent to:

(a) three tenths   (b) seven hundredths

(c) eleven hundredths   (d) four thousandths

(e) sixteen hundredths   (f) sixteen thousandths.

21   Write down the single operation needed [+, −] when you change: For example, to change 0.24 to 0.28, you *add 0.04.*

(a) 5.32 to 5.72   (b) 11.042 to 11.047

(c) 0.592 to 0.392   (d) 0.683 to 0.623.

22   Draw a line from 0.9 to 1.1 with 20 equal divisions

$$\left[\overset{0.9}{\underset{\llcorner\,\llcorner\,\llcorner\,\llcorner}{}} \dots \text{etc} \right]$$

Show these numbers or your line

(a) 0.93   (b) 1.04   (c) 1.0   (d) 0.99   (e) 1.09

Ordering decimals

Consider these three decimals...

0.09, 0.101, 0.1.

Which is the correct order from lowest to highest?

When ordering decimals it is always helpful to write them with the same number of figures after the decimal point.

$$0.09 \longrightarrow 0.090 \quad \text{Empty spaces can be}$$
$$0.101 \longrightarrow 0.101 \quad \text{filled with zeros.}$$
$$0.1 \longrightarrow 0.100$$

Now we can clearly see the correct order of these decimals from lowest to highest... 0.090, 0.1, 0.101.

Exercise 2M

In questions 1 to 20, arrange the numbers in order of size, smallest first.

1 0.21, 0.31, 0.12.

2 0.04, 0.4, 0.35.

3 0.67, 0.672, 0.7.

4 0.05, 0.045, 0.07.

5 0.1, 0.09, 0.089.

6 0.75, 0.57, 0.705.

7 0.41, 0.041, 0.14.

8 0.809, 0.81, 0.8.

9 0.006, 0.6, 0.059.

10 0.15, 0.143, 0.2.

11 0.04, 0.14, 0.2, 0.53.

12 1.2, 0.12, 0.21, 1.12.

13 2.3, 2.03, 0.75, 0.08.

14 0.62, 0.26, 0.602, 0.3.

15 0.5, 1.3, 1.03, 1.003.

16 0.79, 0.792, 0.709, 0.97.

17 5.2 m, 52 cm, 152 cm

18 £1.20, 75p, £0.8

19 200 m, 0.55 km, $\frac{1}{2}$ km

20 1.2 mm, 0.1 cm, 2 mm

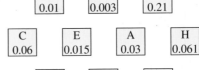

21 Here are numbers with letters

(a) Put the numbers in order, smallest first.
Write down just the letters.

(b) Finish the sentence using letters and numbers of your own. The numbers must increase from left to right.

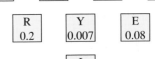

22 Increase the following numbers by $\frac{1}{10}$ th :

    (a) 3.27   (b) 14.8   (c) 0.841

23 Increase the following numbers by $\frac{1}{100}$ th :

    (a) 11.25   (b) 1.294   (c) 0.382

24 Increase the following numbers by $\frac{1}{1000}$ th :

    (a) 3.142   (b) 2.718   (c) 1.414

25 Write the following amounts in pounds:

    (a) 11 pence.   (b) 2 pence.   (c) 5 pence.

    (d) 10 pence.   (e) 20 pence.   (f) 50 pence.

Find the number which the arrow is pointing to on each of the scales.

(a) 4   6   (b) 8.1   8.2

The middle number is 5.   Each division is 0.02.
Each division is 0.2   The arrow points to 8.16.
The arrow points to 4.4.

4.4

4   5   6   8.1   8.2

8.16

                            8.12   8.14   8.18

Exercise 2E

Work out the value indicated by the arrow.

1   40   50   2   2   3   3   14   16

4   15   15.5   5   0   1   6   0   6

7   0   10   8   5   6   9   3.1   3.2

10   0   0.1   11   1   1.04   12   0   1.5

13 0.2 ↓ 0.3

14 100 ↓ 200

15 1 ↓ 2

16 0 ↓ 60

17 60 ↓ 100

18 4 ↓ 4.5

19 2.4 ↓ 2.8

20 3.3 ↓ 3.7

21 0 ↓ 0.3

22 70 ↓ 80

23 18 ↓ 19

24 3.1 ↓ 3.15

Adding and subtracting decimals

Remember: Line up the decimal points

(a) 2.4 + 3.23

(b) 7 − 2.3

(c) 0.31 + 4 + 11.6

put a zero

$$
\begin{array}{r}
2\,.\,40 \\
+\,3\,.\,23 \\
\hline
5\,.\,63
\end{array}
$$

(line up the points)

$$
\begin{array}{r}
{}^{6}\!\!\not{7}\,.\,{}^{1}0 \\
-2\,.\,3 \\
\hline
4\,.\,7
\end{array}
$$

(write 7 as 7.0)

$$
\begin{array}{r}
0\,.\,31 \\
4\,.\,00 \\
+11\,.\,60 \\
\hline
15\,.\,91
\end{array}
$$

(write 4 as 4.00)

Exercise 3M

1 6.1 + 1.7

2 0.4 + 0.9

3 6.7 + 1.8

4 18.4 + 1.6

5 11.9 + 3.2

6 15.6 + 7.8

7 12 + 4.5

8 0.4 + 0.5 + 0.6

9 8.9 − 4.7

10 6.4 − 2.7

11 15.6 − 10.9

12 8 − 2.7

13 5 + 0.26

14 2.9 + 4.37

15 8.6 + 7.99

16 0.078 + 2.05

17 10.04 + 3.005

18 13.47 + 27.084

19 1.97 + 19.7

20 4.56 + 7.890

21 456.7 + 8.901

22 16.374 + 0.947 + 27

23 3.142 + 2.71 + 8

24 0.03 + 11 + 8.74

25 $29.6 - 14$

26 $59.2 - 34.8$

27 $81.8 - 29.9$

28 $8 - 2.7$

29 $6.7 - 4.29$

30 $47.2 - 27.42$

31 $94.63 - 5.9$

32 $2.97 - 1.414$

33 $25.52 - 1.436$

34 $3.142 - 1.414$

35 $2.718 - 1.732$

36 $12 - 3.74$

In questions **37** to **42** find the missing digits

37
$$
\begin{array}{r}
\square.\,8\,\square \\
+\ 1\,.\,\square\,5 \\
\hline
9\,.\,2\,7
\end{array}
$$

38
$$
\begin{array}{r}
\square.\,6\,\square \\
+\ 0\,.\,\square\,5 \\
\hline
3\,.\,9\,0
\end{array}
$$

39
$$
\begin{array}{r}
5\,.\,\square\,7 \\
+\ \square.\,5\,\square \\
\hline
8\,.\,9\,1
\end{array}
$$

40
$$
\begin{array}{r}
8\,.\,2\,\,7 \\
+\ \square\cdot\,7\,\,4 \\
\hline
9\,.\,\square\square
\end{array}
$$

41
$$
\begin{array}{r}
\square.\,8\,\square \\
+\ 2\,.\,\square\,7 \\
\hline
9\,.\,0\,3
\end{array}
$$

42
$$
\begin{array}{r}
6\,.\,9\,\,5 \\
+\ \square.\,2\,\square \\
\hline
9\,.\,\square\,1
\end{array}
$$

Exercise 3E

1 Winston was 1.52 m tall and a year later he had grown 9 cm. How tall was he then?

2 An electrician has 8 m of cable and then cut off 45 cm. How long was the remaining cable?

3 Carlos has £3.20 and wants to buy articles costing £1.10, 66p, £1.99 and 45p. How much more money does he need?

4 Which six different coins make £1.78?

5 Jane went to a shop and bought a book for £2.95 and a CD for £10.95. She paid with a £50 note. What change did she receive?

6 Jackie bought a goldfish for £2.95, a bowl for £5.99 and a bottle of Evian water for 60p. What was the total price?

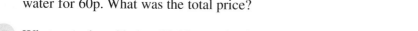

7 What must be added to £5.63 to make £18?

8 Which five different coins make a total of £1.37?

9 Prini bought her local team's replica football kit, shirt costing £10.75, shorts costing £3.99 and socks for £2.59. How much did she spend?

10 Jack spent £5.15 in the supermarket and £10.99 in the music shop. How much change did he get from £20?

In questions 11 to 16 find the missing digits

11
```
   □.5□
 −  4.□3
 ──────
   3.7 3
```

12
```
   4.□7
 +  □.9□
 ──────
   9.0 3
```

13
```
   3.1 7□
 −  □.4□8
 ───────
   0.□4 8
```

14
```
   8.□8
 +  □.8□
 ──────
   9.6 6
```

15
```
   □.9□
 −  2.□6
 ──────
   3.6 6
```

16
```
   2.□5 7
 +  □.3 4□
 ───────
   6.8 □5
```

17 I started with 6.658 and then subtracted a number. The answer was 6.648. What number did I subtract?

18 I started with 0.954 and then added a number. The answer was 0.956. What number did I add?

19 Write down the answers.

(a) 1.242 + 0.03   (b) 9.042 − 0.03   (c) 11.817 + 0.002

(d) 8.679 − 0.001   (e) 6.53 + 0.002   (f) 41.44 − 0.4

(g) 0.473 − 0.2   (h) 0.046 + 0.004   (i) 11.617 − 0.005

20 Write the numbers in order, smallest first, to make a word

I	L	N	E	O	R	T	A
0.501	0.3	4	0.034	0.8	0.03	0.5	0.33

Top Banana! The Banana man of Tesco.

The following article is a true story. Read the article (which deliberately contains blanks) and then answer the questions on the next page.

He is called the Banana man of Tesco. In a special offer Phil Calcott bought almost half a ton of bananas. He then gave it all away and still made a profit on the deal. In a way Mr Calcott made his local store pay him to take away its own fruit.

The offer said that if you bought a 3 lb bunch of bananas for £1.17, you would gain 25 Tesco 'Club Card' points. These points could be used to buy goods worth £1.25.

Mr Calcott asked the store to load up his Peugeot 205 with bananas.

'I took a car load at a time because even with the back seat down and the boot full I could only fit in 460 Ibs of bananas,' he said.

He returned for another load the next day and altogether spent £__buying 942 lbs of the fruit. This earned him almost__, 000 Tesco 'Club Card' points.

1 How much would it cost to buy ten 3 lb bunches of bananas?

2 How many Tesco Club Card points would you get?

3 How much would the points be worth?

4 How much profit would you make on this deal?

5 Do you like bananas?

6 Write down the paragraph, which starts 'He returned …' and fill in the missing numbers.

3.4 Multiplying and dividing with decimals

In section 3.4 you will learn how to:

- multiply and divide numbers by 10, 100, 1000

- multiply decimals by whole numbers

- divide decimals by whole numbers

Multiplying and dividing by 10, 100, 1000

Here are three numbers multiplied by 10

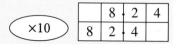

When you multiply by **10** you move the digits **one** place to the left. [Some people prefer to think of moving the decimal point one place to the right. *You* use the method that *you* prefer.]

Similarly when you multiply by **100** you move the digits **two** places to the left and when you multiply by **1000** you move the digits **three** places to the left.

$4.601 \times 100 = 460.1$ $0.231 \times 100 = 23.1$

$0.324 \times 1000 = 324$ $10.24 \times 1000 = 10240$

                                              (add a zero)

When you divide by 10, 100, 1000 and so on the digits move to the right.

$11.7 \div 10 = 1.17$ $235.6 \div 100 = 2.356$

$85 \div 1000 = 0.085$ $25400 \div 10000 = 2.54$

Exercise 1M

Do the following calculations

1. 4.23×10
2. 5.63×10
3. 0.427×100
4. 100×4.63
5. 0.075×10
6. 100×0.0063
7. 1.147×1000
8. 10.7×1000
9. 6.33×100
10. $0.007\,14 \times 10\,000$
11. 100×6.36
12. 8.142×10
13. $10\,000 \times 0.71$
14. 8.9×1000
15. 12×100
16. 10×13
17. 7×1000
18. 10000×9.2
19. 0.7×100
20. $0.5 \times 100\,000$

Copy and Complete

21. $0.8 \times \boxed{} = 80$
22. $\boxed{} \times 1000 = 5500$
23. $\boxed{} \times 10 = 0.52$
24. $1.8 \times 100 = \boxed{}$
25. $0.81 \times \boxed{} = 810$
26. $0.4 \times 1000 = \boxed{}$
27. $7.2 \times \boxed{} = 7.2$
28. $\boxed{} \times 100 = 11.7$
29. $\boxed{} \times 100 = 0.2$

30. Answer true or false: $0.3 \times 10 = 0.03 \times 1000$

Work out

31. $57.2 \div 10$
32. $89.2 \div 10$
33. $5.3 \div 10$
34. $47.1 \div 100$
35. $141.2 \div 100$
36. $19.3 \div 10$
37. $1518 \div 100$
38. $4.7 \div 100$
39. $25.2 \div 1000$
40. $0.63 \div 10$
41. $47.2 \div 100$
42. $27.9 \div 1000$
43. $6.2 \div 1000$
44. $198.7 \div 100$
45. $47 \div 10$
46. $416 \div 1000$

Exercise 1E

Copy and complete

1. $7.5 \times \boxed{} = 7500$
2. $280 \div \boxed{} = 2.8$
3. $\boxed{} \times 1000 = 32$
4. $17 \div 100 = \boxed{}$
5. $36 \times \boxed{} = 36$
6. $56 \div \boxed{} = 0.56$
7. $0.42 \times \boxed{} = 420$
8. $\boxed{} \times 1000 = 6540$
9. $0.07 \times \boxed{} = 0.7$
10. $0.8 \div \boxed{} = 0.8$
11. $0.03 \times \boxed{} = 30$
12. $110 \div \boxed{} = 1.1$

Work out

13 0.414 × 100

14 0.0631 × 1000

15 0.005 × 100

16 0.0063 × 10 000

17 47.4 ÷ 10

18 8.97 ÷ 100

19 54.2 ÷ 1000

20 63 × 100

21 47 × 10

22 0.84 × 10 000

23 0.7 ÷ 100

24 6.2 ÷ 10

25 4.73 × 10

26 0.001 × 1000

27 47 ÷ 100

28 47 × 100

Copy and complete the following

29 | 4.7 | — × 10 → | ☐ | — × 100 → | ☐ | — ÷ 10 → | ☐ |

30 | 0.6 | — × 100 → | ☐ | — ÷ 10 → | ☐ | — × 10 → | ☐ |

31 | 575 | — ÷ 100 → | ☐ | — ÷ 10 → | ☐ | — × 1000 → | ☐ |

32 | ☐ | — × 10 → | 82 | — ÷ 100 → | ☐ | — ÷ 10 → | ☐ |

33 | ☐ | — × 100 → | ☐ | — ÷ 10 → | 95 | — ÷ 10 → | ☐ |

34 | ☐ | — × 10 → | ☐ | — ÷ 1000 → | 7.3 | — × 10 → | ☐ |

35 | ☐ | — ÷ 100 → | ☐ | — ÷ 10 → | ☐ | — × 10 → | 0.4 |

36 | ☐ | — × 10 → | ☐ | — ÷ 100 → | ☐ | — ÷ 10 → | 8.6 |

37 Find the answer to the calculation in each box.

Arrange the answers in order of size, smallest first, what word do you get?

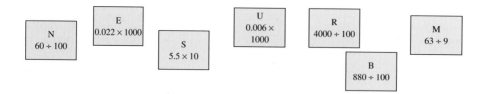

N 60 ÷ 100 E 0.022 × 1000 S 5.5 × 10 U 0.006 × 1000 R 4000 ÷ 100 B 880 ÷ 100 M 63 ÷ 9

Multiplying decimals by whole numbers

Method 1

• $7.93 \times 4 \approx 8 \times 4 = 32$

(Estimate first)

7.93×4 $7.00 \times 4 = 28.00$

$0.90 \times 4 = 3.60$

$0.03 \times 4 = \underline{0.12}$ +

$\,31.72$

• $3.16 \times 6 \approx 3 \times 6 = 18$

(Estimate first)

3.16×6 $3.00 \times 6 = 18.00$

$0.10 \times 6 = 0.60$

$0.06 \times 6 = \underline{0.36}$ +

$\,18.96$

Method 2

• $7.24 \times 4 \approx 7 \times 4 = 28$

(Estimate first)

$$\begin{array}{r} 7.24 \\ \times 4 \\ \hline 28.96 \\ \hline \end{array}$$
$_1$

• $0.096 \times 9 \approx 0.1 \times 9 = 0.9$

(Estimate first)

$$\begin{array}{r} 0.096 \\ \times 9 \\ \hline 0.864 \\ \hline \end{array}$$
$_{8\ 5}$

> The answer has the same number of figures after the point as there are in the numbers being multiplied.

Exercise 2M

Work out the following. Find an estimate first.

1. $\begin{array}{r} 5.1 \\ \times 2 \\ \hline \end{array}$

2. $\begin{array}{r} 2.3 \\ \times 3 \\ \hline \end{array}$

3. $\begin{array}{r} 3.7 \\ \times 4 \\ \hline \end{array}$

4. $\begin{array}{r} 5.6 \\ \times 5 \\ \hline \end{array}$

5. $\begin{array}{r} 6.13 \\ \times 6 \\ \hline \end{array}$

6. $\begin{array}{r} 10.22 \\ \times 7 \\ \hline \end{array}$

7. $\begin{array}{r} 5.34 \\ \times 8 \\ \hline \end{array}$

8. $\begin{array}{r} 1.29 \\ \times 9 \\ \hline \end{array}$

9. 7×0.63

10. 1.452×6

11. 9×0.074

12. 11.3×5

13. 13.6×5

14. 0.074×5

15. 6×2.22

16. 8.4×11

17. Copy and complete with the missing numbers.

(a) $0.3 \times 4 = \boxed{}$

(b) $0.6 \times \boxed{} = 4.2$

(c) $\boxed{} \times 5 = 2.0$

(d) $1.5 = 6 \times \boxed{} + 0.3$

(e) $\boxed{} \times 7 - 2 = 1.5$

(f) $8 \times \boxed{} = 0.16$

18　Find the cost of 6 golf balls at £1.95 each.

19　What is the cost of 2 CDs at £10.95 each?

20　If one brick weighs 1.35 kg, how much do 5 weigh?

Exercise 2E

1　Work out

(a) 6.35×4　　(b) 0.72×9　　(c) 1.45×7　　(d) $0.4 \times 3 \times 10$　　(e) $1.7 \times 3 \times 100$

2　Copy and complete

(a) $\boxed{1.1} \xrightarrow{\times 4} \boxed{} \xrightarrow{\times 10} \boxed{} \xrightarrow{\div 100} \boxed{}$

(b) $\boxed{0.4} \xrightarrow{\times 7} \boxed{} \xrightarrow{\times 3} \boxed{} \xrightarrow{\times 10} \boxed{}$

(c) $\boxed{1.5} \xrightarrow{\times 5} \boxed{} \xrightarrow{\times 3} \boxed{} \xrightarrow{\times 100} \boxed{}$

(d) $\boxed{0.04} \xrightarrow{\times 8} \boxed{} \xrightarrow{\times 100} \boxed{} \xrightarrow{\div 2} \boxed{}$

3　What is the total cost of 6 books at £2.13 each?

4　A new car tyre costs £29.99.
　What is the total cost of 4 new tyres?

5　Find the total cost of 8 batteries at £1.19 each.

6　If 1 kg of cheese costs £4.59, find the cost of 3 kg.

7　Ink cartridges cost £1.25 a packet. What is the cost of 10 packets?

8　A sack of coal costs £6.90. Find the total cost of 9 sacks.

9　If 1 litre equals 1.76 pints, how many pints is 8 litres?

10　　A pair of sandals costs £14.50.
　　A parcel contains 8 pairs of sandals.
　　A van contains 1000 parcels full of sandals.
　　(a) What is the cost of one parcel?
　　(b) What is the cost of the sandals on the van?

In questions 11 to 14 find the total cost.

11 2 jars at £1.75 each

4 boxes at £0.40 each

1 bottle at £1.25

13 4 litres of oil at 97p per litre

6 bags at £0.33 each

3 lb of meat at £2.12 per lb

1 cauliflower at 42p

12 3 tins at £0.51 each

5 packets at £1.10 each

2 pints of milk at 22p per pint.

14 18 eggs at 50p per dozen

$\frac{1}{2}$ lb of cheese at £1.30 per lb

3 lb of leeks at 18p per lb

2 packets at £2.30 each

Division of decimals by whole numbers

(a) $9.6 \div 3$

$$\begin{array}{r} 3.2 \\ 3\overline{)9.6} \end{array}$$

(b) $22.48 \div 4$

$$\begin{array}{r} 5.62 \\ 3\overline{)22^2.48} \end{array}$$

(c) $7.3 \div 4$

$$\begin{array}{r} 1.825 \\ 4\overline{)7.^33^10^20} \end{array}$$

(d) $21.28 \div 7$

$$\begin{array}{r} 3.04 \\ 7\overline{)21.2^28} \end{array}$$

(e) $3.12 \div 4$

$$\begin{array}{r} 0.78 \\ 4\overline{)3.^31^22} \end{array}$$

↑↑
Note the extra zeros.

Exercise 3M

1 $8.42 \div 2$

2 $205.2 \div 6$

3 $18.52 \div 4$

4 $4.984 \div 7$

5 $236.0 \div 5$

6 $18.93 \div 3$

7 $49.92 \div 8$

8 $487.26 \div 9$

9 $6.7 \div 5$

10 A father shares £4.56 between his three children. How much does each receive?

11

1	2		3	4	5
6		7		8	
	9		10		
11			12	13	
14	15			16	17
18			19		

Copy and complete the cross number puzzle. There are decimal points on some lines.

Clues across

1. 4×1.9

3. $6.2 \div 5$

6. $83.2 \div 4$

8. $0.42 \times 2 \times 50$

9. $348 \div 3$

12. $0.95 \times 4 \times 10$

14. $928 + 45$

16. $31.8 \div 6$

18. $2004 - 1989$

19. $5.1 \div 5$

Clues down

1. $36.4 + 35.6$

2. $542 + 5 + 54$

4. $7.2 \div 3$

5. $(85 \times 5) \div 10$

7. 0.081×1000

10. $31.5 \div 5$

11. $200 - (0.9 \times 10)$

13. 0.85×1000

15. $60 \div 8$

17. $0.0032 \times 100 \times 100$

Exercise 3E

1 A length of wood measuring 39.41 cm has to be cut into seven equal lengths. How long is each piece?

2 The total bill for a meal for nine people is £76.23. How much does each person pay if they each paid the same?

3 Work out

    (a) $11.2 \div 5$ (b) $9.01 \div 4$ (c) $12.1 \div 8$

    (d) $0.82 \div 4$ (e) $17 \div 5$ (f) $22 \div 8$

4 If 5 bricks weigh 4.64 kg, find the weight of one brick.

5 Five people share the fuel cost of a car journey which amounts to £18.65. How much does each person pay?

6

Six cows produce 33.84 litres of milk each day. What is the average milk production of each cow?

7 How many times will a 9 litre bucket have to be filled and emptied to completely empty a water drum containing 139.5 litres?

8 Barbecued sausages cost £5.94 for six. How much does each one cost?

9 A steel rod of length 2.86 m is divided into 11 equal pieces. How long is each piece?

10 One hundred ball bearings weigh 2.5 kg. What is the weight of one? Give your answer in grams.

Operator squares

Each empty square contains either a number or an operation (+, −, ×, ÷). Copy each square and fill in the missing details. The arrows are equals signs.

1

32	÷	4	→	
+		×		
		7	→	280
↓		↓		
72	−		→	

2

18	×		→	90
−		+		
7		6	→	42
↓		↓		
		−		→	

3

25	+		→	89
×		+		
	×		→	
↓		↓		
150	−		→	69

4

35	×		→	350
−		÷		
	×		→	
↓		↓		
34.8	+	0.1	→	

5

38	×	8	→	
÷		×		
2	×		→	
↓		↓		
	+	112	→	

6

		574	→	1532
÷		+		
9	×	25	→	
↓		↓		
234	+		→	

7

10	×		→	1
÷		×		
	÷		→	
↓		↓		
2.5	+	1.6	→	

8

19.6	÷	7	→	
×		+		
0.1	×		→	1
↓		↓		
		+		→	

9

8.42	−	0.2	→	
×		×		
100	×		→	1200
↓		↓		
		+		→	

10

20	÷	100	→	
×		÷		
	×	200	→	
↓		↓		
440	×		→	

11

1.22	×	3	→	
+		−		
	+		→	
↓		↓		
5	+		→	7.8

12

	+		→	902
÷		−		
9	×	52	→	
↓		↓		
	+	526	→	

3.5 Properties of numbers

In section 3.5 you will learn about:

- prime numbers
- factors of numbers
- multiples of numbers
- square numbers and cube numbers

Prime numbers

A *prime* number is divisible by only two different numbers: by itself and by one. The first six prime numbers are 2, 3, 5, 7, 11, 13. Note that one is *not* a prime number.

Exercise 1M

1 Draw a number square like the one shown.

1	2	3	4	5	6	7	8	9	10
11	12	13	14	15	16	17	18	19	20
21	22	23	24	25	26	27	28	29	30
31	32	33	34	35	36	37	38	39	40
41	42	43	44	45	46	47	48	49	50
51	52	53	54	55	56	57	58	59	60
61	62	63	64	65	66	67	68	69	70
71	72	73	74	75	76	77	78	79	80
81	82	83	84	85	86	87	88	89	90
91	92	93	94	95	96	97	98	99	100

(a) Cross out in pencil the number 1.

(b) Cross out in pencil all the even numbers, but leave the number 2.

(c) Draw a red circle around all the numbers divisible by 3, but leave the number 3.

(d) Cross out in pencil all the numbers divisible by 5, but leave the number 5.

(e) Draw a green circle around all the numbers divisible by 7, but leave the number 7.

(f) Cross out in red all the numbers divisible by 11, but leave the number 11.

The numbers which have been left blank are all the prime numbers between 1 and 100. You have drawn a square for finding prime numbers known as the 'sieve of Eratosthenes'. Eratosthenes was a famous Greek mathematician working over 2000 years ago.

2 You should be able to see several patterns in the table.

(a) The numbers divisible by 3 form diagonals across the table.

(b) The numbers divisible by 11 form one diagonal across the table.

(c) The numbers divisible by 7 form a pattern which is not so obvious. Can you describe it?

Exercise 1E

1 Write down the one number in each list which is prime.

> Prime numbers are used to generate codes and are used for security in credit cards and internet banking

   (a)   6,   7,   8,   9,   10

   (b)   18,   19,   20,   21,   22

   (c)   36,   37,   38,   39,   40

   (d)   84,   85,   86,   87,   88,   89

2 How many prime numbers are there between 1 and 100?

3 Write down two prime numbers which add up to another prime number. Do this in three ways.

4 How many of the prime numbers are even?

5 How many of the prime numbers between 1 and 100 are odd?

6 Find three pairs of prime numbers with a difference of 4 between the numbers.

7 When two prime numbers are added the answer is 22.

   What could the two numbers be?

8 (a) List the prime numbers ending in 1.

   (b) List the prime numbers ending in 7.

   (c) Apart from 5 why do no prime numbers end in 5?

9 Answer *true* or *false* for the statement below:

   'For all whole numbers greater than one there is at least one prime number between that number and its double.'

10 A rectangle has an area of 23 cm². Its length and width are both a whole number of centimetres. What is the perimeter of the rectangle?

11 Find three prime numbers which add up to another prime number.

12 (Harder) Use a calculator to find which of the following are prime numbers.

   (a) 103   (b) 145   (c) 151   (d) 188

> Hint: Divide by the prime numbers 2, 3, 5, 7, ...

   (e) 143   (f) 108   (g) 221   (h) 293

   (i) 493   (j) 323   (k) 1999   (l) 2639

146

Factors

- The number 12 can be written as two numbers multiplied together in three different ways

    | 1 × 12 | | 2 × 6 | | 3 × 4 |

    The numbers 1, 12, 2, 6, 3, 4 are all the *factors* of 12.

- | 1 × 8 | = 8 | 2 × 4 | = 8

    The factors of 8 are 1, 2, 4, 8.

Exercise 2M

Write down all the factors of the following numbers

1 6 2 4 3 10 4 7 5 15

6 18 7 24 8 21 9 36 10 40

11 32 12 31 13 60 14 63 15 85

16 Find two 1-digit numbers that have 4 factors.

17 Find two numbers less than 20 that have 6 factors.

18 The number in each circle is the product of the numbers in the squares on either side.
Find the missing numbers.

(a)
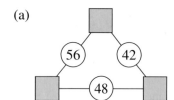

(b)
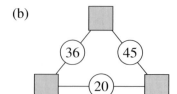

(c)
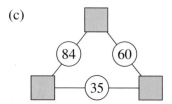

(d)
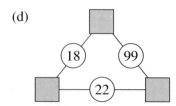

Exercise 2E

1 Write down all the factors of the following numbers

   (a) 50   (b) 44   (c) 100   (d) 29

2 Factors of a number which are also prime numbers are called *prime factors*. We can find
   these prime factors using a 'factor tree'

   (a) Here is a factor tree for 60   (b) Here is a factor tree for 24

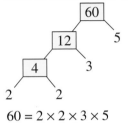

$$60 = 2 \times 2 \times 3 \times 5$$

   All prime numbers

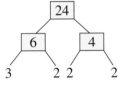

$$24 = 3 \times 2 \times 2 \times 2$$

   (c) You can turn the diagram upside down and then draw a
       trunk around the number and branches to give a real 'tree
       shape'. Some people like to draw the prime factors inside
       apples, pears, bananas and so on.

   (d) Draw a factor tree for 36.

In questions 3 to 14 draw a factor tree for each number.

   3 28   4 32   5 34   6 81

   7 84   8 216   9 294   10 200

   11 1500   12 2464   13 4620   14 98175

15 What is the smallest number with exactly 3 factors?

16 What is the smallest number with exactly

   (a) 4 factors

   (b) 5 factors?

Multiples

The *multiples* of 5 divide by 5 with no remainder.

The first four multiples of 5 are 5, 10, 15, 20.

The first four multiples of 6 are 6, 12, 18, 24.

> The multiples of 5 are the numbers in
> the 5 times table

148

Exercise 3M

Write down the first four multiples of:

1. 3   2. 4   3. 2   4. 7   5. 10

Write down the first six multiples of:

6. 5   7. 8   8. 9   9. 11   10. 20

11. Copy and complete

    (a) 25, 30, 35 and 60 are all multiples of ☐

    (b) 14, 21, 35 and 70 are all multiples of ☐

    (c) 8, 12, 20 and 28 are all multiples of ☐ and ☐

In questions 12 to 16 find the 'odd one out'. (The number which is not a multiple of the number given.)

12. Multiples of 6:   18, 24, 32, 48, 54.   13. Multiples of 11:   33, 77, 101, 132.

14. Multiples of 10:   5, 10, 20, 30, 60.   15. Multiples of 9:   18, 27, 45, 56, 72.

16. Multiples of 7:   49, 77, 91, 105, 18.

17.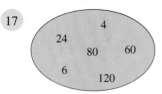
    Write down the numbers in the hoop which are:

    (a) multiples of 12

    (b) factors of 12

18. Write each line with either 'multiple' or 'factor' in the space.

    (a) 15 is a ☐ of 5

    (b) 8 is a ☐ of 32

    (c) 9 is a ☐ of 90

    (d) 6 is a ☐ of both 18 and 30

19. Find three numbers that are multiples of both 3 and 4.

20. Find three numbers that are multiples of both 2 and 5.

21. Find three numbers that are multiples of 2, 3 and 5.

22. Find two numbers that are multiples of 2, 4 and 6.

L.C.M. and H.C.F.

The first few multiples of 4 are 4, 8, 12, 16, ◯, 24, 28 ...

The first few multiples of 5 are 5, 10, 15, ◯, 25, 30, 35 ...

The *Least Common Multiple* (L.C.M) of 4 and 5 is 20.

It is the lowest number which is in both lists.

Exercise 3E

1 (a) Write down the first six multiples of 2

(b) Write down the first six multiples of 5

(c) Write down the L.C.M. of 2 and 5

2 (a) Write down the first four multiples of 4

(b) Write down the first four multiples of 12

(c) Write down the L.C.M. of 4 and 12

3 (a) Write down the first six multiples of 3

(b) Write down the first six multiples of 5

(c) Write down the L.C.M. of 3 and 5

4 Find the L.C.M. of

(a) 6 and 9   (b) 8 and 12   (c) 14 and 35

(d) 2, 4 and 6   (e) 3, 5 and 10   (f) 4, 7 and 9

The factors of 12 are 1, 2, 3, ◯, 6, 12

The factors of 20 are 1, 2, ◯, 5, 10, 20

The *Highest Common Factor* (H.C.F.) of 12 and 20 is 4

It is the highest number which is in both lists.

5 The table shows the factors and common factors of 24 and 36

number	factors	common factors
24	1, 2, 3, 4, 6, 8, 12, 24	⎫
36	1, 2, 3, 4, 6, 9, 12, 18, 36	⎬ 1, 2, 3, 4, 6, 12 ⎭

Write down the H.C.F. of 24 and 36.

6   The table shows the factors and common factors of 18 and 24

number	factors	common factors
18	1, 2, 3, 6, 9, 18	1, 2, 3, 6
24	1, 2, 3, 4, 6, 8, 12, 24	

Write down the H.C.F. of 18 and 24.

7   Find the H.C.F. of

(a) 12 and 18   (b) 22 and 55   (c) 45 and 72

(d) 12, 18 and 30   (e) 36, 60 and 72   (f) 20, 40 and 50

8   Don't confuse your L.C.M. s with your H.C.F. s!

(a) Find the H.C.F. of 12 and 30.

(b) Find the L.C.M. of 8 and 20.

(c) Write down two numbers whose H.C.F. is 11

(d) Write down two numbers whose L.C.M. is 10

Hint: make a table like that in question 6

9   Given that $30 = 2 \times 3 \times 5$ and $165 = 3 \times 5 \times 11$, find the highest common factor of 30 and 165 [i.e. The highest number that goes into 30 and 165]

10 If $315 = 3 \times 3 \times 5 \times 7$ and $273 = 3 \times 7 \times 13$, find the highest common factor of 315 and 273

Square numbers and cube numbers

Exercise 4M

1

$1 \times 1 = ①$

④
$2 \times 2 = ④$

⑨
$3 \times 3 = ⑨$

$4 \times 4 = ⑯$

(a) The first four *square* numbers are 1, 4, 9, 16

(b) Draw diagrams with labels to show the next three square numbers.

2 A square number is obtained by multiplying a number by itself.

3×3 is written 3^2 (We say '3 squared . . .')

4×4 is written 4^2

Work out

(a) 5^2 (b) 8^2 (c) 10^2 (d) 1^2

3 Work out

(a) $3^2 + 4^2$ (b) $1^2 + 2^2 + 3^2$ (c) $9^2 + 10^2$

4 The sum of the square numbers 9 and 81 is 90. Find a pair of square numbers with a sum of

(a) 13   (b) 73   (c) 40   (d) 181

(e) 125   (f) 97   (g) 74   (h) 113

5 Here is a 6×6 square divided into 9 smaller squares.

Draw a 5×5 square and design a pattern which divides it into eight smaller squares.

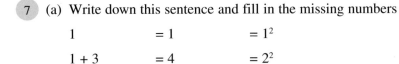

6 Which square number is between

(a) 50 and 70   (b) 70 and 100   (c) 150 and 180?

7 (a) Write down this sentence and fill in the missing numbers

1	= 1	= 1^2
1 + 3	= 4	= 2^2
1 + 3 + 5	= ☐	= ☐²
1 + 3 + 5 + 7	= ☐	= ☐²

(b) Write down the next five lines of the sequence.

Exercise 4E

1 Which numbers below are *not* square numbers?

     1   4   8   25   49   84

2 What number when multiplied by itself gives

(a) 49   (b) 121   (c) 169

3   Look at the numbers in the pentagon.

Write down the numbers which are:

(a) factors of 16

(b) prime numbers

(c) multiples of 3

(d) square numbers

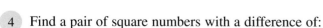

4   Find a pair of square numbers with a difference of:

(a) 7   (b) 80   (c) 84   (d) 300

(e) 45   (f) 32   (g) 39   (h) 105

5   The *square root* of a number is the number which is multiplied by itself to give that number. The symbol for square root is $\sqrt{\ }$.

So $\sqrt{9} = 3$, $\sqrt{16} = 4$, $\sqrt{100} = 10$

Work out

(a) $\sqrt{25}$ (b) $\sqrt{81}$ (c) $\sqrt{49}$ (d) $\sqrt{1}$

6   Copy the following and fill in the spaces

(a) $7^2 = 49$, $\sqrt{49} = \square$ (b) $14^2 = 196$, $\sqrt{196} = \square$

(c) $21^2 = 441$, $\sqrt{\square} = 21$ (d) $3.3^2 = 10.89$, $\sqrt{\square} = 3.3$

7   *Lagrange's theorem.* A famous mathematician called Lagrange proved that every whole number could be written as the sum of four or fewer square numbers.

For example: $21 = 16 + 4 + 1$

$19 = 16 + 1 + 1 + 1$

$35 = 25 + 9 + 1$

Check that the theorem applies to the following numbers.

(a) 10   (b) 24   (c) 47

(d) 66   (e) 98   (f) 63

(g) 120   (h) 141   (i) 423

If you can find a number which needs more than four squares you will have disproved Lagrange's theorem and a new theorem will be named after you.

8 The numbers 1, 8, 27 are the first three *cube* numbers.

$1 \times 1 \times 1 = 1^3 = 1$ (we say '1 cubed')

$2 \times 2 \times 2 = 2^3 = 8$ (we say '2 cubed')

$3 \times 3 \times 3 = 3^3 = 27$ (we say '3 cubed')

Work out the next three cube numbers.

9 Look at the diagram in question ⑶.

Write down the numbers which are cube numbers.

10 The odd numbers can be added in groups to give an interesting sequence:

$$1 \qquad\qquad = 1 \qquad\qquad = 1^3$$

$$3 + 5 \qquad\qquad = 8 \qquad\qquad = 2^3$$

$$7 + 9 + 11 \qquad\qquad = 27 \qquad\qquad = 3^3$$

Write down the next three rows of the sequence to see if the sum of each row always gives a cube number.

Satisfied numbers

The number 4 is an even number *and* a square number. It *satisfies* both categories.

1 Copy the grid below and use a pencil for your answers (so that you can rub out mistakes.)

Write the numbers from 1 to 9, one in each box, so that all the numbers satisfy the conditions for both the row and the column.

	Number between 5 and 9	Square number	Prime number
Factor of 6	6	?	?
Even number	?	?	?
Odd number	?	?	?

2 Copy the grid and write the numbers from 1 to 9, one in each box.

	Prime number	Multiple of 3	Factor of 16
Number greater than 5			
Odd number			
Even number			

3   This one is more difficult. Write the numbers from 1 to 16, one in each box. There are several correct solutions. Ask a friend to check yours.

	Prime number	Odd number	Factor of 16	Even number
Numbers less than 7				
Factor of 36				
Numbers less than 12				
Numbers between 11–17				

4   Design a grid with categories of your own and ask a friend to solve it.

Happy numbers

- (a) Take any number, say 23.
  - (b) Square the digits and add: $2^2 + 3^2 = 4 + 9 = 13$
  - (c) Repeat (b) for the answer: $1^2 + 3^2 = 1 + 9 = 10$
  - (d) Repeat (b) for the answer: $1^2 + 0^2 = 1$

  23 is a so-called 'happy' number because it ends in one.

- Take another number, say 7.

  Write 7 as 07 to maintain the pattern of squaring and adding the digits.

  Here is the sequence:

$$07$$
$$0 + 49 = \quad 49$$
$$16 + 81 = \quad 97$$
$$81 + 49 = \quad 130$$
$$1 + 9 + 0 = \quad 10$$
$$1 + 0 = 1$$

So 7 is a happy number also.

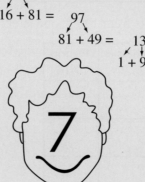

With practice you may be able to do the arithmetic in your head and write:

$07 \rightarrow 49 \rightarrow 97 \rightarrow 130 \rightarrow 10 \rightarrow 1$.

You may find it helpful to make a list of the square numbers $1^2, 2^2, 3^2, \dots 9^2$.

- Your task is to find all the happy numbers from 1 to 100 and to circle them on a grid like the one shown. This may appear to be a very time-consuming and rather tedious task! But remember: Good mathematicians always look for short cuts and for ways of reducing the working.

So think about what you are doing and good luck!

As a final check you should find that there are 20 happy numbers from 1 to 100.

1	2	3	4	5	6	7	8	9	10
11	12	13	14	15	16	17	18	19	20
21	22	23	24	25	26	27	28	29	30
31	32	33	34	35	36	37	38	39	40
41	42	43	44	45	46	47	48	49	50
51	52	53	54	55	56	57	58	59	60
61	62	63	64	65	66	67	68	69	70
71	72	73	74	75	76	77	78	79	80
81	82	83	84	85	86	87	88	89	90
91	92	93	94	95	96	97	98	99	100

CHECK YOURSELF ON UNITS 3.1, 3.2, 3.3, 3.4 AND 3.5

1   Using coordinates with positive and negative numbers

Draw a grid like this…

(a) Plot these points on the grid and join them up in the order given:

   (2, 2), (3, 3), (3, 4), (2, 5), (5, 5), (4, 4), (4, 3), (5, 2), (2, 2)

(b) How many lines of symmetry does the shape have?

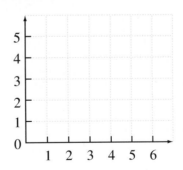

Draw a grid like the one shown.

(c) Plot the points A(–2, 1) B(2, 3) C(2, 0) D(–2, –2)

(d) Join the points to make a shape. Name the shape.

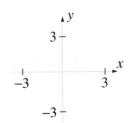

2 Solving problems involving shapes

(a) Points A, D and E are three vertices of a rectangle. Write down the coordinates of the other vertex.

(b) C, E and D are three vertices of a square. Write down the coordinates of the other vertex.

(c) B, C and E are three vertices of a parallelogram. Write down the coordinates of the other vertex.

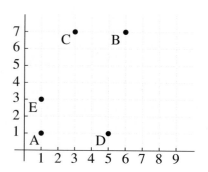

3 Long multiplication and division

Workout

(a) 27 × 16   (b) 54 × 36   (c) 1872 ÷ 13

4 Solving word problems

(a) Find the total cost of 52 magazines at 75p each.

(b) It costs £744 to hire a coach for 31 football supporters. How much does each person pay?

5 Measuring shapes and using place value with decimals

Use a ruler to measure the length of each object.

(a)   (b)   (c)

Write the decimal number equivalent to:

(d) seven tenths   (e) three hundredths   (f) fifteen hundredths

6 Writing numbers in order of size

Arrange the numbers in order of size, smallest first

(a) 0.5, 0.31, 0.08, 0.411

(b) 0.007, 0.62, 0.602, 0.1

(c) Work out the value indicated at A and at B

7 Adding and subtracting decimals

Work out

(a) $5 + 0.27$ (b) $6.7 - 3.25$ (c) $0.03 + 8 + 1.4$

(d) Rio spent £6.40 in a newsagent and £9.78 in the post office. How much change did he get from £20?

8 Multiplying and dividing by 10, 100, 1000

Work out

(a) 3.61×10 (b) $11.94 \div 10$ (c) 1.4×100 (d) $6 \div 100$

Copy and complete

(e) $6.4 \times \square = 6400$ (f) $6300 \div \square = 6.3$ (g) $0.06 \times \square = 0.6$

9 Multiplying decimals by whole numbers

Work out

(a) 2.7×5 (b) 0.64×6 (c) 1.54×8

(d) Find the total cost of 2 tins at £1.65 each and 7 bottles at £0.40 each.

10 Dividing decimals by whole numbers

Work out

(a) $9.42 \div 2$ (b) $31.8 \div 6$ (c) $22 \div 4$

(d) A cake weighing 2.24 kg is shared equally between seven people. How much does each person get?

11 Prime numbers, factors and multiples

Look at these numbers   55   17   9   25

(a) Which number is a prime number?

(b) Which number is a multiple of 11?

(c) Which number is a factor of 36?

(d) Find a number less than 20 which has six factors.

12 Square numbers and cube numbers

Work out

(a) 7^2

(b) 1^3

(c) $3^3 + 4^2$

(d) $10^2 - 2^3$

Find a pair of square numbers with a difference of:

(e) 13

(f) 16

(g) 99

3.6 Straight line graphs

In section 3.6 you will learn about:

- lines which are parallel to the axes

- sloping lines

- finding the equation of a line

- drawing straight line graphs

Lines parallel to the axes

- The points P, Q, R and S have coordinates (4, 4), (4, 3), (4, 2) and (4, 1) and they all lie on a straight line. Since the x-coordinate of all the points is 4, we say the *equation* of the line is $x = 4$.

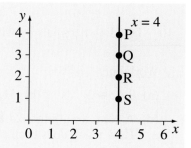

- The points A, B, C and D have coordinates (1, 3), (2, 3), (3, 3) and (4, 3) and they all lie on a straight line. Since the y-coordinate of all the points is 3, we say the *equation* of the line is $y = 3$.

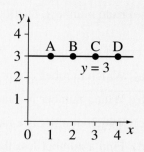

Exercise 1M

1 Write down the equations for the lines marked A, B and C.

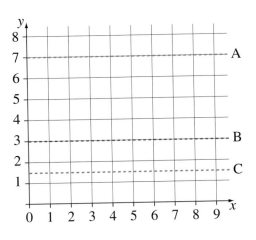

2 Write down the equations for the lines marked P, Q and R.

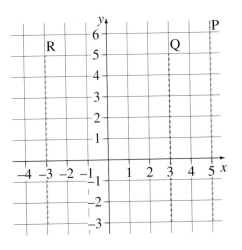

In questions 3 and 4 below there is a red line A, a blue line B and a green line C.

Write down the equations of the lines in each question.

3

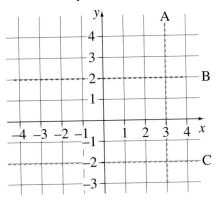

4

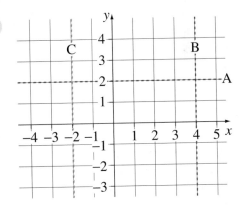

5 On squared paper

(a) Draw the lines $y = 2$ and $x = 3$. At what point do they meet?

(b) Draw the lines $y = 5$ and $x = 1$. At what point do they meet?

(c) Draw the lines $x = 7$ and $y = 3$. At what point do they meet?

6 In the diagram, E and N lie on the line with equation $y = 1$. B and K lie on the line $x = 5$. In parts (a) to (h) find the equation of the line passing through the points given:

(a) A and D

(b) A, B and I

(c) M and P

(d) I and H

(e) L and E

(f) D, K and G

(g) C, M, L and H

(h) P and F

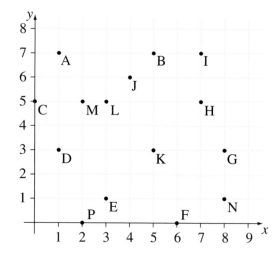

Relating x and y

● The sloping line passes through the following points:
(1, 1), (2, 2), (3, 3), (4, 4), (5, 5).

For each point, the y coordinate is equal to the x coordinate.

The equation of the line is $y = x$ (or $x = y$)

This is the rule for any point on the line

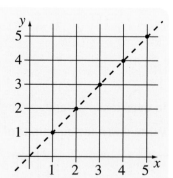

● This line passes through:
(0, 1), (1, 2), (2, 3), (3, 4), (4, 5).

For each point the y coordinate is one more than the x coordinate.

The equation of the line is $y = x + 1$

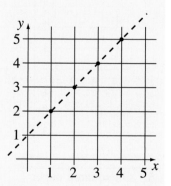

We could also say that the x coordinate is always one less than the y coordinate. The equation of the line could then be written as $x = y - 1$.

[Most mathematicians use the equation beginning '$y = $'].

- This line slopes the other way and passes through: (0, 5), (1, 4), (2, 3), (3, 2), (4, 1), (5, 0).

  The sum of the x coordinate and the y coordinate is always 5.

  The equation of the line is $x + y = 5$

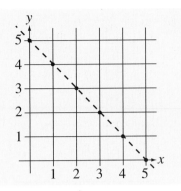

Exercise 1E

For each question write down the coordinates of the points marked. Find the equation of the line through the points.

1

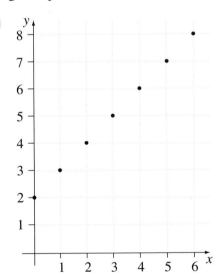

2

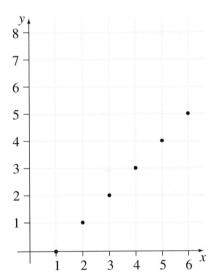

3

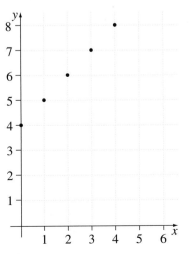

4

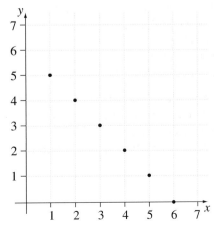

5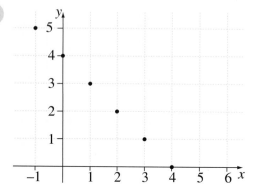

6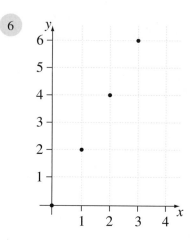

7 Look at the graph. Find the equation for

(a) line A

(b) line B

(c) line C

(d) line D

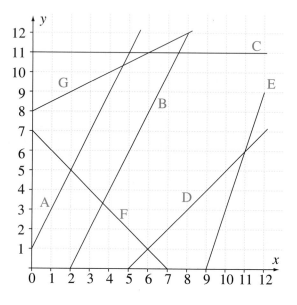

8 This is the table of the points on line G

x	0	2	4	6
y	8	9	10	11

Find the equation for line G.
[Hint: It starts $y = \frac{1}{2}x + \ldots$]

9 This is the table for the points on line E.

x	9	10	11	12
y	0	3	6	9

Find the equation of line E.

10 Make a table for the points on line F.

x	0	1	2	3
y	7			

Find the equation of line F.

Finding points on a line

The rule (or equation) for a line is $y = x + 1$.

Points which lie on the line satisfy the equation $y = x + 1$

So when $x = 3$, $y = 3 + 1 = 4$. The point $(3, 4)$ is on the line.

when $x = 5$, $y = 5 + 1 = 6$. The point $(5, 6)$ is on the line.

Exercise 2M

1   For the line $y = x + 4$, find the y values for

   (a) $x = 3$ (b) $x = 5$ (c) $x = 0$

2   For the line $y = x - 3$, find the y values for

   (a) $x = 6$ (b) $x = 8$ (c) $x = 10$

3   For the line $y = 3x$, find the y values for

   (a) $x = 2$ (b) $x = 5$ (c) $x = 0$

4   Which of the points below lie on the line $y = x + 7$?

   A(3, 10)   B(6, 1)   C(5, 12)

5   Which of the points below lie on the line $y = 2x - 1$?

   A(0, 1)   B(2, 3)   C(5, 9)

6   Here are two lines: $y = x + 2$ and $y = 2x$.
   On which of these lines do the following points lie?

   A(5, 7)   B(4, 8)   C (0, 0)

   D(1, 2)   E(10, 12)   F(0, 2)

7   Here are two lines: $y = x - 3$ and $y = 3x - 2$.
   On which of these lines do the following points lie?

   P(2, 4)   Q(3, 0)   R(5, 2)

   S(0, -2)   T(3, 7)   U(7, 4)

164

8 Look at the graph. Decide which of the equations below matches each line.

$y = x - 2$ $y = 4$

$y = 8 - x$ $y = 2x$

$x = 4$

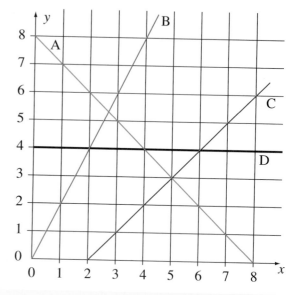

Drawing graphs

- The equation of a line is $y = x + 2$. Here is a list of five points on the line: (0, 2), (1, 3), (2, 4), (3, 5), (4, 6)

  The points are plotted on a graph and the line $y = x + 2$ is drawn. Notice that the line extends beyond (0, 2) and (4, 6)

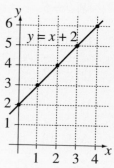

Exercise 2E

1 The equation of a line is $y = x + 3$. Copy and complete a list of points on the line:

(0, 3) (1, 4) (2, ☐) (3, ☐) (4, ☐)

Draw the graph of $y = x + 3$

2 The equation of a line is $y = x + 5$. Copy and complete a list of points on the line:

(0, 5) (1, 6) (2, ☐) (3, ☐) (4, ☐)

Draw the graph of $y = x + 5$

In questions 3 to 10 you are given the equation of a line and a list of points on the line. Fill in the missing numbers and then draw the graph.

3 $y = x - 2$;   (0, −2), (1, −1), (2, ☐), (3, ☐), (4, ☐)

4 $y = x - 4$;   (0, − 4), (1, −3), (2, ☐), (3, ☐), (4, ☐)

5 $y = 2x$;   (0, 0), (1, 2), (2, ☐), (3, ☐), (4, ☐)

6 $y = 2x + 1$;   (0, ☐), (2, ☐), (4, ☐)

7 $y = 2x - 2$;   (0, ☐), (2, ☐), (4, ☐)

8 $y = 6 - x$;   (1, ☐), (3, ☐), (5, ☐), (6, ☐)

9 $y = 4 - x$;   (0, ☐), (2, ☐), (4, ☐)

10 $y = 3x + 2$;   (0, ☐), (1, ☐), (2, ☐)

11 Draw the lines $y = 5 - x$ and $y = 2x - 1$ on the same graph.
Write down the co-ordinates of the point where the lines meet.

3.7 Handling data

In section 3.7 you will learn about:

- bar charts and bar-line graphs

- data in groups and line graphs

- pie charts

- problems answered using statistics

Bar charts and bar-line graphs

When you do a survey the information you collect is called *data*. This data is usually easier for someone else to understand if you display it in some sort of chart or graph.

(a) The scores of 35 golfers competing in a
tournament were

68 74 71 72 71 68 70
74 69 71 70 67 73 71
70 74 69 72 73 74 71
72 74 71 72 72 70 73
67 68 72 73 72 71 71

(b) A tally chart/frequency table is made
for the scores.

score	tally	frequency
67	‖	2
68	‖‖	3
69	‖	2
70	‖‖‖	4
71	卌 ‖‖	8
72	卌 ‖	7
73	‖‖‖	4
74	卌	5

166

(c) This data can be displayed on either a bar chart or on a bar-line graph. The '⌇' shows that a section on the horizontal axis has been cut out.

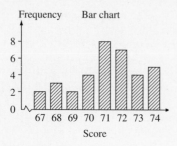
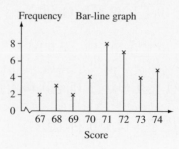

Exercise 1M

1. In a survey children were asked to name their favourite sport.

    (a) What was the most popular sport?

    (b) How many children chose Athletics?

    (c) How many children took part in the survey?

    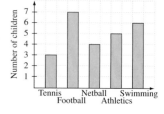

2. Here is a *bar-line graph* showing the number of children in the families of children in a school.

    (a) How many families had three children?

    (b) How many families were there altogether?

    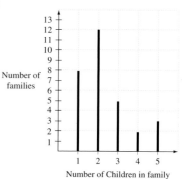

3. Collect your own data for a bar line graph like the one in question 2. Ask lots of people to state the number of children in their families.

    Draw a graph of the results and use colour to make it more attractive.

4. This table shows the number of different sorts of snacks sold by a shop.

    (a) How many snacks were sold on Thursday?

    (b) Each Aero costs 35p. How much was spent on Aeros in the whole week?

    (c) Draw a bar chart to show the number of each kind of snack sold in a week.

	Mon	Tu	Wed	Th	Fri
Mars	3	1	0	0	3
Snickers	0	4	1	2	2
Twix	2	2	1	3	4
Aero	5	0	0	1	4
Crunchie	2	3	4	1	1
Kit Kat	5	0	2	1	1

    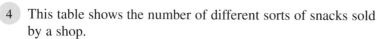

5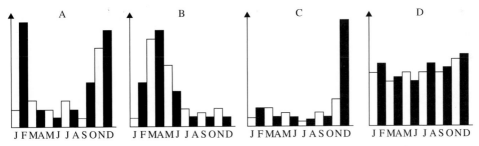

The monthly rainfall in the Lake District is shown left.

(a) How much rain fell in August?

(b) Which was the driest month in the year?

(c) Which was the wettest month in the year?

(d) In which months did 25 cm of rain fall?

(e) In which months did 30 cm of rain fall?

Exercise 1E

1 The bar charts show the sale of different things over a year but the labels on the charts have been lost. Decide which of the charts A, B, C or D shows sales of:

(a) Christmas trees

(b) Crisps

(c) Flower seeds

(d) Greetings cards [including Christmas, Valentine's Day, etc.]

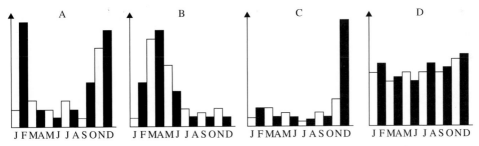

2 The number of people staying in two different hotels in each month of the year is shown below.

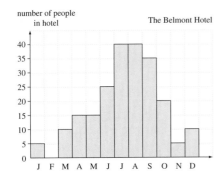

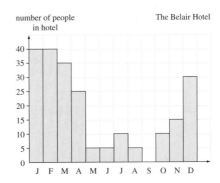

(a) How many people stayed in the 'Belmont' in July?

(b) How many people stayed in the 'Belair' in July?

(c) What was the total number of people staying in the two hotels in April?

(d) One hotel is in a ski resort and the other is by the seaside. Which is in the ski resort?

3

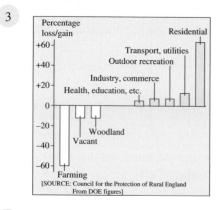

This chart shows changes of land use in rural areas in England between 1960 and 2000.

(a) What was the change in the area of land used for farming?

(b) Write down three activities that would go in the 'outdoor recreation' category.

(c) Describe the main features of the chart.

4 The chart shows the agricultural production figures for four crops in Pakistan. Pakistan has low rainfall but in recent years major irrigation schemes have been introduced. About 50% of the population is employed in agriculture.

Describe how the production of the four crops has changed over the years from 1960 to 2000.

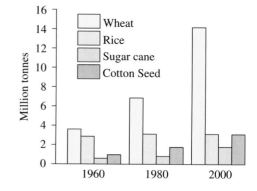

5 Here are details of the official languages spoken in countries around the world.

English	27% of the world population	French	4%
Chinese	19 %	Arabic	3%
Hindi	14%	Portuguese	3%
Spanish	6%	Malay	3%
Russian	5%	Bengali	3%
		Japanese	2%

(a) Draw a bar chart to illustrate this data.

(b) England is a fairly small country compared to China. How can you explain the figures given?

6   Some children were asked to state which was their favourite
T.V. programme from the list below.

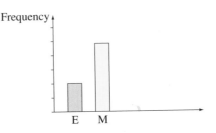

East Enders	E
MTV	M
Football Highlights	F
Neighbours	N
The Simpsons	S

The replies were: S N S M N E M F N M E M M M E N

F S N M M E S E N S E N N E N

N M E N N E M F N S E M N F N

Make a tally chart and then draw a bar chart to show the results

		Tally	Total
East Enders	E		
MTV	M		
Football Highlights	F		
Neighbours	N		
The Simpsons	S		

Frequency

E   M

7   Here are two paragraphs: one in English and one in French.
There is the same number of letters in each paragraph.

Luciano Gaucci Perugia's
"Chairman Gau" signed Al Saadi
Gaddafi, the son of the Libyan
dictator, who was described by an
Italian paper as "twice as slow as
slow itself". He then attempted to
sign a Sweden international – Hanna
Ljungberg, a star of women's
football. He also tried to dismiss
Ahn Jung Hwan because the South
Korea forward scored against Italy in
the 2002 World Cup finals.

Eurogoals Magazine
Les plus beaux buts des champi-
onnats européens de football Ce
magazine hebdomadaire de
cinquante-deux minutes présente
une sélection des meilleures ren-
contres du Championnat espagnol,
portugais, belge, néerlandais ou
français. L'acent est mis sur les
buts, et les matchs se soldant par un
0–0 sont systématiquement écartés.
Les grandes équipes telles que
l'Ajax d'Amsterdam ou le Real

(a) For each paragraph make a tally chart to record how many
letters there are in each word.

(b) Draw a bar chart for each language and write a sentence
about the main differences in the two charts.

Word length	Tally
1	
2	
3	

Data in groups and line graphs

- Here are the ages of the people at a wedding.

  33 11 45 22 50 38 23 54 18 72   5 58

  37   3 61 51   7 62 24 57 31 27 66 29

  25 39 48 15 52 25 35 18 49 63 13 74

  With so many different numbers over a wide range
  it is helpful to put the ages into *groups*.

- Here is the start of a tally chart

Ages	Tally	Total (Frequency)
0–9	III	3
10–19	IIII	5
20–29	IIII II	7
30–39		
40–49		
50–59		
60–69		
70–79		

- Here is the start of a frequency chart

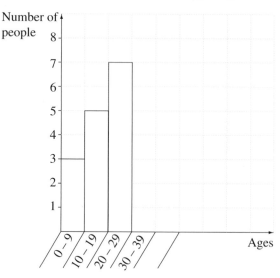

- Finish the tally chart and the frequency diagram.
  Notice that when the data is in groups the bars
  are touching.

Exercise 2M

1 Shruti started with one frog but it laid eggs and now she has lots!
   One day she measures all her little pets. Here are the lengths in mm.

   82 63 91 78 27 93 87 48 22 15

   42 28 84 65 87 55 79 66 85 38

   (a) Make a tally chart and then draw the frequency diagram.

Length (mm)	Tally	Frequency
0–20		
21–40		
41–60		
61–80		
81–100		

   (b) How many frogs were more than 60 mm long?

2   The heights, in cm, of 30 children are shown below

    134 146 141 147 151 141 137 159 142 146

    151 157 143 154 146 143 149 151 141 148

    136 144 147 152 147 137 133 140 139 155

(a) Put the heights into groups

class interval	frequency
130 ≤ h < 135	
135 ≤ h < 140	
140 ≤ h < 145	
145 ≤ h < 150	

(b) Draw a frequency diagram

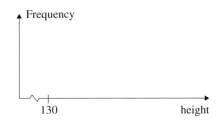

3   Tom has lots of snakes and he likes to weigh them every week. The weights are shown.

(a) How many snakes weigh between 61 and 80 grams?

(b) How many snakes weigh less than 41 grams?

(c) How many snakes does he have altogether?

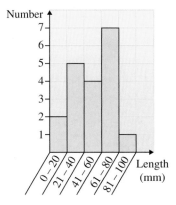

4   Farmer Gray rears pigs. As an experiment, he decided to feed half of his pigs with their normal diet and the other half on a new high fibre diet. The diagrams show the weight of the pigs in the two groups.

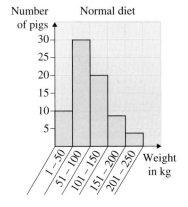

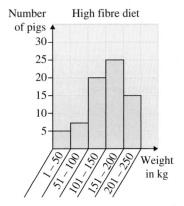

In one sentence describe what effect the new diet had.

Exercise 2E

1 A teacher has a theory that pupils' test results are affected by the amount of T.V. watched at home.

With the willing cooperation of the children's parents, the pupils were split into two groups:

Group X watched at least two hours of T.V. per day.

Group Y watched a maximum of half an hour per day.

The pupils were given two tests: one at the start of the experiment and another test six months later. Here are the results:

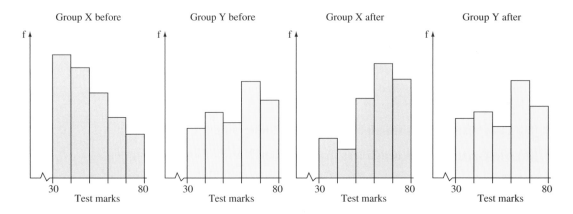

Look carefully at the frequency diagrams. What conclusions can you draw? Was the teacher's theory correct? Give details of how the pupils in group X and in group Y performed in the two tests.

2 Here is some information about fireworks.

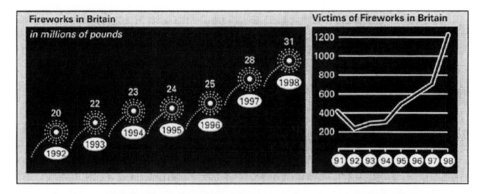

In which year were the lowest number of people injured by fireworks?

3   A car went on a five hour journey starting at 12.00 with a full tank of petrol. The volume of petrol in the tank was measured after every hour; the results are shown below.

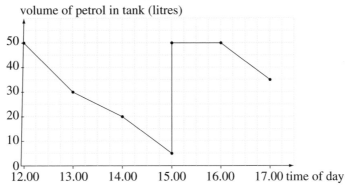

(a) How much petrol was in the tank at 13.00?

(b) At what time was there 5 litres in the tank?

(c) How much petrol was used in the first hour of the journey?

(d) What happened at 15.00?

(e) What do you think happened between 15.00 and 16.00?

(f) How much petrol was used between 12.00 and 17.00?

4   This diagram shows the temperature and rainfall readings in one week.

The rainfall is shown as the bar chart.

The temperature is shown as the line graph.

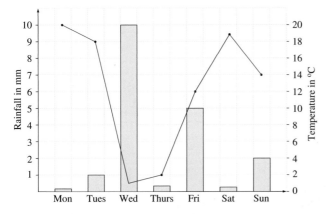

(a) Use both graphs to describe the weather on Monday.

(b) On which day was the weather cold and wet?

(c) Compare the weather on Thursday and Saturday.

Pie charts

In a pie chart a circle is divided into sectors to display information. Pie charts are often used to show the results of a survey. The sectors of the circle show what *fraction* of the total is in each group. Here are two pie charts.

- How children go to a school in the Alps.
- People in a Spanish jail.

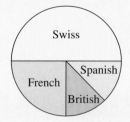

$\frac{1}{2}$ of the children walk to school

$\frac{1}{4}$ of the children swim to school

$\frac{1}{4}$ of the children hang glide to school

$\frac{1}{8}$ of the people were Spanish

$\frac{1}{8}$ of the people were British

$\frac{1}{4}$ of the people were French

$\frac{1}{2}$ of the people were Swiss

Exercise 3M

1 The pie chart shows the contents of a box of chocolates.

   (a) What fraction of the contents is chocolate?

   (b) What fraction of the contents is toffee?

   (c) If the total weight of the packet is 400 g, what is the weight of nuts?

2 In a survey children said what pets they had at home.

   (a) What fraction of the children had a hamster?

   (b) What fraction of the children had a dog?

   (c) 40 children took part in the survey. How many of these children had a pet spider?

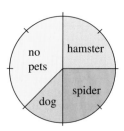

3 In another survey children were asked what *pests* they had at home. One third of the children said, 'my sister'.

What angle would you draw for the 'my sister' sector on a pie chart?

4 The pie chart shows the results of a survey in which 80 people were asked how they travelled to work. Copy this table and fill it in.

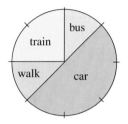

Method	car	walk	train	bus
Number of people				

Exercise 3E

1 In 2007 and 2008 children were asked in a survey to say which country they would most like to go to for a holiday. The pie charts show the results.

2007

100 children
answered in
each year

Countries in the
'others' section
had only one or
two votes each.

2008

(a) Which was the most popular country in the 2007 survey?

(b) Which country was less popular in 2008 than in 2007?

(c) *Roughly* how many children said 'Jamaica' in the 2007 survey?

2 A hidden observer watched Philip in a 40 minute maths lesson.

He spent: 20 minutes talking to a friend.

10 minutes getting ready to work,

5 minutes working,

5 minutes packing up.

Draw and label a pie chart to show Philip's lesson.

3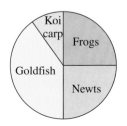

Jodie counted the different animals in her pond. Altogether there were 200 animals or fish.

(a) *About* how many frogs were there?

(b) *About* how many goldfish were there?

4　The children at a school were asked to state their favourite colour. Here are the results.

Boys

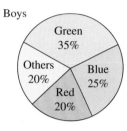

Girls

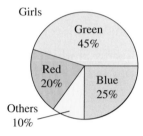

There were 40 boys　　　　　There were 25 girls

John says 'The same number of boys and girls chose red.'

Tara says 'More boys than girls chose blue.'

(a) Use both charts to explain whether or not John is right.

(b) Use both charts to explain whether or not Tara is right.

Problems answered using statistics

Many problems in mathematics and other subjects, like science or geography can be solved by statistical methods.

The data relevant to such problems might be obtained from:

● a survey of a sample of people;

● an experiment;

● published material, such as tables or charts, from reference books.

Here are two examples of problems which can be answered using statistical methods.

1　Do different newspapers use words of different length or sentences of different length? Why would they do this?

In this case you could conduct an experiment by choosing a similar page from different newspapers.
Record your results in a table.

Number of words in a sentence	1–5	6–10	11–15	16–20	21 or more
Times					
Sun					
Mail					

2　What factors are most important to the customers of supermarkets?
In this case you could conduct a survey asking about price of food, quality of food, speed of checkouts, ease of car parking and so on.

You would need questions designed so that shoppers could state the importance, or otherwise, of the factors you include.

Reporting on results

Most work of this nature is easier to understand if data is presented in the form of graphs and charts. You should *justify* the choice of the data you present. You might find it helpful to include calculations of mean or range depending on the context.

Your report should highlight the main findings of your work and you should write a clear *summary* which relates back to the original problem.

3.8 Probability 1

In this section you will learn about:

- the probability scale
- experimental probability
- equally likely outcomes
- expected probability

In probability we ask questions like…

'How likely is it?'

'What are the chances of…?'

Here are some questions where we do not know the answer…

'Will it rain tomorrow?'

'Who will win the next World Cup?'

'Will the school be struck by lightning?'

Some events are certain. Some events are impossible.

Some events are in between certain and impossible.

The probability of an event is a measure of the chance of it happening.

The probability (or chance) of an event occurring is measured on a scale like this…

| impossible | unlikely | evens | likely | certain |

178

Exercise 1M

Draw a probability scale like this…

impossible   unlikely   evens   likely   certain

①

Draw an arrow to show the chance of the events below happening.

Draw more scales if needed

[The arrow for question 1 has been done for you.]

1   When a card is selected from a pack it will be an 'ace'.

2   When a coin is tossed it will show a 'head'.

3   The letter 'a' appears somewhere on the next page of
    this book.

4   When a drawing pin is dropped it will land 'point up'.

5   There will be at least one baby born somewhere in Great
    Britain on the first day of next month.

6   You have the same birthday as the Prime Minister.

7   The day after Monday will be Tuesday.

8   There will be a burst pipe in the school heating system
    next week and the school will have to close for 3 days.

9   You will blink your eyes in the next minute.

10   You will be asked to tidy your room this week.

11   When a slice of toast is dropped, it will land on the
     floor buttered side down.

12   You will discover a tarantula in your bed tonight.

13   England will win the next World Cup at football.

14   Your maths teacher has a black belt in Judo.

15   You will be captured by aliens tonight.

Probability as a number

Different countries have different words for saying how likely or unlikely any particular event is.

All over the world people use probability as a way of doing this, using numbers on a scale instead of words.

The scale looks like this…

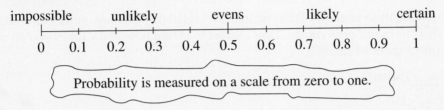

Probability is measured on a scale from zero to one.

Exercise 1E

Look at the events in the last exercise and for each one estimate the probability of it occurring using a probability from 0 to 1.

As an example in question 1 you might write 'about 0.1'. Copy each question and write your estimate of its probability at the end.

Experimental probability

The chance of certain events occurring can easily be predicted. For example the chance of tossing a head with an ordinary coin. Many events, however, cannot be so easily predicted.

Experiment: To find the experimental probability that the third word in the third line on any page in this book contains the letter 'a'. (You could use a non-mathematical book if you prefer.)

Step 1. We will do 50 *trials*. Write down at random 50 page numbers between 1 and 180 (say 3, 15, 16, 21, 27, etc.).

Step 2. For each page look at the third word in the third line. This is a *trial*. If there is not a third word on the third line it still counts as a trial. (The third line might be all numbers.)

> 37
>
> **Angles in triangles**
> Draw a triangle of any shape on a piece of card and cut it out accurately. Now tear off the three corners as shown.

third line, third word

Step 3. If the word contains the letter 'a' this is a *success*.

Step 4. Make a tally chart like this…

Number of trials	Number of successes
⊥⊦⊦⊦ ⊥⊦⊦⊦ ‖	⊥⊦⊦⊦ ‖

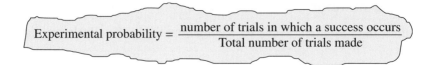

$$\text{Experimental probability} = \frac{\text{number of trials in which a success occurs}}{\text{Total number of trials made}}$$

Exercise 2M

Carry out experiments to work out the experimental probability of some of the following events. Use a tally chart to record your results. Don't forget to record how many times you do the experiment (the number of 'trials').

1   Roll a dice. What is the chance of rolling a six? Perform 100 trials.

2   Toss two coins. What is the chance of tossing two tails? Perform 100 trials.

3   Pick a counter from a bag containing counters of different colours. What is the chance of picking a red counter? Perform 100 trials.

4   Roll a pair of dice. What is the chance of rolling a double? Perform 100 trials.

5   Butter a piece of toast and drop it on the floor. What is the chance of it landing buttered side down? Would you expect to get the same result with margarine? How about butter and jam? Suppose you don't toast the bread?
If you run into difficulties at home, blame your maths teacher, not the authors of this book.

Equally likely outcomes

When you roll a fair dice there are six *equally likely outcomes*.

You are equally likely to roll a 1, 2, 3, 4, 5 or 6.

So, for example, the probability of rolling a 3 is $\frac{1}{6}$.

You also have equally likely outcomes when you use a spinner with equal sectors.

In this spinner there are four equal sectors.

The probability of spinning yellow is $\frac{1}{4}$.

Exercise 3M

For each spinner what is the probability of getting red?

1    2    3 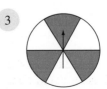   4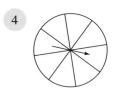

5   6   7   8

9   What is the probability of getting blue on each spinner?

  (a)   (b)   (c)   (d)

10   For this question you need a dice.

  (a) copy the table below and fill in the second row.

Number of rolls of dice	12	24	36	48	60
Number of 4s expected					
Actual number of 4s					

  (b) Now roll the dice 60 times, filling in the third row every 12 rolls.

11   One peg is selected at random from those shown.

     What is the probability of selecting a red peg?

Expected probability

For simple events, like throwing a dice or tossing a coin, we can work out the expected probability of an event occurring.

For a fair dice the *expected probability* of throwing a '3' is $\frac{1}{6}$,

For a normal coin the expected probability of tossing a 'head' is $\frac{1}{2}$

$$\text{Expected probability} = \frac{\text{the number of ways the event can happen}}{\text{the number of possible outcomes}}$$

Random choice: If a card is chosen at random from a pack it means that every card has an equal chance of being chosen.

Nine identical discs numbered 1, 2, 3, 4, 5, 6, 7, 8, 9 are put into a bag.
One disc is selected at random.
In this example there are 9 possible equally likely outcomes of a trial.

(a) The probability of selecting a '4' = $\frac{1}{9}$

This may be written p (selecting a '4') = $\frac{1}{9}$

(b) p (selecting an odd number) = $\frac{5}{9}$

(c) p (selecting a number greater than 5) = $\frac{4}{9}$

Exercise 3E

1   A bag contains a red ball, a blue ball and a yellow ball. One ball is chosen at
random. Copy and complete these sentences.

(a) The probability that the red ball is chosen is . . . $\frac{\square}{3}$

(b) The probability that the blue ball is chosen is . . . $\frac{\square}{\square}$

(c) The probability that the yellow ball is chosen is . . . $\frac{\square}{\square}$

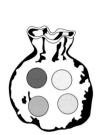

2   One ball is chosen at random from a bag which contains a red ball, a blue
ball, a yellow ball and a green ball. Write down the probability that the
chosen ball will be

(a) red   (b) blue   (c) yellow

3   One ball is chosen at random from a box which contains 2 red balls and
2 blue balls. Write down the probability that the chosen ball will be

(a) red

(b) blue

(c) yellow

4   A hat contains 2 white balls and 1 black ball. One ball
is chosen at random. Find the probability that it is

(a) white

(b) black

5   A pencil case contains pencils of the following colours:-
6 red, 3 black, 1 green and 1 blue. One pencil is selected
without looking. Find the probability that the pencil is

(a) red

(b) black

(c) green

6   I roll an ordinary dice. Find the probability that I score

(a) 3

(b) 1

(c) less than 5

7   Eight identical discs numbered 1, 2, 3, 4, 5, 6, 7, 8
are put into a bag. One disc is selected at random.
Find the probability of selecting

(a) a '5'   (b) an odd number   (c) a number less than 6

8   Nine identical discs numbered 1, 3, 4, 5, 7, 8, 10, 11, 15 are
put into a bag. One disc is selected at random. Find the
probability of selecting

(a) a '10'   (b) an even number   (c) a number more than 6

9   I buy a fish at random from a pond containing 3 piranhas,
2 baby sharks and 7 goldfish. Find the probability that
the fish I choose is

(a) a goldfish.   (b) a baby shark

(c) dangerous   (d) glad I rescued it!

10 A bag contains 4 red balls and 7 white balls. One ball
is selected at random. Find the probability that it is

(a) red   (b) white

11 A bag contains 2 red balls, 4 white balls and 5 blue balls.
One ball is selected at random.
Find the probability of selecting

(a) a red ball   (b) a white ball   (c) a blue ball

12 One card is selected at random from the cards shown.
    Find the probability of selecting

(a) the king of hearts   (b) a Joker

(c) a 2   (d) an Ace

CHECK YOURSELF ON UNITS 3.6, 3.7 AND 3.8

1   Lines parallel to the axes

ABCD is a rectangle.

(a) Write down the coordinates of A.

(b) Write down the equation of line AD.

(c) Write down the equation of line DC.

(d) N is in the middle of the rectangle.
    What are the coordinates of N?

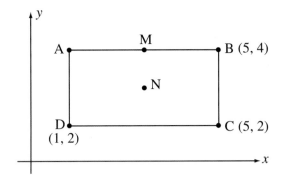

2   Finding the equation of a line and drawing graphs

(a) Which is the equation of line C?

$y = 2x$, $y = x$, $y = x - 2$

Write down the equation of

(b) line A

(c) line B

(d) Which of the points below lie on the line $y = x + 1$?

P (4, 5)   Q (6, 5)   R (0, 1)

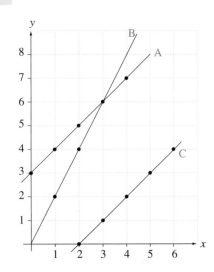

3   Bar charts and bar-line graphs

(a) This chart shows the number of packets of different
flavours of crisps sold by a shop.

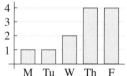

	M	Tu	W	Th	F
Ready Salted	3	1	2	4	0
Salt 'n Vinegar	4	2	5	3	1
Cheese 'n Onion	5	1	3	1	4
Roast Beef	3	2	6	4	1
Prawn	1	1	2	4	4

(i)   How many packets of crisps were sold on
Wednesday?

(ii) Each packet of Ready Salted crisps costs 35p.
How much was spent on Ready Salted crisps in
the whole week?

(iii) This is a graph of one flavour of crisps.
Which flavour is it?

(b) Number of houses

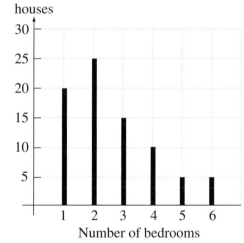

Number of bedrooms

This bar line graph shows the number of
bedrooms in the houses in one road.

(i)   How many houses had 4 bedrooms?

(ii) How many houses are in the road?

(iii) Why would it not be sensible to join the
tops of the bars to make a line graph?

4   Data in groups and line graphs

(a) Eggs are sorted into size by weight. The
weight is then converted into an egg size.
The sizes range from 1 to 7.

Here are the weights of eggs produced
by a farmer's chickens:

65, 56, 62, 69, 64, 51, 53, 57, 60, 59, 45,
59, 50, 57, 54, 58, 53, 59, 55, 58, 56, 46,
55, 44, 61, 55, 52, 70, 60, 56, 70, 66, 62,
42, 49, 63, 50, 57, 64, 72.

Copy and complete this table:

Weight (grams)	Size	Tally	Frequency
Under 45g	7		
45–49	6		
50–54	5		
55–59	4		
60–64	3		
65–69	2		
70g or over	1		

(b) Some keen gardeners collect rain water from the roofs of their homes into rain barrels. They use the water from the barrel when the ground is dry to save using tap water.

Look at this graph and write down what you think is happening. Use the labels A, B, C...

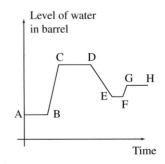

Level of water in barrel

Time

5   Pie charts

In a survey the children at a school were asked to state their favourite sport in the Olympics.

(a) Estimate what fraction of the children chose gymnastics.

(b) There are 120 children in the school. Estimate the number of children who chose athletics.

6   The probability scale and experimental probability

(a) Draw a probability scale like this...

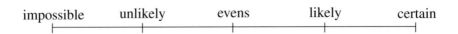

impossible   unlikely   evens   likely   certain

(b) Draw an arrow to show the chance of the events below happening.

   (i) A dice will show a six on its next roll.

   (ii) Your school will be struck by lightning tomorrow.

(c) Describe a simple experiment where the probability of success is very high.

7   Equally likely outcomes

For each spinner state the probability of getting green.

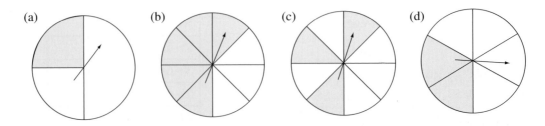

(a)   (b)   (c)   (d)

One card is selected at random from a normal pack of 52 playing cards.
Find the probability of selecting:

(e) the king of diamonds

(f) an ace

(g) a red card

8   Expected probability

(a) Here are two spinners. Say whether the
    following statements are true or false.
    Explain why.

Gill's spinner

Nick's spinner

(i)   'Gill is more likely than Nick to spin a 4.'

(ii) 'Gill and Nick are equally likely to spin an even number.'

(iii) 'If Nick spins his spinner eight times he is bound to get at least one 8'.

(b) A bag contains 1 blue ball, 3 red balls and 7 white balls.

(i) If I select a ball at random from the bag without looking,
    what colour ball am I most likely to select?

What is the probability I select:

(ii)   a white ball?

(iii) a red ball?

(iv)   a green ball?

(v)   a blue ball?

3.9   Applying mathematics in a range of contexts

In section 3.9 you will:

- solve problems in a variety of real life situations

- solve a range of puzzles

- investigate problems with more than one solution

Exercise 1M

1   It cost six people a total of £25.50 for a taxi.

What did it cost each person?

2 Work out

(a) 480 − 55   (b) (4 + 57) × 0   (c) 348 ÷ 6   (d) 6241 + 582

(e) 5 × 607   (f) 747 − 682   (g) 4 × 5 × 6   (h) 0.34 × 1000

3 In a new office building there are 82 doors.

(a) If each door is fastened by 3 hinges, how many hinges are needed altogether?

(b) If each hinge requires 6 screws, what is the total number of screws required to fit all the doors?

4 Use the table to write the calculation 2 × 4 = 8 using Chinese symbols.

(Use × for the multiplication unless you know the Chinese symbol.)

絵 Picture	水 Water	月 Moon	楽 Fun	朝 Morning	考 Think	雪 Snow	鳥 Bird
夢 Dream	人 Person	火 Fire	友 Friend	心 Heart	七 Seven	雨 Rain	宝 Treasure
金 Gold	花 Flower	夜 Night	八 Eight	空 Sky	風 Wind	強 Strength	土 Earth
猫 Cat	星 Star	二 Two	九 Nine	一 One	二 Two	三 Three	四 Four

5 Anil has read 97 of the 448 pages in his book. How many more pages must be read to reach the middle?

6 There are 15 piles of magazines. Eight piles have 20 magazines each, of the other piles each have 25 magazines. How many magazines are there altogether?

7 Write the number 'twelve thousand and eleven' in figures.

8 The area of the 'U' shape is 175 cm².

(a) Find the area of each small square.

(b) Work out the length of the perimeter of the shape.

9 There are 208 pupils in year 7 of a school.
How many teams of six can be formed?
How many pupils will be left over?

10 (a) What is the length of line PQ in millimetres?

(b) What is this length in centimetres?.

P   Q

Exercise 2M

1. Write the next number in each sequence

   (a) 1   5   9   13   ☐

   (b) 32   27   22   17   ☐

   (c) 3   6   12   24   ☐

   (d) 0.2   2   20   ☐

2. In a 'magic square' all rows (←→), columns (↕),
   and main diagonals (⤢) add up to the same
   'magic number'. Copy and complete this magic square.

	10		7
16		2	16
4	17	13	
11			

3. A multi-storey office block has 126 offices altogether.
   If there are 9 offices on each floor, how many storeys does the building have?

4. Write 30 million pence in pounds and pence.

5.  The Coliseum had 2680 windows when it was built. The
   local window cleaner charged a quarter of a shekel per
   window and cleaned all the windows once a week.

   (a) What was his total income in 3 weeks?

   (b) Where is the Coliseum?

6. (a) Copy and shade one fifth of this shape.

   (b) What percentage of the shape is left unshaded?

7. Look at this group of numbers…

   17, 11, 16, 36, 8

   (a) Which of the numbers is a multiple of both 3 and 4?

   (b) Which of the numbers are prime numbers?

   (c) Which of the numbers are square numbers?

8. Numbers are missing on four of these calculator buttons.
   Copy the diagram and write in numbers to make the answer 35.

[3] [8] [+] [ ] [ ] [–] [ ] [ ] [=] [3] [5]

9 (a) How many 8 centimetre pieces of string can be cut from a piece of string which is 1 metre in length?

   (b) How much string is left over?

10 What number, when divided by 7 and then multiplied by 9, gives an answer of 81?

Exercise 3M

1 Write down these calculations and find the missing digits.

   (a) 5 ☐ 5
        + 3 2 ☐
        ─────────
          9 0 1

   (b) 3 ☐ 9
        + 5 8 ☐
        ─────────
        ☐ 5 3

   (c) ☐ 1 ☐
        + 5 ☐ 4
        ─────────
          7 5 0

2 Find the remainder when 370 is divided by 20.

3 The rule for the number sequences below is 'double and add 1'
   Write down each sequence and fill in the missing numbers.

   (a) 2 → 5 → 11 → ☐

   (b) ☐ → 7 → 15 → ☐

   (c) ☐ → 13 → ☐ → ☐

4 A mixed school has a total of 852 pupils.
   There are 24 more girls than boys.
   How many girls are there?
   [Hint: check your answer.]

5 Draw a copy of the grid shown. The sum of the numbers in each column ↕ is the same as the sum of the numbers in each diagonal ↗ or ↘ .

   What number goes in the centre?

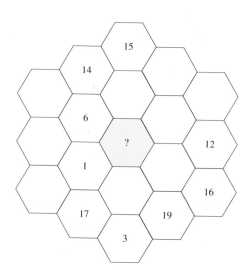

6 How many grams of flour must be added to 2.4 kg to make 4kg altogether?

7 How many minutes are there from 06.40 to 08.05?

8 A book has 648 pages. Gina has read 42 pages
   in 3 days. At that rate how long will it take her
   to read the whole book?

9 Ronnie has the same number of 10p and 20p coins.
   The total value of the coins is £6.
   How many of each coin does he have?

10 Work out the missing numbers

   (a) 204 + 360 = ☐   (b) 270 + ☐ = 800   (c) 25 × ☐ = 500

   (d) ☐ + 305 = 500   (e) ☐ − 220 = 450   (f) ☐ ÷ 12 = 8

Exercise 4M

1 The ingredients for a chocolate cake cost £1.25 and the chef charges £1.10 to make each
   cake. A shop sells the cakes at £11.99. Calculate the total profit made if 200 cakes are sold.

2 Find two numbers which multiply together to give 65
   and which add up to 18

   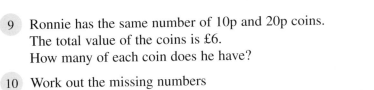

   ◯ × ◯ = 65   ◯ + ◯ = 18

3 A car uses 5 litres of petrol for every 80 km travelled.
   Petrol costs 98p per litre. Calculate the cost in £s of travelling 400 km.

4 Place the numbers in order of size, smallest first.

   0.32   0.201   0.2   0.03   0.4

5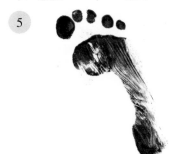

   An artist won the Turner art prize by 'carefully' walking
   across his canvas with bare feet. Unfortunately his prize
   winning piece was thrown in the bin by the cleaner at
   his studio.

   The painting was on sale for £620 000. The cleaner
   offered to make up for her mistake by paying the artist
   £20 per week. How many years would it take to pay the
   full amount?

6 The tenth number in the sequence 1, 3, 9, 27, …. is 19683.
   What is the ninth number?

7 Copy each calculation and find the missing numbers.

(a)
```
    5  7  □
    3  □  2
  + □  4  7
 ──────────
  □  0  4  3
```

(b)
```
  □  3  2  4
  3  □  0  2
+ 2  3  □  5
──────────────
  8  1  4  □
```

8 I think of a number, add 3.6 and then multiply by 5.
   The answer is 21.6. What is the number I am thinking of?

9
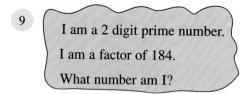
> I am a 2 digit prime number.
>
> I am a factor of 184.
>
> What number am I?

Exercise 5M

1 Draw each chain and fill in the missing numbers

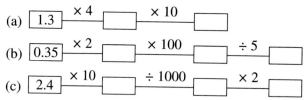

(a) | 1.3 | ×4 | □ | ×10 | □

(b) | 0.35 | ×2 | □ | ×100 | □ | ÷5 | □

(c) | 2.4 | ×10 | □ | ÷1000 | □ | ×2 | □

2 Look at the photo of the pile of matches.

(a) How many matches are there in each layer?

(b) Each match is 3 mm thick. How many
    matches are there in a tower of height 3 cm?

(c) How high a tower can you build
    with 14 boxes of matches if each
    box contains 48 matches?

3
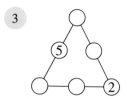
This is a number triangle.
The numbers along each edge add up to 9.

Copy and complete the triangle.

The six numbers are 1, 2, 3, 4, 5, 6.

4 A box has a mass of 230 g when empty.
   When it is full of sugar the total mass is 650 g.
   What is its mass when it is half full?

5 Write the number 'five and a quarter million' in figures.

6 A piece of A4 size paper measures 297 mm by 210 mm.

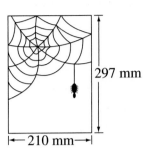

297 mm

210 mm

(a) A money spider starts at a corner and decides to walk around all sides of the paper. How far will the spider walk in millimetres?

(b) Change your answer in part (a) into centimetres.

(c) Has the spider travelled more or less than one metre?

7 In this calculation use each of the digits 1, 2, 3, 4, 5, 6
   Put one digit in each box to make the statement true

☐ ☐ × ☐ = ☐ ☐ 2

8 Copy and complete this multiplication square

×	3	7		
		35		20
			48	
	27			
			16	8

9 The rule for the number sequences is 'treble and subtract 1'.
   Write down each sequence and fill in the missing numbers.

(a) 1 ──→ 2 ──→ 5 ──→ ☐

(b) 4 ──→ 11 ──→ ☐ ──→ ☐

(c) 3 ──→ ☐ ──→ ☐ ──→ ☐

10 Measure the sides of the rectangle and work out

(a) the area

(b) the perimeter

Investigation – Number rings

● This is a number ring
  Start with any number and multiply the units digit by 4 and then add the tens digit.

  For example (14) ──→ 4 × 4 + 1 ──→ (17)

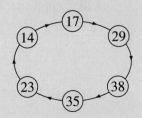

The rule is then repeated on 17.

$(17) \longrightarrow 4 \times 7 + 1 \longrightarrow (29)$

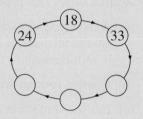

- Use the same rule to complete this number ring.

- Does it matter where you start in the ring?
  In the ring on the last page could you start at 35? .... or 23?

- Do you get a closed ring when you start with any 1 or 2 digit number? Hint: Write 1 digit numbers with a zero. (e.g. 02)

- Do any numbers get 'stuck'?

Find out as much as you can and then write a few sentences to show what you discovered.

UNIT 3   MIXED REVIEW

Part one

1 Copy and complete.

(a) $0.71 \times 10 = \square$

(b) $1.52 \times \square = 152$

(c) $86.2 \div \square = 8.62$

(d) $406 \div \square = 0.406$

(e) $0.014 \times \square = 1.4$

(f) $0.1 \times 1000 = \square$

2 The letters from A to Z are shown on the grid.
Decipher the following messages

(a) (5, 5) (4, 0) (1, 3) (2, 5) $\square$ (4, 2) (–4, 2)
     $\square$ (–5, –3) (–4, 2) (–2, 5) $\square$ (–2, –2)
     (1, 3) (–5, –5) (–5, –5) $\square$ (1, 3) $\square$ (4, –4)
     (1, 3) (0, 1) $\square$ (5, 5) (–2, 1) (2, 5) (4, 0)
     $\square$ (1, 3) $\square$ (5, –2) (–5, 4) (1, 3) (4, 2)
     (–2, 2) $\square$ (–2, 1) (0, 1) $\square$ (4, 0) (–2, 1)
     (5, –2) $\square$ (4, 0) (–2, 2) (1, 3) (4, 2) ? $\square$
     (4, 2) (–4, 2) (–2, 5) (4, 4) !

(b) Change the seventh word to: (5, 5) (–2, 1)
     (2, 5) (4, 0) (–4, 2) (–2, 5) (2, 5).
     Change the last word to: (4, 2) (–4, 2)
     (–2, 5) (4, 4) (–5, –5) (1, 3) (5, –2).

(c) (5, 5) (4, 0) (1, 3) (2, 5) $\square$ (4, 2) (–4, 2)
     $\square$ (–5, –3) (–4, 2) (–2, 5) $\square$ (–2, –2)
     (1, 3) (–5, –5) (–5, –5) $\square$ (1, 3) $\square$ (4, 2)
     (–2, 2) (1, 3) (4, 2) $\square$ (–5, 4) (1, 3) (–3, –4)
     (–3, –4) (–4, 2) (2, 5) ? $\square$ (–5, 4) (–4, 2)
     (–5, –5) (–5, –3) (4, 4) (–4, 2) (0, 1) !

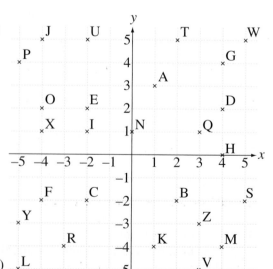

3 Look at the graph in question 2 . Write down the equation of the line through

    (a) T and B   (b) P and G   (c) G and C

4 (a) Write down the first five multiples of 4

  (b) Write down the factors of 12

  (c) Which of the factors of 12 are prime numbers?

5 (a) What is the probability of rolling a dice and getting a six?

  (b) What is the probability of not getting a six?

6   Different batteries were tested to see how long a set of 'clattering teeth' keep working. The winning battery worked for eight minutes. Each battery costs 90p. How much would it cost to keep the teeth clattering for four hours?

7 Find the missing digits.

(a)
$$
\begin{array}{r}
3 \cdot 2\ \square \\
+\ 1 \cdot \square\ 4 \\
\hline
\square \cdot 0\ \ 1
\end{array}
$$

(b)
$$
\begin{array}{r}
\square \cdot 5\ \ 5 \\
+\ 0 \cdot \square\ 3 \\
\hline
5 \cdot 1\ \ \square
\end{array}
$$

(c)
$$
\begin{array}{r}
3 \cdot 6\ \ \square \\
-\ \square \cdot \square\ 7 \\
\hline
2 \cdot 0\ \ 7
\end{array}
$$

8 Write the numbers in order of size, smallest first.

  (a) 0.71, 0.605, 0.65, 0.7

  (b) 0.99, 0.08, 0.079, 0.1

  (c) 2^3, 3^2, 1^3, (2×3)

9 Find the number

(a)
| a 2-digit number |
| a multiple of both 3 and 4 |
| the sum of its digits is 15 |

(b)
| a 3-digit number |
| a square number |
| the product of its digits is 2 |

10 This pie chart shows how 72 people travelled to the same hotel. Write down how many people travelled by:

  (a) train   (b) car   (c) plane

11 The equation of a line is $y = x - 2$. Some points on the line are:

  $(0, -2)$ $(1, -1)$ $(2, \square)$ $(3, \square)$ $(4, \square)$

  Fill in the missing numbers and then draw a set of axes and the line $y = x - 2$.

12   What is the probability of spinning a red on each spinner?

(a)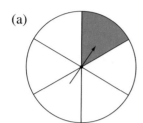

(b)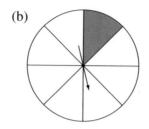

(c)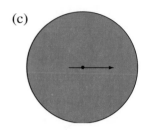

13   An ice cream and a can of drink together cost 85p.
     Two ice creams and a can of drink together cost £1.40.

   (a) How much does one ice cream cost?

   (b) How much would you pay for three ice creams
       and two cans of drink?

14   Write down the probability of the following events occurring …

   (a) When a fair coin is tossed it will come down 'heads'.

   (b) You will roll a number greater than 4 on a fair dice.

   (c) From a bag containing six red balls and one yellow ball,
        you select a red ball.

15   Copy and complete each chain.

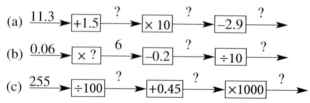

(a) $\dfrac{11.3}{}$ ▶ +1.5 — ? ▶ × 10 — ? ▶ −2.9 — ? ▶

(b) $\dfrac{0.06}{}$ ▶ × ? — 6 ▶ −0.2 — ? ▶ ÷10 — ? ▶

(c) $\dfrac{255}{}$ ▶ ÷100 — ? ▶ +0.45 — ? ▶ ×1000 — ? ▶

Part two

1   This bar chart shows the marks achieved by children in
    a test.

   (a) How many children scored between 41 and 60
       marks?

   (b) How many children scored over 60 marks?

   (c) How many children took the test?

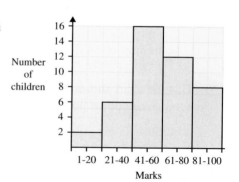

2 Find the number.

(a)
> a multiple of 11
> a multiple of 7
> the product of its digits is 6

(b)
> a square number
> a 3-digit number
> the product of its digits is 20

3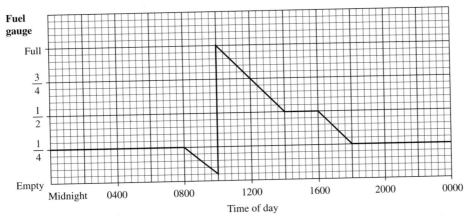

It is not easy to burn a match completely.
In fact it takes thirteen seconds.
A box contain 47 matches.
How long would it take to completely burn
the matches one after the other in 10 boxes?

4 (a) Write down the first seven multiples of four.

   (b) Write down the first six multiples of seven.

   (c) Write down the lowest common multiple of four and seven.

5 The line graph below shows the fuel gauge reading of a car at different times throughout a day…

(a) Was the car moving or stationary between midnight and 8.00 am?

(b) What happened to the car at 10.00 am?

(c) How much petrol was used between 10.00 am and 2.00 pm?

(d) At what time in the evening was the car put in the garage?

6 The smiley face with banana and berries won a competition to
promote healthy eating. The prize was £95. How many euros
was that? [£1 = €1.5]

7 The winner of the World Apple Peeling Championship peeled an unbroken length of 231 cm from a Bramley. His prize was $35 per cm. How much did he win?

8 A book has pages numbered 1 to 200 and the thickness of the book, without the covers is 10 mm. How thick is each page?

9

20%

1

30%
2 hours

10% 0

3+ 3 hours

10%

30%

This pie chart shows the number of hours in one evening spent watching television by 40 children. Copy and complete the table

HOURS	CHILDREN
0	
1	
2	
3	
3+	

10 A bag contains 4 balls. The probability of selecting a white ball from the bag is 0.5. A white ball is taken from the bag and left on one side. What is the probability of selecting a white ball from the bag now?

11 Copy and complete

(a) 3.25 + ☐ = 5

(b) 100 × ☐ = 3.7

(c) ☐ − 0.23 = 2.5

(d) (☐ + 1.2) × 10 = 25

12 A 10p coin is 2 mm thick. Alex has a pile of 10p coins which is 16.6 cm tall. What is the value of the money in Alex's pile of coins?

2 mm

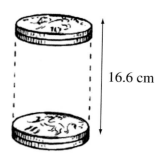

16.6 cm

13 A mixed school has a total of 918 pupils. There are 54 more girls than boys. How many girls are there?

14 How many spots are there on twenty-four ordinary dice?

15 Answer true or false:

(a) $4^2 = 2^3$ (b) $10 \div 100 = 0.1$ (c) 20% of 20 = 5

(d) $0.001 \times 100 = 0.01$ (e) 3^3 is greater than 4^2

16 The graph converts Australian dollars into pounds.

(a) Convert 84 dollars into pounds.

(b) Convert 100 dollars into pounds.

(c) Convert 20 pounds into dollars.

(d) Convert 16 pounds into dollars.

(e) A boomerang costs 140 dollars. How much does it cost in pounds?

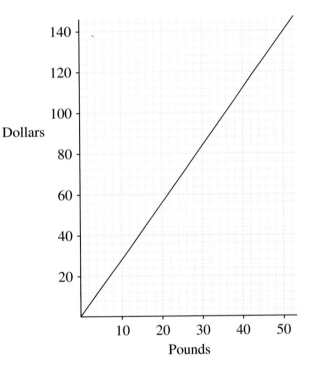

Puzzles and Problems 3

1 The totals for the rows and columns are given. Unfortunately some of the totals are hidden by blue ink blots. Find the values of the letters.

(a)

A	A	A	A	28
A	B	C	A	27
A	C	D	B	30
D	B	B	B	(blot)
(blot)	25	30	24	

(b)

A	B	A	B	B	18
B	B	E	C	D	21
A	B	B	A	B	18
C	B	C	B	C	19
E	B	D	E	D	26
27	10	25	23	17	

This one is more difficult

(c)

A	A	A	A	24
C	A	C	D	13
A	B	B	A	18
B	B	D	C	12
(blot)	18	15	18	

(d)

A	B	B	A	22
A	A	B	B	22
A	B	A	B	22
B	B	A	B	17
27	17	22	17	

2 In these triangle puzzles the numbers a, b, c, d are connected as follows:

$a \times b = c$

$c \times b = d$

  For example:

Copy and complete the following triangles:

(a)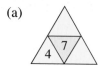

(b)

(c)

(d)

(e)

(f)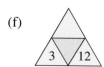

3 Draw four straight lines which pass through all 9 points, without taking your pen from the paper and without going over any line twice. [Hint: Lines can extend beyond the square].

• • •
• • •
• • •

4 Write the digits 1 to 9 so that all the answers are correct.

☐ − ☐ = ☐
        ×
☐ ÷ ☐ = ☐
        ‖
☐ + ☐ = ☐

5 Draw six straight lines to pass through all 16 points, subject to the same conditions as in question **3** .

• • • •

• • • •

• • • •

• • • •

A long time ago! 3

Pounds, shillings and pence

In horse racing, the length of a race is often measured in furlongs.
Do you know how many furlongs make one mile?
A person throwing a party might buy a firkin of beer. How many gallons would this be?
These are imperial units which are covered later in this book.
Actually 8 furlongs make one mile and 9 gallons make one firkin.
Your grandparents (and maybe parents!) used to buy things with shillings, tanners and two bob coins.
One penny was written as 1d. 12 pennies made 1 shilling (written as 1s.)
20 shillings made 1 pound
21 shillings made 1 guinea
(A 'tanner' was a 6d. coin and 2s. was sometimes called a 'two bob' coin)

1s. = 12d.
£1 = 20s.

Mary wants to buy a car for £27 16s. 4d. and a bike for 5s. 10d. How much does she spend in total?

£	s.	d.
27	16	4
	5	10
28	2	2
¹	¹	

Add the pennies first. Every 12 pennies are carried over as 1 shilling. Next add the shillings. Every 20 shillings are carried over as 1 pound.

Mary spends a total of £28 2s. 2d.

Exercise

Try these questions from a 1927 arithmetic test.

1 £   s.   d.
   5   3   7
 + 2   5   9

2 £   s.   d.
   3   14   8
 + 6   12   3

3 £   s.   d.
   8   13   4
 + 4   17   10

4   £ s. d.
from 8 19 3
take 4 13 9

5   £ s. d.
from 16 4 8
take 7 10 4

6   £ s. d.
from 17 3 2
take 10 14 8

7 How many $\frac{1}{2}$ d. stamps could I buy with a 'two bob' coin?

8 How many oranges can I get for 3s. at the cost of seven oranges for 6d.?

9 How much must be added to 15s. 6d. to make a guinea?

10 I have bought a cake for 1s. 3d. and some jam for 5d. How much change should I have out of 2 shillings?

11 I have been for a week's holiday and spent 6d. a day while I was away. How much should I have left out of 4s.?

RESEARCH: There were many units used in the nineteenth century for length, weight and capacity. Examples are 'barleycorns' and 'kilderkins'.

(a) How many different units can you find?
(b) Can you discover where any of the names come from?

Mental Arithmetic Practice 3

There are two sets of mental arithmetic questions in this section. Ideally a teacher will read out each question twice, with pupils' books closed. Each test of 20 questions should take about 20 minutes.

Test 1

1 What is three quarters of sixty pounds?

2 What is the product of ten and thirty-five?

3 What is nought point two as a percentage?

4 How much change from a ten pound note will I receive if I spend three pounds and sixty-nine pence?

5 What is the sum of 6, 7, 8, 9, 10?

6 Two angles in a triangle are thirty-five and seventy-five degrees. What is the third angle?

7 Change seventeen thirty-five into twelve hour clock time.

8 How many 2p coins are worth the same as forty 5p coins?

9 How many centimetres are equal to eighty-five millimetres?

10 What is the area of a triangle with a base of 6 cm and a height of 8 cm?

11 I am facing south-east and turn through one right angle in a clockwise turn. In which direction am I now facing?

12 What is the next prime number after eleven?

13 I bought a magazine for 79p and paid with a £1 coin. My change consisted of five coins. What were they?

14 What is the probability that I will roll an odd number on a fair dice?

15 What is the perimeter of a square whose area is four centimetres squared?

16 Write down the number that is halfway between twenty-three and sixty-seven.

17 How many seconds are there in one hour?

18 Answer true or false: 1 km is longer than 1 mile.

19 A 'lottery' win of four million pounds is shared equally between one hundred people. How much does each person receive?

20 What is the mean average of 8, 12 and 13?

Test 2

1 What is the area of a rectangle eight metres by seven metres?

2 Round off six hundred and fifty-seven to the nearest hundred.

3 How many twelve pence pencils can you buy for one pound?

4 Write the number three thousand two hundred and nine in figures.

5 One quarter of a number is nine. What is the number?

6 How many twenty pence coins make four pounds?

7 What number is 10 less than one thousand?

8 How many thirds are there in one and two-thirds?

9 Write down a sensible estimate for eleven multiplied by forty-nine.

10 What is the probability of scoring more than a one on a fair dice?

11 Write seven tenths as a decimal number.

12 Write a hundred million pence in pounds.

13 I think of a number, divide it by six and the answer is five. What number did I think of?

14 What decimal number is forty-seven divided by one hundred?

15 What is the name given to a triangle which has two sides the same length and a pair of equal angles.

16 What number is squared to produce sixty-four?

17 How many millimetres are there in one metre?

18 In a survey seven tenths of people like watching soaps. What percentage of people like watching soaps?

19 What is the median of 6, 7 and 4?

20 How many hours are two hundred and forty minutes?

UNIT 4

4.1 Constructing triangles

In section 4.1 you will learn how to:

- construct triangles with a protractor and ruler

A triangle is an extremely rigid structure. It is used extensively in the real world to support many objects such as the roof on your house or the brackets holding up your bookshelf.

Draw the triangle ABC full size and measure the length x.

(a) Draw a base line *longer than* 8.5 cm

(b) Put the centre of the protractor on A and measure an angle 64°. Draw line AP.

(c) Similarly draw line BQ at an angle 40° to AB.

(d) The triangle is formed.
Measure $x = 5.6$ cm.

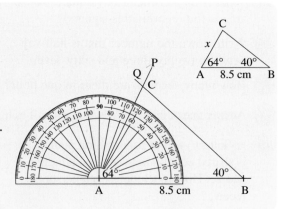

Exercise 1M

1 Measure the angles below to make sure you can still use a protractor accurately.

(a)

(b)

(c)

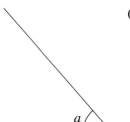

2 (a) Use a protractor and ruler to
       draw AB = 7 cm and CÂB = 50° as
       shown below.

(b) Put the centre of the protractor
    on B and measure an angle of
    50° as shown below.

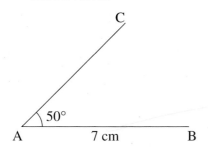

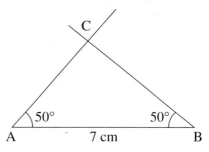

(c) Measure AĈB. It should be 80°.

3 Construct each triangle below. Measure the third angle in each triangle. Is it what you would
   expect?

   (a)

   (b)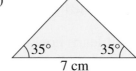

   (c)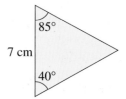

4 Construct triangles with the angles given below. Measure the third angle in each triangle. Is it
   what you would expect?

   (a) 65°, 65°   (b) 35°, 80°   (c) 50°, 75°

5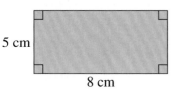

   Construct this rectangle accurately using a ruler and
   protractor.
   Measure the length of the diagonal of the rectangle.

Exercise 1E

Construct the triangles and measure the lengths of the sides marked x.

1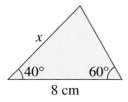

2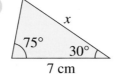

3

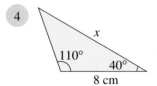

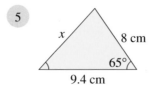

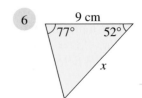

7 Construct the rhombus shown below.

8 Construct the parallelogram shown below.

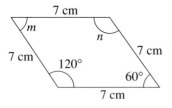

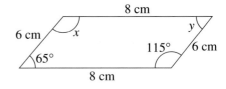

Measure the size of *m* and *n*.

Measure the size of *x* and *y*.

4.2 Two dimensional shapes

In section 4.2 you will learn how to:

- recognise parallel, perpendicular, horizontal and vertical lines
- recognise different types of triangle
- recognise different types of quadrilateral
- recognise different polygons

Lines
- A straight line has infinite length.

  A *line segment* is part of a straight line and has finite length.

  A ——————————— B   AB is a line segment

- Lines which are at right angles are *perpendicular* to each other.

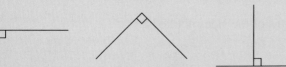

- A *horizontal* line is parallel to the horizon.

- A *vertical* line is perpendicular to the surface of the earth.

For each of the letters of the word 'LINES' use the following 'key' to indicate ...

1. perpendicular lines ⟶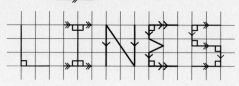

2. parallel vertical lines ⟶

3. parallel horizontal lines ⟶

... like this:-

Exercise 1M

Copy out the key given in the above example and the stencil of the alphabet below onto squared paper. Use the key to show on all the letters any:

(a) perpendicular lines (b) parallel vertical lines (c) Parallel horizontal lines

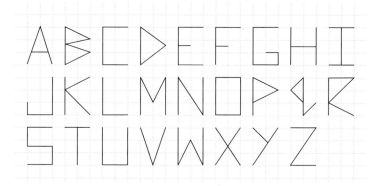

Exercise 1E

In questions 1 to 3 write the sentence choosing the correct word.

1

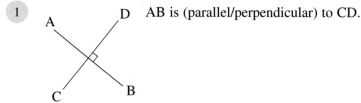

D   AB is (parallel/perpendicular) to CD.

2

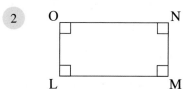

LM is (parallel/perpendicular) to MN.

ON is (parallel/perpendicular) to LM.

OL is (parallel/perpendicular) to MN.

208

3 Look at the diagram on the right. Copy and complete.

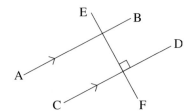

CD is _____ to EF.

AB is _____ to CD.

4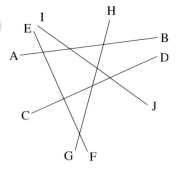

Which lines are perpendicular to each other?

5 Copy the diagram on the right.

(a) Draw a line through C which is perpendicular to AB

(b) Draw a line through D which is parallel to AB

(c) Draw a line through D which is perpendicular to the line AB.

6 In the rectangle WXYZ, XY is perpendicular to WX.

(a) Which other line is perpendicular to WX?

(b) Which line is parallel to ZY?

7 Use the sides of a ruler to draw a four-sided shape (quadrilateral) with two pairs of parallel sides. Mark the parallel sides with arrows.

8

Copy the diagram on the left.

(a) Draw a line through R which is parallel to PQ.

(b) Draw a line through R which is perpendicular to PQ.

Triangles

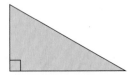

A triangle with three different sides and three different angles is a *scalene* triangle.

A triangle which contains a right angle is a *right angled* triangle.

Reminder:

An *isosceles* triangle has two equal sides and two equal angles.

An *equilateral* triangle has three equal sides and three equal angles.

Quadrilaterals

A quadrilateral has four sides and four angles. Special types of quadrilateral

square

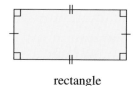

rectangle

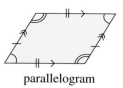

parallelogram

rhombus

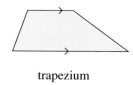

trapezium

kite

Polygons

A polygon is a shape with straight sides.

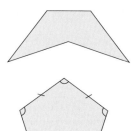

This is a five-sided polygon or pentagon.

A *regular* polygon has all its sides and angles equal.

This is a *regular* pentagon.

Names of common polygons:

hexagon (6 sides),   heptagon (7 sides),   octagon (8 sides),

nonagon (9 sides),   decagon (10 sides).

Exercise 2M

1. For each of the following triangles state whether it is scalene, isosceles, equilateral or right-angled. (Lines of the same length are indicated by dashes and equal angles are marked)

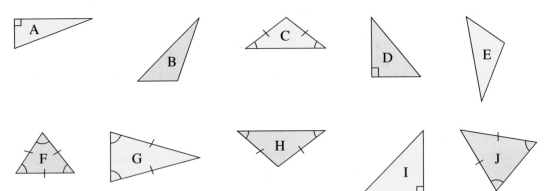

2. Write down the name for each shape below. If the shape has a special name like 'parallelogram', or 'kite' write that name. If not, write 'quadrilateral', 'hexagon', 'regular pentagon' and so on.

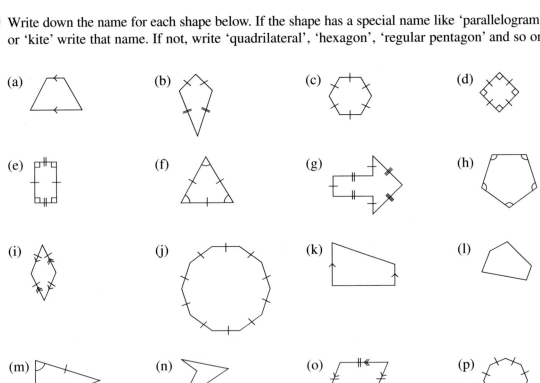

Exercise 2E

1　Write down the letter for which bucket each of the 6 quadrilaterals will drop into when they pass through the sorting machine.

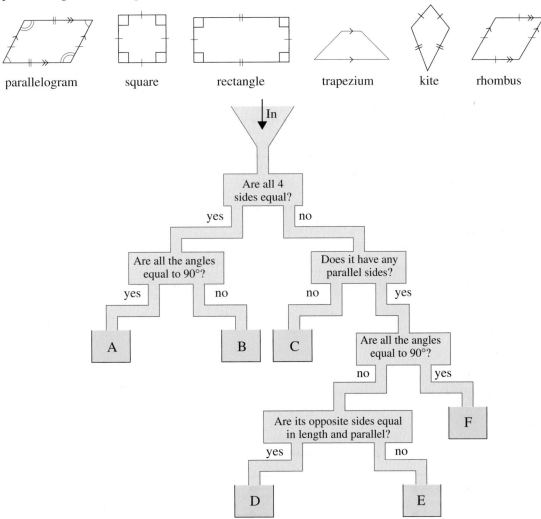

2　Copy the diagram of each quadrilateral in question ① . For each quadrilateral, write its name and describe the rules that make it that particular shape. Discuss these rules with a partner then as a class.

3　Which shape below is not a regular polygon?

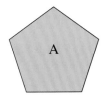

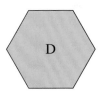

212

 A diagonal joins one corner (vertex) of a polygon to another corner.

Draw any rhombus. Write as many facts as possible about the diagonals of a rhombus.

5 Draw a hexagon which has exactly four obtuse angles.

Investigation – triangles and quadrilaterals

On a square grid of 9 dots it is possible to draw several different triangles with vertices on dots. A vertex (plural vertices) is where two lines meet. Look at the three examples below:

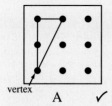 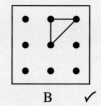 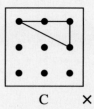

vertex

A ✓   B ✓   C ✗

A and B are different triangles but C is the same as A. If a triangle could be cut out and placed exactly over another triangle then the two triangles are the same. The two triangles are called *congruent*.

PART A

Copy A and B above and then draw as many different triangles as you can.
Check carefully that you have not repeated the same triangle.

PART B

On a grid of 9 dots it is also possible to draw several different *quadrilaterals*.

Copy the three shapes above and then draw as many other different quadrilaterals as possible. You are doing well if you can find 12 shapes but there are a few more!

Check carefully that you have not repeated the same quadrilateral. (Congruent shapes are not allowed.)

CHECK YOURSELF ON SECTIONS 4.1 AND 4.2

1   Constructing triangles with a protractor and ruler

Construct each triangle below:

(a)

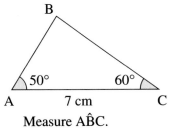

Measure AB̂C.

(b)

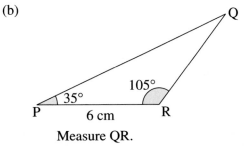

Measure QR.

2   Recognising parallel, perpendicular, horizontal and vertical lines

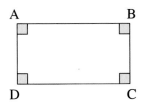

(a) Name a horizontal line.

(b) Name a side perpendicular to AD.

(c) Name a vertical line.

(d) Name a side parallel to AD.

3   Recognising different types of triangle

Match each triangle to the correct name below.

(a)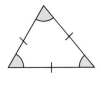

(b)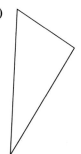

(c)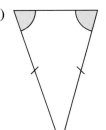

(d)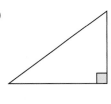

isosceles   right-angled   equilateral   scalene

(e) Write down the rules that make an isosceles triangle.

4   Recognising different types of quadrilateral

Match each quadrilateral to the correct name below:

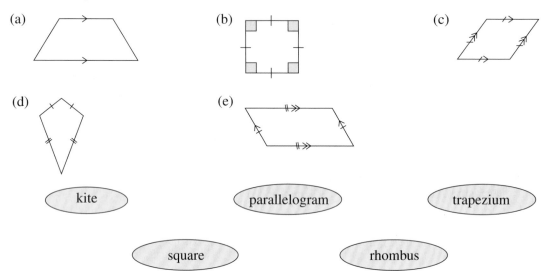

(a)

(b)

(c)

(d)

(e)

kite   parallelogram   trapezium

square   rhombus

(f) Write down the rules that make a rhombus.

5   Recognising different polygons

(a) Write down which shapes below are polygons.

P   Q   R   S

(b) How many sides has a decagon?

(c) 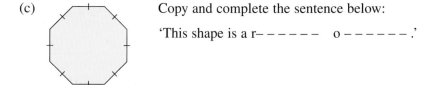   Copy and complete the sentence below:

'This shape is a r– – – – – –   o – – – – – – .'

4.3 Percentages

In section 4.3 you will:

- review the conversion of fractions, decimals and percentages
- learn how to recognise common percentages
- learn how to find a percentage of a number

Fractions, decimals and percentages review

Reminder (from section 2 work)

$\dfrac{3}{10} = 0.3$ $\dfrac{7}{100} = 0.07$ $\dfrac{9}{25} = \dfrac{36}{100} = 0.36$

convert denominator to 10, 100, etc

$0.35 = \dfrac{35}{100} = \dfrac{7}{20}$ $28\% = \dfrac{28}{100} = \dfrac{7}{25}$

cancel down fractions

'per cent' means 'out of 100'

$\dfrac{19}{50} = \dfrac{38}{100} = 38\%$ $64\% = \dfrac{64}{100} = 0.64$

Exercise 1M

1 Copy and complete the following statements.

  (a) $\dfrac{3}{5} = \dfrac{\square}{10} = 0 \cdot \square$

  (b) $\dfrac{11}{20} = \dfrac{\square}{100} = 0 \cdot \square\square$

  (c) $0.9 = \dfrac{\square}{10} = \dfrac{\square\square}{100} = \square\square\%$

  (d) $0.17 = \dfrac{\square\square}{100} = \square\square\%$

2 5% of people who go to the beach get sunburnt.

  What fraction of people who go to the beach get sunburnt?

3 Change these percentages into decimals.

  (a) 37%   (b) 60%   (c) 6%   (d) 19%

  (e) 45%

4 Write True or False for each of the following statements.

  (a) $0.09 = \dfrac{1}{9}$ (b) $0.25 = \dfrac{1}{4}$ (c) $0.2 = \dfrac{1}{5}$

  (d) $0.4 = 4\%$ (e) $65\% = 0.65$ (f) $\dfrac{3}{5} = 35\%$

5 Change these decimals into fractions. Give the fractions in their most simple form.

  (a) 0.8   (b) 0.47   (c) 0.16   (d) 0.85   (e) 0.75

6 Copy and complete this table.

	fraction	decimal	percentage
(a)	$\frac{7}{10}$		
(b)			24%
(c)		0.46	
(d)			95%
(e)	$\frac{3}{20}$		

Exercise 1E

1 Convert these fractions into decimals.

(a) $\frac{17}{50}$ (b) $\frac{19}{25}$ (c) $\frac{13}{20}$ (d) $\frac{90}{200}$

2 Write the numbers below in order of size, smallest first.

(a) $\frac{3}{4}$, 0.8, $\frac{7}{10}$ (b) 0.57, $\frac{11}{20}$, 60% (c) 24%, $\frac{1}{4}$, $\frac{1}{5}$ (d) $\frac{21}{25}$, 0.8, 82%

3 Mary uses 39 out of 52 cards to build a tower of cards.

(a) What fraction of all the cards did she use?

(b) What percentage of all the cards did she use?

4 Write down which fractions are equivalent to the given percentage.

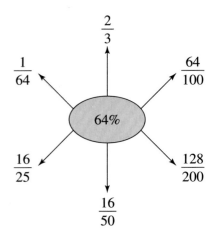

5 Convert these percentages into fractions.

(a) 49% (b) 8% (c) 56% (d) 15%

6   There are five groups of *equivalent* fractions, decimals and percentages below. Write down each group. For example $\frac{3}{4}$, 0.75, 75% would be a group (beware: there are two odd ones out).

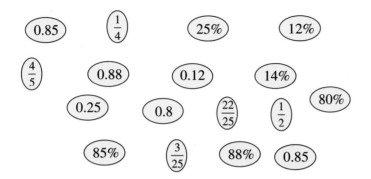

$\boxed{0.85}$ $\boxed{\frac{1}{4}}$ $\boxed{25\%}$ $\boxed{12\%}$

$\boxed{\frac{4}{5}}$ $\boxed{0.88}$ $\boxed{0.12}$ $\boxed{14\%}$

$\boxed{0.25}$ $\boxed{0.8}$ $\boxed{\frac{22}{25}}$ $\boxed{\frac{1}{2}}$ $\boxed{80\%}$

$\boxed{85\%}$ $\boxed{\frac{3}{25}}$ $\boxed{88\%}$ $\boxed{0.85}$

Common Percentages

You should learn

$25\% = \frac{1}{4}$ $50\% = \frac{1}{2}$ $75\% = \frac{3}{4}$

$33\frac{1}{3}\% = \frac{1}{3}$ $66\frac{2}{3}\% = \frac{2}{3}$

$10\% = \frac{10}{100} = \frac{1}{10}$ $20\% = \frac{20}{100} = \frac{1}{5}$

Exercise 2M

For each shape in questions 1 to 8 , (a) what *fraction* is shaded pink?
                                    (b) what *percentage* is shaded pink?

1 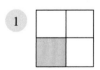   2 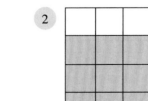   3 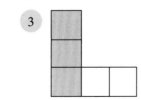   4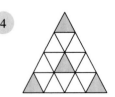

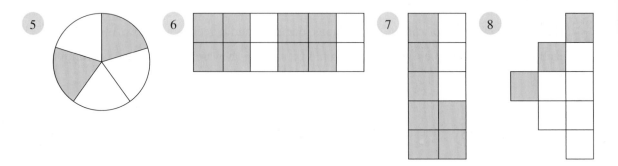

5   6   7   8

9   Draw a diagram of your own design and shade in 30%.

10 What percentage could be used in each sentence below?

(a) Zak scored 12 out of 20 in a test.

(b) Three quarters of the students in year 7 went on a school trip.

(c) One in three cats prefer 'Pepsi'.

(d) Half the people in a pub were over 40 years-old.

(e) One in five adults think children should spend more time playing computer games and watching TV.

11 Becky spends 80% of her money shopping. What *fraction* of her money does she have left?

12 Boris drank one third of his drink. What *percentage* of his drink did he have left?

13 Three tenths of Lorna's books were Science Fiction. What *percentage* of her books were *not* Science Fiction?

14 These pictures show how much petrol is in a car. E is Empty and F is Full.

What percentage of a full tank is in each car?

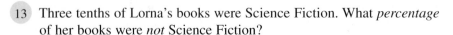

(a) E   F   (b) E   F

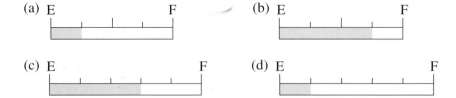

(c) E   F   (d) E   F

15    What percentage of these apples is green?

Percentage of a number

Use common percentages

(a) 25% of 36

$= \dfrac{1}{4} \times 36$

$= 36 \div 4 = 9$

(b) 75% of 20

$= \dfrac{3}{4} \times 20$

$= (20 \div 4) \times 3 = 15$

(c) $66\frac{2}{3}$% of 30

$= \dfrac{2}{3}$ of 30

$= (30 \div 3) \times 2 = 20$

Use multiples of 10% $\qquad 10\% = \dfrac{1}{10}$

To work out 20%, find 10% then multiply by 2.

To work out 30%, find 10% then multiply by 3 and so on.

Exercise 3M

Do not use a calculator.

1 Work out

(a) 25% of £60
(b) 75% of £24
(c) 10% of £70
(d) 20% of £70
(e) 30% of £90
(f) $33\frac{1}{3}$% of £60

2 There are 48 dolphins in a pod.
Seventy-five per cent of the
dolphins are adults.
How many adult dolphins are there?
[The word for a group of dolphins is 'pod'.]

3 Matt scores 40% in a test.
If full marks in the test were 50, how
many marks did Matt get?

4 There are 220 children in a school. 60%
of the children have school meals.
How many children have school meals?

5 Work out

(a) 80% of £200
(b) $66\frac{2}{3}$% of £33
(c) 70% of £400
(d) 20% of £60
(e) 5% of £80
(f) 15% of £80

6 Which is larger? (30% of £40) or (25% of £60)

7 Which is larger? (50% of £70) or (5% of £700)

8 Find the odd one out

(a) 75% of £200   (b) 70% of £210   (c) 30% of £500

9 Find the odd one out

(a) 10% of £90   (b) 20% of £40   (c) 5% of £160

10 A hammer costs £12. A shop decides to 'knock' 25% off the price of the hammer. How much money will be 'knocked' off the price?

In a sale the price of a shirt is reduced by 20%. Find the 'sale price' if the normal price is £30.

20% is the same as $\frac{1}{5}$

20% of 30 = $\frac{1}{5}$ of 30 = 6

sale price = 30 − 6 = £24

Exercise 3E

Do not use a calculator.

1 Find the sale price of each item below. The normal prices are shown in boxes.

(a) £60
30% off
marked price

(b) £20
25% off!

(c) £700
20% off
normal price

(d) £16
75% off

(e) £36

$33\frac{1}{3}$% discount

off the shown price

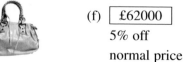

(f) £62000
5% off
normal price

2 A car is worth £5200. After an accident, its value falls by 40%. How much is the car worth now?

3 The price of a caravan is £9400. One year later the price has dropped by 10%. What is the new price of the caravan?

4. In a particular area, there are 4000 penguins. Six months later the population has decreased by 20%. How many penguins are there now?

5. A train company increases its prices by 15%. If a ticket costs £40 now, how much will it cost after the price increase?

6. A marathon runner weighs 60kg at the start of a race. During the race his weight is reduced by 5%. How much does he weigh at the end of the race?

7. One Saturday 320 people go to the cinema. 40% more people go on the following Saturday.
   How many people
   go to the cinema on the following Saturday?

8. A shop puts all its prices *up* by 5%. Find the new prices of the following.

   (a) a dress at £120   (b) a skirt at £70   (c) a scarf at £20

9. A lizard weighs 500g. While escaping from a predator it loses its tail and its weight is reduced by 5%. How much does it weigh now?

10. A shop 'slashes' its prices by $66\frac{2}{3}$%. Find the reduced price of a guitar costing £390.

Harder percentages of a number

$1\% = \dfrac{1}{100}$ To find 1% of a number, divide the number by 100.

Find 16% of a number.

Divide the number by 100 to find 1% then multiply by 16 to find 16% of the number.

(a) Work out 29% of £18.

1% of $18 = 18 \div 100$

29% of $18 = (18 \div 100) \times 29$

$\qquad = 5.22 = £5.22$

(b) Increase a price of £60 by 8%.

1% of $60 = 60 \div 100$

8% of $60 = (60 \div 100) \times 8$

$\qquad = 4.8 = £4.80$

New price $= £60 + £4.80$

$\qquad\qquad = £64.80$

Exercise 4M

Use a calculator when needed.

1 Work out 1% of £2600.

2 Find 1% of:
   (a) £375   (b) £370   (c) £49   (d) £180

3 Work out
   (a) 8% of £460   (b) 3% of £690   (c) 32% of £240
   (d) 73% of £3800   (e) 19% of £510   (f) 94% of £1200

4 2700 people watch a film. 12% of the people did not enjoy the film. How many people did not enjoy the film?

5 Which is larger? (8% of £23) or (9% of £21)

6 Work out the following, giving the correct units in your answers.
   (a) 73% of 3000 kg   (b) 14% of 530 km   (c) 3% of $235
   (d) 86% of 17 km   (e) 47% of 600 m   (f) 98% of 7100 g

7 Find 3.2% of £7000.

Exercise 4E

Use a calculator when needed.

1 A ticket to New York City costs £230. The price of the ticket is increased by 4%. What is the new price of the ticket?

2 A mail order firm reduces its prices by 7%. What will be the reduced price of each of the following items?
   (a) fridge £230   (b) TV £750
   (c) dishwasher £470   (d) cooker £860

3 John weighs 80kg. Over the next year his weight increases by 6%. What is his new weight?

4 (a) Increase £70 by 16%.
   (b) Decrease £190 by 2%.
   (c) Decrease £280 by 28%.

5 A hen weighs 3kg. After laying an egg, her weight is reduced by 2%. How much does she weigh now?

6 A plane ticket is advertised as being £160. It is then increased by 14%. What is the new plane ticket price?

7 During the day a person might shrink in height by 0.5% to 1%. Donald is 1.8 m when he wakes up. If he shrinks by 0.7% during the day, how tall is he at the end of the day?

8 Marie earns £340 each week. She is given a 6.5% pay rise. How much does she earn each week after the pay rise?

9 John Terry earns £130 000 per week. How much does he earn after a 4.8% pay rise?

4.4   Proportion and ratio

In section 4.4 you will learn how to:

- tackle problems involving direct proportion

- express proportions

- deal with ratios

Direct proportion

(a) If 4 books cost £24, find the cost of 3 books. We are assuming that the 4 books are identical. Find the cost of 1 book first.

4 books cost £24

1 book costs £24 ÷ 4 = £6

3 books cost £6 × 3 = £18

(b) If 4 bottles of lemonade contain 10 litres, how much lemonade is there in 7 bottles?

4 bottles contain 10 litres

1 bottle contains 10 ÷ 4 = 2.5 litres

7 bottles contain 2.5 × 7 = 17.5 litres

Exercise 1M

1 Diving masks cost £200 for 10. Find the cost of 5 diving masks.

2 Find the cost of 20 mugs if 5 mugs cost £20.

3 If 3 pens cost £6, find the cost of 6 pens.

4 The total weight of 7 CDs is 84 grams. How much do 10 CDs weigh?

5 Five oranges cost 95p. How much will 9 oranges cost?

6 Eight coats cost £560. Find the cost of 11 coats.

7 Five tea pots cost £7.50. Find the cost of 50 tea pots.

8 Find the cost of 7 skateboards if 4 skateboards cost £168.

9 A machine fills 800 bottles in 5 minutes. How many bottles will it fill in 20 minutes?

10 If 16 bottles of cola hold 32 litres, how much cola will 9 bottles hold?

11 Seven bikes cost £1750. How much will 3 bikes cost?

12 Twelve cinema tickets cost £60. Find the cost of 20 cinema tickets.

13 A train travels 100 km in 20 minutes. How long will it take to travel 50 km?

14 The total cost of 8 magazines is £12. What is the total cost of 12 magazines?

15 Usually it takes 12 hours for 5 men to build a wall.
How many men are needed to build a wall twice as big in 12 hours?

Proportion

Proportion is used to compare part of something to the whole. A proportion is expressed as a fraction, decimal or percentage.

(a) There are 8 boys and 11 girls in a class of 19 children. The proportion of girls in the class is $\frac{11}{19}$.

(b) The proportion of material to make a shirt which is cotton is 80%.

Exercise 1E

1. There are 40 people on a bus. 23 people are female. What proportion of the people are male?

2.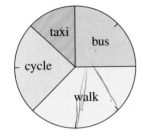
   The chart shows how children travel to Maxwell High School.

   (a) What proportion travel by bus?

   (b) What proportion walk?

3. A soup contains 150g of water and 50g of vegetables. What proportion of the soup is vegetables?

4. Count the children in your class. What proportion of the class went to the same junior school as you?

5. The diagram shows how the government spends money on transport. Estimate, as a percentage, what proportion is spent on roads.

   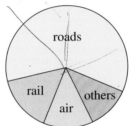

6. £30 can be exchanged for 48 dollars. How many dollars can be exchanged for £150?

7. £30 can be exchanged for 51 euros. How many euros can be exchanged for £90?

8. £1 is worth 1.92 dollars. How many dollars will I get for £100?

9. Jack uses 32 litres of petrol to travel 270 km. How much petrol does Jack use to travel 810 km?

10. £1 is worth 196 yen (money used in Japan). How many yen will I get for £40?

Ratio

Ratio is used to compare parts of a whole.

There are 29 children in a class. 16 are boys and 13 are girls.

The ratio of boys to girls is written as 16:13.

Ratios can be simplified.

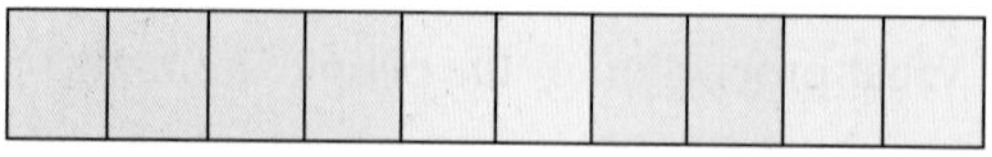

ratio of blue squares to green squares = 6:4

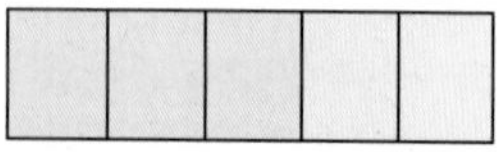

ratio of blue squares to green squares = 3:2

The ratio 6:4 is *equivalent* to 3:2. In both cases, every 5 squares contains 3 blue squares and 2 green squares.

6 and 4 can both be divided by 2 to give 3 and 2 so 6:4 simplifies to 3:2.

5:10:30 simplifies to 1:2:6 (divide each number by 5)

0.5:4 simplifies to 1:8 (multiply each number by 2)

Exercise 2M

For questions 1 to 4 , write down the ratio of yellow squares to green squares (make ratios as simple as possible):

1

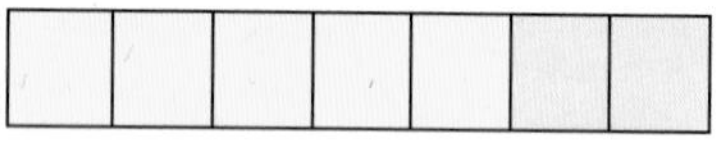

2

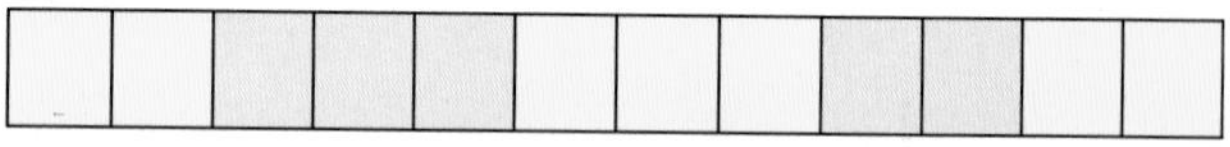

3

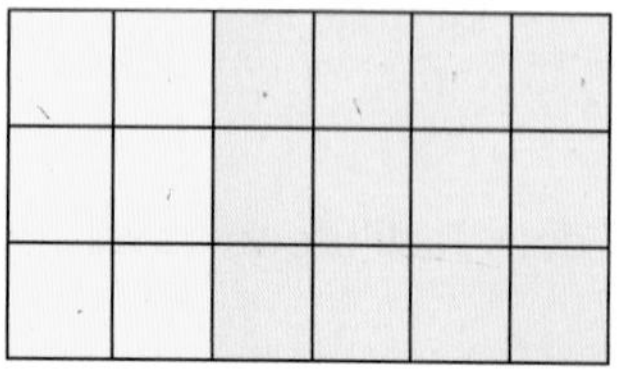

4

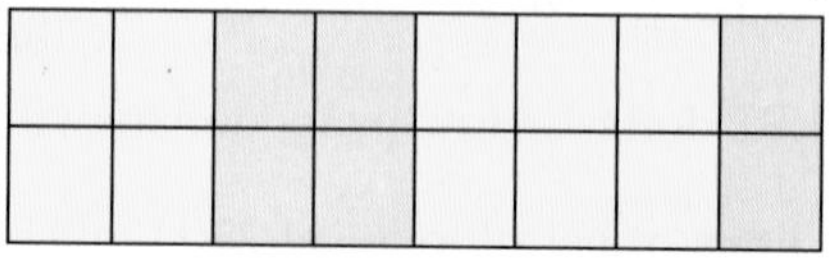

5 There are 27 children in a class. 11 are boys and 16 are girls. Write down the ratio of boys to girls.

6 One evening a vet sees 10 dogs and 6 cats. Find the ratio of dogs to cats.

7 Make diagrams like those in questions 1 to 4 to show the ratio of yellow squares to green squares is:

(a) 3:2 (b) 7:3 (c) 4:5

8 There are 33 people on a bus. 19 are men. Write down the ratio of men to women.

9 At one moment in a chess match, there are 10 black pieces on the board and 14 white pieces. Write down the ratio of black pieces to white pieces in its simplest form.

10 Write these ratios in simplified form.

(a) 5:20   (b) 8:10   (c) 4:44

(d) 16:12   (e) 10:8:6   (f) 21:35

(g) 65:25   (h) 16:24:80   (i) 5:15:33

11 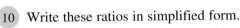 Copy this diagram. Colour in so that the ratio of blue squares to green squares is 2:3.

12 For each pair of ratios below, write down the value of *n* which makes the ratios *equivalent* to each other.

(a) 8:2 = *n*:1   (b) 4:12 = 1:*n*   (c) 70:40 = *n*:4

(d) 24:30 = 12:*n*   (e) 22:33 = 2:*n*   (f) 48:32 = 6:*n*

Share £35 in the ratio 5:2

The ratio 5:2 means we are dividing into '5 + 2' = 7 parts.
£35 is split into 7 parts so 1 part = £5.

5 parts = 5 × £5 = £25 and 2 parts = 2 × £5 = £10

Exercise 2E

1 Share £36 in the ratio   (a) 3:1   (b) 1:5   (c) 2:1

2 Share £50 in the ratio   (a) 1:4   (b) 3:2   (c) 3:7

3 Share £75 in the ratio   (a) 2:3   (b) 11:14   (c) 8:7

4 There are 28 children in a class. The ratio of boys to girls is 4:3.

(a) How many boys are in the class?

(b) How many girls are in the class?

5   In a hall, the ratio of chairs to tables is 9:2.
    If there is a total of 99 chairs and tables,
    how many chairs are there?

6   There are 30 chocolates in a box. The ratio of
    dark chocolates to milk chocolates is 2:3.
    How many milk chocolates are in the box?

7   Natasha and Andy are given £24 in the ratio 5:3.
    How much does each person get?

8   Mark and Helen share 45 sweets in the ratio 4:5.
    How many sweets does each person get?

9   Neil, Pippa and Mel have newspaper rounds. Each week they earn a total of £28 in the ratio
    3:5:6. How much money does Pippa earn?

10 In a kitchen drawer, there is a total of 36 knives, forks and spoons in the ratio 4:3:5.
    How many knives are there?

11 Sasha mixes some blue paint and some yellow paint in the ratio 7:4 to make up 33 litres of
    paint. How much yellow paint did she use?

12 Sachin and Ellie have a total of £60 between them. Sachin has three times as much money as
    Ellie. How much money does Sachin have?

CHECK YOURSELF ON SECTIONS 4.3 AND 4.4

1   Conversion of fractions, decimals and percentages

Copy and complete this table.

	fraction	decimal	percentage
(a)		0.08	
(b)	$\frac{4}{5}$		
(c)		0.9	
(d)			32%
(e)	$\frac{18}{25}$		

2   Recognising common percentages

(a) What percentage of the shape is shaded green?

(b) Before cooking, Roger finds that two-fifths of his vegetables are rotten. What *percentage* of his vegetables are not rotten?

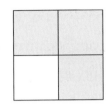

(c) Bev knocks over a bottle and loses two-thirds of her coke. What *percentage* of her coke does she still have?

3   Finding a percentage of a number

(a) Find 30% of £60.

(b) A camera costs £300. It is reduced in price by 5%. What is the new price?

(c) Find 12% of £800.

4   Tackling problems involving direct proportion

(a) Find the cost of 7 toys if 9 toys cost £72.

(b) 6 doughnuts cost £2.40. How much will 5 doughnuts cost?

5   Expressing proportions

(a) 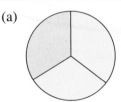 What proportion of this circle is green?

(b) 22 children are playing football. Nine of the children are in year 7. What proportion of the children are in year 7?

6   Dealing with ratios

(a)  Write down the ratio of black circles to white circles.

(b) Write the ratio 12:32 in simplified form.

(c) Share £40 in the ratio 7:1.

(d) During one week Urma and Terry eat 15 ice-creams in the ratio 3:2. How many ice-creams does Urma eat?

4.5 Negative numbers

In section 4.5 you will learn how to:

- compare negative numbers
- multiply and divide negative numbers
- add and subtract negative numbers

Comparing negative numbers

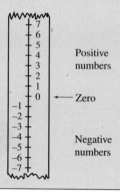

- All numbers above zero are positive numbers.
- Zero is not positive or negative.
- All numbers below zero are negative numbers.

- Temperatures are given in degrees Celsius (°C).
- Water freezes at 0°C.

Exercise 1M

1

(a) Which of these temperatures is the hottest?

(b) Which of these temperatures is the coldest?

(c) Which temperatures are below freezing?

2 Copy and complete the table below.

Temperature °C	Change °C	New temperature°C
7	falls by 9	
−3	rises by 6	
−8	rises by 2	
−10	falls by 2	
12	falls by 15	

3 The graph shows the temperatures for one day in Greenland.

(a) What was the temperature at 6 pm?

(b) What was the temperature at 9 am?

(c) What was the lowest temperature recorded?

(d) At what times was it −12°C?

(e) By how many degrees did the temperature go up between 6 am and 6 pm?

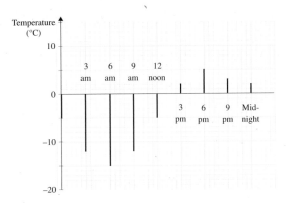

4 Write down each statement with either > or < in place of the box.

(a) −5 ☐ −4   (b) 0 ☐ −2   (c) −3 ☐ −6

5

−10 −9 −8 −7 −6 −5 −4 −3 −2 −1 0 1 2 3 4 5 6 7 8 9 10

Find the difference between

(a) −4 and 2   (b) −8 and −3   (c) 5 and −2

(d) −7 and 0   (e) −6 and 6   (f) −9 and −1

6 Write down these temperatures in order, coldest first.

(a) 5°C   −4°C   −9°C   −2°C   6°C   −7°C

(b) −4°C   5°C   −13°C   23°C   −5°C   4°C

(c) −5°C   14°C   3°C   −2°C   −7°C   5°C

(d) −3°C   0°C   −2°C   5°C   −5°C   −1°C

7 The temperature in London is −3°C. It rises by 9°C then drops by 7°C. What is the new temperature?

8 In a test there are +2 marks for a correct answer and −1 mark for an incorrect answer. Find the total marks in the tests below:

Test A ✓, ✓, ✗, ✗, ✗, ✓, ✓, ✗, ✓, ✗,

Test B ✗, ✗, ✓, ✓, ✗, ✓, ✗, ✗, ✗, ✗,

9 A diver is below the surface of the water at −25 m. She dives a further 9 m then rises 4 m. At what depth is she now?

10 The heights of places on a map are always measured in relation to sea level. For example a hill marked 510 m is 510 m above sea level.

(a) Think of something which could be at a height of –20 m.

(b) Some places in Holland are at a height of –3 m. What problems does this cause and what do the people do about it?

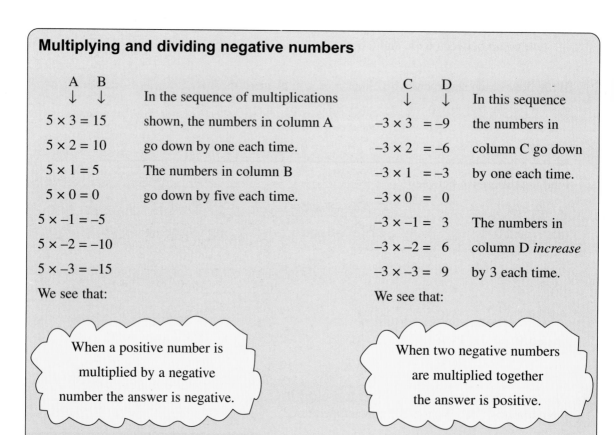

Multiplying and dividing negative numbers

A	B
↓	↓

In the sequence of multiplications shown, the numbers in column A go down by one each time.

The numbers in column B go down by five each time.

$5 \times 3 = 15$
$5 \times 2 = 10$
$5 \times 1 = 5$
$5 \times 0 = 0$
$5 \times -1 = -5$
$5 \times -2 = -10$
$5 \times -3 = -15$

We see that:

C	D
↓	↓

In this sequence the numbers in column C go down by one each time.

$-3 \times 3 = -9$
$-3 \times 2 = -6$
$-3 \times 1 = -3$
$-3 \times 0 = 0$
$-3 \times -1 = 3$
$-3 \times -2 = 6$
$-3 \times -3 = 9$

The numbers in column D *increase* by 3 each time.

We see that:

When a positive number is multiplied by a negative number the answer is negative.

When two negative numbers are multiplied together the answer is positive.

For division, the rules are the same as for multiplication.

$-4 \times (-6) = 24$ $7 \times (-3) = -21$ $-15 \div 3 = -5$

$40 \div (-4) = -10$ $-60 \div (-20) = 3$ $(-2) \times (-3) \times (-2) = -12$

$(-3) \times 15 = -45$ $(-12) \div (-1) \times (5) = 60$ $(-7) \times (-8) = 56$

Exercise 1E

Work out

1 (a) $4 \times (-2)$ (b) $5 \times (-4)$ (c) -3×4 (d) $-2 \times (-3)$

   (e) -6×3 (f) $8 \times (-2)$ (g) $-5 \times (-6)$ (h) -1×7

2 (a) $12 \div (-3)$ (b) $20 \div (-4)$ (c) $-8 \div 2$ (d) $-12 \div (-4)$

   (e) $-18 \div (-6)$ (f) $25 \div (-5)$ (g) $-15 \div 3$ (h) $-30 \div (-10)$

3 (a) $-40 \div 20$ (b) $8 \times (-6)$ (c) $-4 \times (-7)$ (d) $4 \times (-8)$

   (e) $-50 \div (-25)$ (f) $24 \div (-8)$ (g) $10 \times (-9)$ (h) $-63 \div (-7)$

4 Write down two negative numbers which multiply together to make 8. Are there any other pairs of negative numbers which will multiply together to make 8? Write them down.

5 Copy and complete the square below:

(a)

×	−3	6	−1	4
5	−15			
−2				
7				
−5				

(b)

×	−4	−7	2	0	−8	5
3	−12					
−9						
6						
−4						
−6						
−1						

6 Work out

   (a) $(-2) \times (-4) \times (-1)$ (b) $3 \times (-5) \times (-2)$

   (c) $(-3)^2$ (d) $(-6)^2$

   (e) $4 \times (-2) \times 4$ (f) $(-5) \times (-2) \times (-4)$

   (g) $(-10)^2$ (h) $(-1)^2$

7 What is the missing number for each box below?

   (a) $-4 \times \square = -28$ (b) $-6 \times \square = 42$ (c) $32 \div \square = -16$

   (d) $-45 \div \square = 5$ (e) $\square \div (-10) = 5$ (f) $\square \div (-9) = -8$

Adding and subtracting negative numbers

For adding and subtracting with negative numbers a number line is very useful.

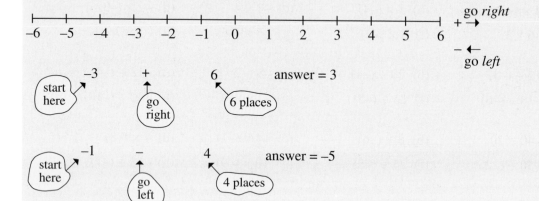

Exercise 2M

1. Use a number line to work out

    (a)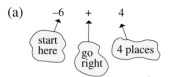

    (b)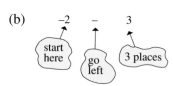

2. Use a number line to work out

    (a) $4 - 7$ (b) $-3 + 5$ (c) $-1 - 3$ (d) $-5 + 8$

    (e) $6 - 9$ (f) $-9 + 3$ (g) $6 - 12$ (h) $-7 + 6$

    (i) $-2 - 6$ (j) $-2 + 8$ (k) $-8 + 8$ (l) $10 - 14$

3. Work out

    (a) $-9 + 3$ (b) $5 - 11$ (c) $-4 - 4$ (d) $7 - 20$

    (e) $-6 + 8$ (f) $7 - 3$ (g) $-6 - 5$ (h) $-10 + 6$

    (i) $-3 + 3$ (j) $1 - 10$ (k) $-8 + 1$ (l) $-8 - 4$

4. Now work out these

    (a) $-3 + 12$ (b) $-7 + 7$ (c) $-6 - 1$ (d) $-5 - 4$

    (e) $-10 + 10$ (f) $3 - 15$ (g) $-7 + 8$ (h) $-4 - 1 + 3$

    (i) $30 - 60$ (j) $-6 - 14$ (k) $-60 + 20$ (l) $5 - 7 - 2$

5. Finally try this:

    $-4 + 1 - 6 - 3 + 2 + 5 - 3$

In the sequence of subtractions on the right the numbers in column A go down by one each time.

The numbers in column B increase by one each time.

	A	B
	↓	↓

$8 - (+3) = 5$

$8 - (+2) = 6$

$8 - (+1) = 7$

$8 - (0) = 8$

Continuing the sequence downwards:

$8 - (-1) = 9$

$8 - (-2) = 10$

We see that $8 - (-3)$ becomes $8 + 3$.

$8 - (-3) = 11$

This always applies when subtracting negative numbers. It is possible to replace *two* signs next to each other by *one* sign as follows:

Remember: 'same signs: +'

'different signs: –'

$$+ \quad + \; = \; +$$
$$- \quad - \; = \; +$$
$$- \quad + \; = \; -$$
$$+ \quad - \; = \; -$$

When two signs next to each other have been replaced by one sign in this way, the calculation is completed using the number line as before.

(a) $-3 + (-5)$

$= -3 - 5$

$= -8$

(b) $6 + (-12)$

$= 6 - 12$

$= -6$

(c) $4 - (-3)$

$= 4 + 3$

$= 7$

(d) $5 - (-2) + (-6)$

$= 5 + 2 - 6$

$= 1$

236

Exercise 2E

1 Work out

(a) $7 + (-3)$ (b) $9 - (-2)$ (c) $4 - 9$ (d) $-5 + 2$

(e) $-4 + (-5)$ (f) $-8 + (-3)$ (g) $10 - 12$ (h) $6 - (-4)$

(i) $12 - (-4)$ (j) $-6 + (-6)$ (k) $-4 - (-4)$ (l) $-5 + (-6)$

2 Work out

(a) $8 + (-7)$ (b) $-5 + (-1)$ (c) $-2 - (-3)$ (d) $-9 - (-9)$

(e) $8 - 12$ (f) $6 + (-9)$ (g) $-4 - (-3)$ (h) $3 + (-3)$

(i) $-7 - 5$ (j) $6 + (-13)$ (k) $-5 - (-6)$ (l) $3 + (-10)$

3 What is the missing number for each box below?

(a) $\square - (-3) = 7$ (b) $\square + (-4) = 6$ (c) $3 + \square = 1$

(d) $4 - \square = 8$ (e) $\square - 6 = -8$ (f) $8 + \square = -1$

4 Copy and complete each number wall below. The number in each box is found by adding the two numbers below it.

(a)

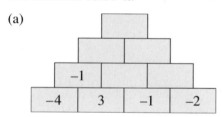

(b)

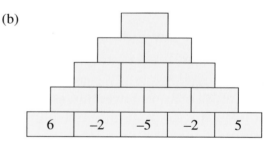

5 Write down whether each statement below is true or false.

(a) $4 + (-6) = -2$ (b) $8 - (-2) = 6$ (c) $-7 - 2 = -9$

(d) $8 - (-4) = 12$ (e) $5 + (-5) = -10$ (f) $2 - (-2) = 0$

(g) $16 + (-3) = 13$ (h) $10 + (-3) = 13$ (i) $-6 - (-8) = -14$

6 Work out the calculation in each box and put the answers in order of size, smallest first, to make a word.

A		Y	C	N		D
$(-1)^3$	I	$-8 - 4$	$-3 - (-12)$	$-6 + (-3)$	M	$(-7) \times 6$
	$5 - (-3)$				$(-2) \times (-3)$	

4.6 More algebra

In section 4.6 you will:

- review substituting numbers into a formula
- learn how to solve equations
- learn how to multiply out single brackets

Review of substituting numbers into a formula

(a) $y = 5(x - 4)$ Find y when $x = 7$

$y = 5(7 - 4)$

$y = 5 \times 3$

$y = 15$

(b) $m = 8 + 3n + nc$

Find m when $n = 5$ and $c = 7$

$m = 8 + (3 \times 5) + (5 \times 7)$

$m = 58$

Exercise 1M

A formula is given in each of questions 1 to 10 . Find the value of the letter required in each case.

1   $y = 3x + 7$

Find y when $x = 4$

2   $m = 4n + 12$

Find m when $n = 7$

3   $w = 25 - 4n$

Find w when $n = 5$

4   $a = 2(b - 6)$

Find a when $b = 10$

5   $c = 8(d + 3)$

Find c when $d = 6$

6   $y = x^2$

Find y when $x = 7$

7   $p = 2q + 5r$

Find p when $q = 6$ and $r = 7$

8   $f = gh$

Find f when $g = 9$ and $h = 8$

9   $m = \dfrac{n}{4}$

Find m when $n = 48$

10   $a = b\,(c - 7)$

Find a when $b = 10$ and $c = 15$

11 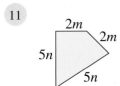

The perimeter p of this shape is given by the formula

$$p = 4m + 10n$$

Find p when $m = 8$ and $n = 13$

238

12 The average speed s of a sprinter is given by the formula

$$s = \frac{d}{t}$$

where d is the distance covered and t is the time taken.
Find the value of s when $d = 200$ and $t = 25$

13 The cost in pounds C for hiring a van is given by the formula $C = 3n + 65$ where n is the number of miles travelled.

Find C when $n = 60$

14 $V = IR$ is an electrical formula. Find the value of V when $I = 0.5$ and $R = 68$

Negative numbers can be substituted into formulas

$m = 6 - n$

Find m when $n = -2$.

$m = 6 - (-2)$

$m = 6 + 2$

$m = 8$

$y = 3x + w$

Find y when $x = 4$ and $w = -8$.

$y = (3 \times 4) + (-8)$

$y = 12 - 8$

$y = 4$

Exercise 1E

1 Copy and complete the following:

(a) $x = -7 - (-4)$

$x = -7 \;\square\; 4$

$x = \square$

(b) $y = -3 + (-10)$

$y = -3 \;\square\; 10$

$y = \square$

2 $a = 7 + b$
Find a when $b = -5$

3 $w = 16 - p$
Find w when $p = -3$

4 $m = 3n$
Find m when $n = -9$

5 $h = 3g - 6$
Find h when $g = -6$

6 $c = 2d + e$
Find c when $d = -4$ and $e = -7$

7 $n = 5x - y$
Find n when $x = -10$ and $y = -40$

8 $p = m^2$

Find p when $m = -6$

9 $a = \dfrac{b}{7}$

Find a when $b = -63$

10 $y = 3(8 - x)$

Find y when $x = -2$

11 $p = -2(8 + q)$

Find p when $q = -3$

12 $a = 2b + 2c$

Find a when $b = -4$ and $c = -5$

13 $c = \dfrac{d}{-3}$

Find c when $d = -36$

14 $y = mx + c$

Find y when $m = 4$,
$x = -6$ and $c = 3$

15 $p = uw - t$

Find p when $u = 7$,
$w = -2$ and $t = -8$

Solving equations

● Tom is thinking of a mystery number. He knows that if he doubles the number and then adds nine, the answer is twenty-three.

He could write $\boxed{?}$ for the mystery number.

So $2 \times \boxed{?} + 9 = 23$ This is an *equation*. It contains an '=' sign. There is one unknown number shown by the question mark.

● People prefer to use *letters* to stand for unknowns when they write equations.

Tom's equation would be

$\qquad 2 \times n + 9 = 23$ where n is the mystery number,

or $2n + 9 = 23$ (any letter could be used)

What is Tom's mystery number?

● Equations are like weighing scales which are balanced. The scales remain balanced if the same weight is added or taken away from both sides.

On the left pan is an unknown weight x plus a 6 kg weight. On the right pan there is a 6 kg weight and a 3 kg weight.

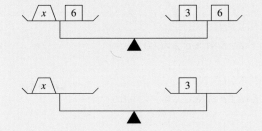

If the two 6 kg weights are taken from each pan, the scales are still balanced so the weight x is 3 kg.

Exercise 2M

Find the weight x by removing weights from both pans. Weights are in kg.

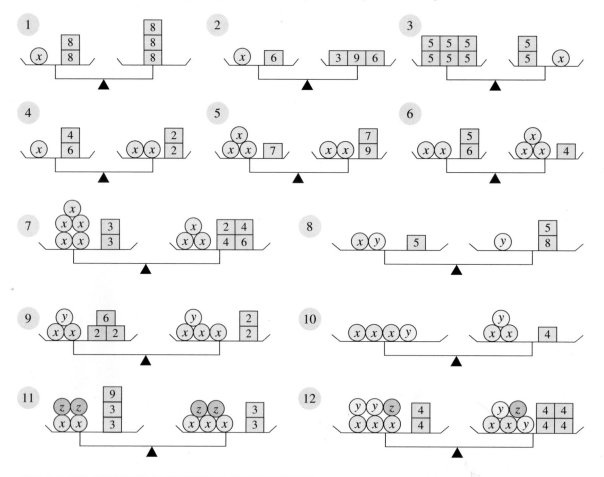

Rules for solving equations

Equations can be solved in the same way as the weighing scale problems were solved.

The main rule is

> Do the same thing to both sides

If you need to, you may:

     add the same thing to both sides

     subtract the same thing from both sides

     multiply both sides by the same thing

     divide both sides by the same thing

Solve the equations. The circles show what is done to both sides of the equation.

(a) $x + 4 = 16$

$\ominus 4$ $\ominus 4$

$x = 12$

(b) $x - 5 = 14$

$\oplus 5$ $\oplus 5$

$x = 19$

(c) $3x = 18$

$\div 3$ $\div 3$

$x = 6$

(d) $\dfrac{x}{2} = 6$

$\times 2$ $\times 2$

$x = 12$

Exercise 3M

Solve the equations below.

1   $x + 5 = 12$

2   $x + 6 = 19$

3   $x - 4 = 8$

4   $x - 9 = 8$

5   $3 + x = 11$

6   $7 + x = 17$

7   $5 = x + 3$

8   $6 = x - 2$

9   $2 = x - 6$

10   $3 + x = 3$

11   $x - 14 = 10$

12   $17 = 5 + x$

Questions 13 to 27 involve multiplication and division.

13   $7n = 21$

14   $4n = 12$

15   $5n = 45$

16   $10 = 2n$

17   $8 = 8n$

18   $2n = 1$

19   $4n = 100$

20   $6n = 0$

21   $\dfrac{n}{3} = 2$

22   $\dfrac{n}{5} = 4$

23   $70 = 7n$

24   $2n = 1000$

25   $\dfrac{n}{8} = 3$

26   $\dfrac{n}{4} = 1$

27   $10 = \dfrac{n}{2}$

In questions 28 to 45 find a.

28   $a - 17 = 21$

29   $4a = 32$

30   $9 + a = 60$

31   $5 = a + 5$

32   $63 = 9a$

33   $15a = 45$

34   $a + 36 = 120$

35   $a - \dfrac{1}{3} = \dfrac{2}{3}$

36   $3a = 1$

37 $65 = a - 25$	38 $140 = a - 20$	39 $4a = 412$
40 $109 = a - 206$	41 $\dfrac{a}{3} = 9$	42 $\dfrac{a}{5} = 100$
43 $0 = 15a$	44 $a + 14 = 14$	45 $\dfrac{a}{10} = 6$

Equations with two operations

(a) $6n - 5 = 19$

$(+5)$ $(+5)$

$6n = 24$

$(\div 6)$ $(\div 6)$

$n = 4$

Check: $6 \times 4 - 5 = 19$

(b) $3n + 4 = 31$

(-4) (-4)

$3n = 27$

$(\div 3)$ $(\div 3)$

$n = 9$

Check: $3 \times 9 + 4 = 31$

Exercise 3E

Solve the equations below. Check by substituting the answer back in the equation.

1 $4n - 1 = 11$	2 $2n + 3 = 17$	3 $6n - 9 = 15$
4 $5n + 6 = 16$	5 $4n - 9 = 11$	6 $2n - 10 = 8$
7 $3n + 7 = 37$	8 $9n + 4 = 13$	9 $7n - 6 = 15$
10 $7n - 10 = 25$	11 $4n - 7 = 73$	12 $3n + 8 = 26$

In questions 13 to 24 solve the equations to find x.

13 $7x + 2 = 30$	14 $5x - 9 = 31$	15 $6x - 40 = 20$
16 $8x + 3 = 59$	17 $2 + 4x = 30$	18 $19 + 3x = 19$
19 $12 + 6x = 42$	20 $10x - 13 = 27$	21 $7x - 40 = 100$
22 $2x - 38 = 62$	23 $7 + 2x = 19$	24 $2x + 6 = 7$

Using equations to solve problems

Tina is thinking of a number. She tells us that when she trebles it and adds 8, the answer is 23. What number is Tina thinking of?

Let n be the number Tina is thinking of.

She tells us that $\qquad\qquad\qquad\qquad 3n + 8 = 23$

Subtract 8 from both sides: $\qquad\qquad\qquad 3n = 15$

Divide both sides by 3: $\qquad\qquad\qquad\qquad n = \dfrac{15}{3} = 5$

So Tina is thinking of the number 5.

Exercise 4M

In questions ① to ⑦ I am thinking of a number.

Write down an equation then solve it to find the number.

① I multiply the number by 4 and then add 9. The answer is 17.

② I multiply the number by 6 and then add 2. The answer is 50.

③ I multiply the number by 9 and then subtract 5. The answer is 22.

④ I double the number and then add 17. The answer is 37.

⑤ I multiply the number by 5 and then subtract 11. The answer is 24.

⑥ I treble the number and then subtract 13. The answer is 2.

⑦ I multiply the number by 4 and then add 15. The answer is 135.

⑧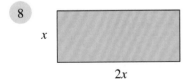

x $2x$

The length of a rectangle is twice its width. If the perimeter is 48 cm, find its width.

⑨ The length of a rectangle is four times its width. If the perimeter of the rectangle is 50 cm, find its width. [Hint: Let the width be x.]

⑩ The length of a rectangle is 5 cm more than its width. If the perimeter of the rectangle is 38 cm, find its width.

11 For each triangle, write down an equation then solve it to find x.

(a)

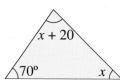

(b)

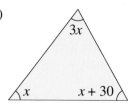

12 The angles of a triangle are A, B and C. Angle B is three times as big as angle A. Angle C is 45° bigger than angle A. Find the size of angle A. (Hint: let the size of angle A be $x°$)

Mixed equations

Solve the equations where the 'n' terms are on the right hand side.

(a) $7 = 5n - 8$

    (+8)   (+8)

    $15 = 5n$

    (÷5)   (÷5)

    $3 = n$

(b) $11 = 3 + 2n$

    (–3)   (–3)

    $8 = 2n$

    (÷2)   (÷2)

    $4 = n$

Exercise 4E

Solve the equations below. Check by substituting the answer back in the equation.

1 $37 = 4n + 1$

2 $7 = 2n - 5$

3 $7 = 20n - 13$

4 $33 = 2n + 9$

5 $3n + 16 = 25$

6 $55 = 15 + 8n$

7 $16 = 16 + 3n$

8 $19 = 2n - 11$

9 $59 = 4n + 3$

In questions 10 to 21 find the value of the letter in each question.

10 $6t - 9 = 45$

11 $50 = 7y + 8$

12 $11 = 3 + 8c$

13 $3x + 10 = 85$

14 $0 = 4m - 36$

15 $16 + 2p = 106$

16 $7 + 5n = 62$

17 $8w - 25 = 47$

18 $10a - 15 = 205$

19 $3y - 70 = 260$

20 $156 = 26 + 2q$

21 $540 = 3x - 63$

Multiply out single brackets

$6 (4 + 3) = 6 (7) = 6 \times 7 = 42$

We also get the correct answer if the number outside the brackets multiplies each number inside the brackets.

$6 (4 + 3) = 6 \times 4 + 6 \times 3 = 24 + 18 = 42$

(a) Multiply out $3 (a + b)$

$3 (a + b) = 3 \times a + 3 \times b$

$\qquad = 3a + 3b$

(b) Multiply out $6 (n - 3)$

$6 (n - 3) = 6 \times n - 6 \times 3$

$\qquad = 6n - 18$

Exercise 5M

Multiply out

1. $2 (x + 3)$
2. $6 (x + 4)$
3. $3 (x + 9)$
4. $5 (x + 8)$
5. $4 (x - 7)$
6. $2 (x - 8)$
7. $9 (x - 4)$
8. $6 (x - 8)$
9. $4 (x + y)$
10. $7 (a + b)$
11. $3 (m - n)$
12. $5 (2x + 3)$
13. $6 (4x - 7)$
14. $4 (2a + b)$
15. $9 (m + 2n)$
16. $4 (x + 3y)$
17. $2 (4m + n)$
18. $7 (5x - 3)$
19. $8 (3 - x)$
20. $6 (4 - 2x)$
21. $5 (3a + 5b)$
22. $9 (2m + 1)$
23. $11 (2t - 3)$
24. $4 (a - 2c)$
25. $3 (x + y + z)$
26. $5 (a + 2b + c)$
27. $7 (2x + y + 3)$
28. $4 (3x - 5)$
29. $6 (8 - x)$
30. $8 (x + 2y - 1)$

'Expand' means 'multiply out'.

(a) Expand $m(n + y)$

$m(n + y) = m \times n + m \times y$

$\qquad = mn + my$

(b) Expand $w(w - 3)$

$w(w - 3) = w \times w - 3 \times w$

$\qquad = w^2 - 3w$

Exercise 5E

Expand

1 $p(q + r)$

2 $m(n - p)$

3 $a(b + c)$

4 $a(b - e)$

5 $x(y + 3)$

6 $m(n - 6)$

7 $x(y - 9)$

8 $p(q - 5)$

9 $a(c + 7)$

10 $d(e + 8)$

11 $a(a + 4)$

12 $m(m - 6)$

13 $p(p - 2)$

14 $x(x + 9)$

15 $a(7 - a)$

16 $x(2 + y)$

17 $5(2a + 3)$

18 $9(3m - 2)$

19 $6(4x - 1)$

20 $4(8n + 7)$

21 $b(4 - b)$

CHECK YOURSELF ON SECTIONS 4.5 AND 4.6

1   Comparing negative numbers

(a) Write these temperatures in order, hottest first.

   –8°C,   1°C,   –4°C,   –3°C,   2°C,   –9°C

(b) Which number is larger $\boxed{-5}$ or $\boxed{-6}$?

2   Multiplying and dividing negative numbers

Work out

(a) $3 \times (-5)$ (b) $-16 \div (-2)$ (c) $-30 \div 10$ (d) $-8 \times (-4)$

3   Adding and subtracting negative numbers

Work out

(a) $-6 + 2$ (b) $-3 - 4$ (c) $2 + (-5)$ (d) $-8 - (-6)$

4   Review of substituting numbers into a formula

(a) $m = 4(n + 5)$
Find m when $n = 2$.

(b) $y = 3x + 4z$
Find y when $x = 8$ and $z = -5$.

5   Solving equations

Solve

(a) $x - 9 = 17$
(b) $\frac{m}{6} = 5$

(c) $3n - 7 = 23$
(d) $54 = 7a + 5$

6   Multiplying out single brackets

Expand (multiply out)

(a) $5(x + 7)$
(b) $n(p - 3)$
(c) $x(x + 8)$

UNIT 4 MIXED REVIEW

Part one

1   The price of a computer game is £40 but it is increased by 5%. What is the new price?

2   Gwen and Tim are given £99 in the ratio 8:3. How much money does Tim get?

3   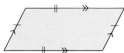   Name this shape.

4   The temperature in Manchester one day is 1°C. During the night it drops
    by 5°C. What is the new temperature?

5   Solve   (a) $3n = 18$ (b) $4n - 9 = 11$ (c) $7 = \frac{n}{8}$

6   If you buy 3 tins of cat food for £2.16,
    how much would 5 tins cost?

7   If 76% of people wear a wristwatch, what
    percentage does not?

8   What is 70% as a fraction?

9   A small boat travels 300 km on 135 litres of fuel.
    How much fuel is needed for a journey of 1200 km?

10 A laptop costs £450. In a sale the price is reduced by 20%.
What does the laptop now cost?

11 Use a protractor and ruler to construct this
triangle. Measure the side marked x.

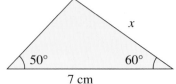

12 Simplify these fractions.

(a) $\frac{15}{20}$ (b) $\frac{30}{35}$ (c) $\frac{46}{50}$ (d) $\frac{21}{35}$

13 Look at the following numbers …

$-8, \quad 3, \quad 0, \quad -3, \quad 6$

(a) Write down the positive numbers.

(b) Write down the negative numbers.

(c) Write the numbers in order, lowest to highest.

(d) Write down the difference between the highest and lowest numbers.

14 Multiply out   (a) $5(x-3)$ (b) $3(2x+4)$

15 Write the ratio 18:30 in simplified form.

Part Two

1

London	$-5°C$
Paris	$-3°C$
Rome	$+1°C$
Melbourne	$+11°C$
New York	$-8°C$

(a) From the table above, what is the
difference in temperature between
Rome and London?

(b) At 12:00 the temperature in New
York has risen by 5°C. What is the
temperature in New York at 12:00?

2. A recipe uses 3 eggs and 2 apples for every cake. A chef has an order for several cakes. He uses 24 eggs. How many apples does he use?

3. On squared paper draw these shapes:

   (a) a quadrilateral with just one right angle.

   (b) an isosceles triangle.

   (c) a quadrilateral with no right angles and no parallel sides.

4. Which is larger? $\boxed{\dfrac{7}{25}}$ or $\boxed{27\%}$

5. Solve (a) $\frac{x}{4} = 6$ (b) $5x + 6 = 51$ (c) $58 = 3x - 8$

6. There are 30 children in class 7C. One day 80% of the class are on a school trip. How many children do *not* go on the school trip?

7. Three friends share a prize of £5000 in the ratio 2:3:5. How much was the largest share?

8. Write down an expression for the area of this rectangle. Expand your answer.

n

$n + 4$

9.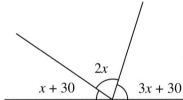

   $2x$

   $x + 30$ $3x + 30$

   Find the value of x and then write down the size of each of the three angles.

10. Look at the diagram.

    (a) Write down the ratio shaded length: unshaded length.

    (b) As a percentage, what proportion of the diagram is shaded?

11. If $y = 3x - c$, find the value of y when $x = 3$ and $c = -8$.

12. Draw a scalene triangle.

13. The price of a dress costing £45 was decreased by 10%. Six months later the price was increased by 10%. Calculate the final price of the dress.

250

Puzzles and Problems 4

Coordinates puzzles

1 Draw a pair of axes with the values shown.

Plot the points below and join them up with a ruler in the order given.

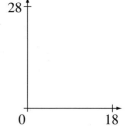

(10, 28)	(16, 28)	(18, 26)	(18, 24)	(16, 22)
$(14\frac{1}{2}, 20)$	(14, 18)	(14, 8)	(12, 6)	(12, 1)

ON THE SAME PICTURE plot the points below and join them up with a ruler in the order given.

DO NOT JOIN THE LAST POINT IN THE BOX ABOVE WITH THE FIRST POINT IN THE NEW BOX.

(5, 1)	(7, 3)	(7, 5)	(6, 6)	(5, 6)	(4, 7)	(6, 7)	(8, 7)	(10, 8)

ON THE SAME PICTURE plot the points below and join them up with a ruler in the order given.

(4, 7)	(3, 8)	(4, 9)	(6, 9)

ON THE SAME PICTURE plot the points below and join them up with a ruler in the order given.

(4, 9)	(4, 10)	(5, 10)

ON THE SAME PICTURE plot the points below and join them up with a ruler in the order given.

(7, 12)	(6, 13)	(5, 13)	(4, 12)	(4, 11)	(5, 10)	(6, 10)
(7, 11)	(7, 12)	(8, 13)	(9, 13)	(10, 12)	(10, 11)	(9, 10)
(8, 10)	(7, 11)					

ON THE SAME PICTURE plot the points below and join them up with a ruler in the order given.

(10, 28)	(8, 26)	(7, 24)	$(6\frac{1}{2}, 22)$	(6, 20)	$(5\frac{1}{2}, 18)$	
(5, 16)	(5, 13)	$(5, 13\frac{1}{2})$	(7, 14)	(9, 14)	(12, 13)	(12, 6)

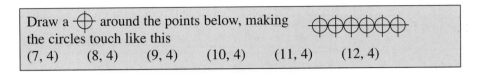

Draw a ⊕ around the points below, making the circles touch like this

(7, 4)   (8, 4)   (9, 4)   (10, 4)   (11, 4)   (12, 4)

Draw a • at (6, 11) and a • at (9, 11)

2 Draw a pair of axes with the values shown.

Plot the points below and join them up with a ruler in the order given.

(4, 2) (4, 4) (2, 6) (0, 6) (−1, 4) (−1, 2) (0, 1)

(2, 1) (4, 2) (6, 2) (6, 1) (5, 1)

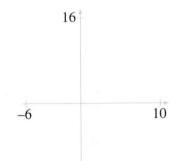

ON THE SAME PICTURE plot the points below and join them up with a ruler in the order given.

DO NOT JOIN THE LAST POINT IN THE BOX ABOVE WITH THE FIRST POINT IN THE NEW BOX.

(−3, 13)   (−3, 1)   (−2, 1)

ON THE SAME PICTURE plot the points below and join them up with a ruler in the order given.

(0, −4)   (−2, −3)   (−2, −1)   (−4, −1)   (−4, 1)   (−3, 1)

ON THE SAME PICTURE plot the points below and join them up with a ruler in the order given.

(3, −5)   (4, −5)   (5, −4)   (4, −3)   (4, −2)   (3, −2)

(−1, −1)   (−1, −2)   (1, −3)   (1, −1$\frac{1}{2}$)

ON THE SAME PICTURE plot the points below and join them up with a ruler in the order given.

(4, −3)   (1, −3)   (3, −3)   (3, −2)   (7, −2)   (7, 1)

(6, 1)   (7, 1)   (8, 2)   (8, 4)   (7, 6)

ON THE SAME PICTURE plot the points below and join them up with a ruler in the order given.

(−3, −1)   (−3, −6)   (−4, −6)   (6, −6)   (4, −6)   (4, −5)

ON THE SAME PICTURE plot the points below and join them up with a ruler in the order given.

(4, 4)	(5, 6)	(7, 6)	(7, 13)	(6, 14)	(6, 13)	(5, 14)
(5, 13)	(4, 14)	(4, 13)	(3, 14)	(3, 13)	(2, 14)	$(1\frac{1}{2}, 13)$ $(\frac{1}{2}, 14)$
(0, 13)	(–1, 14)	(–1, 13)	(–2, 14)	(–2, 13)	$(-3\frac{1}{2}, 14)$	(–3, 13)

Draw a • at (1, 4) and a • at (6, 4)   Who am I?   Colour me in?

A long time ago!   4

Roman numerals

Many clock faces still use roman
numerals like IV and XI. At the end of a film, the
year in which the film was made is often given
using roman numerals.
MCMLXXX means 1980.

1	one	XI	eleven
II	two	XII	twelve
III	three	XX	twenty
IV	four (one before five)	XXX	thirty
V	five	XL	forty (ten before fifty)
VI	six	L	fifty
VII	seven	LX	sixty
VIII	eight	C	hundred
IX	nine (one before ten)	CM	nine hundred
X	ten	M	thousand

Note

When we reach 10 before 50, we write XL not XXXX. Your teacher may explain this more fully.

Exercise

1 Write down the value of each of the numbers written below in roman numerals.

(a) VII   (b) XIII   (c) XVI   (d) XXVII

(e) XVIII   (f) XIX   (g) XLV   (h) LXXII

(i) CCCXXVII   (j) XCIV   (k) MMVI   (l) CMXLIX

2 Write these numbers in roman numerals.

(a) 8   (b) 17   (c) 22

(d) 58   (e) 39   (f) 84

(g) 78   (h) 123   (i) 339

(j) 1265   (k) 1066   (l) 3194

3 Write this year in roman numerals.

4 Work out the questions below, giving your answers in roman numerals.

(a) VI + III   (b) IX + VIII   (c) XIII + XVII

(d) XL − VI   (e) LIII − XVIII   (f) C − XLVII

(g) LXXV + CCXXXVI   (h) V × II   (i) IV × IX

(j) CCCXII − CLXXIX   (k) VII × VI   (l) VII × XII

(m) XXIV ÷ III   (n) L ÷ X   (o) CXX ÷ XX

(p) XXXVI ÷ IX   (q) MCC ÷ XXX   (r) MCCV + CCXXVIII − XCIV

5 **RESEARCH:**

(a) In the ancient Greek number system, Δ was the symbol for 10. Find out the ancient Greek symbol for (i) 100   and   (ii) 50.

(b) Find the ancient Egyptian symbols for (i) 10   (ii) 100   and   (iii) 1000.

(c) Find out three more ancient Egyptian symbols and sketch them as carefully as you can.

(d) Can you find out why particular letters are used for certain roman numerals?
For example, why is C used for 100?

Mental Arithmetic Practice 4

Here are two sets of mental arithmetic questions. Ideally a teacher will read out each question twice, with pupils books closed. Each test of 20 questions should take about 20 minutes.

Test 1

1 What is half of half of eighty?

2 How many twenty pence coins make three pounds?

3 What is the perimeter of a rectangular room twelve metres by six metres?

4 I am facing South-West and the wind is hitting me on my back. What direction is the wind coming from?

5 If six per cent of pupils of a school are absent, what percentage of pupils are present?

6 Write nought point seven as a fraction.

7 What is twenty-fifteen in twelve hour clock time?

8 Write the number six thousand two hundred and four in figures.

9 What number is twelve more than fifty-seven?

10 If pears cost eleven pence each, how many can I buy for one pound?

11 With three darts I score six, double five and treble five. What is my total score?

12 A film lasting one and half hours starts at six twenty p.m. What time does the film finish?

13 If I buy a card for sixty-five pence and a stamp for thirty-two pence, how much change do I get from one pound?

14 What number is nine less than sixty-two?

15 How many degrees are there in one tenth of a right angle?

16 A fifth of my wages is taken in tax. What percentage have I got left?

17 How many grams are there in half a kilogram?

18 What four coins make forty pence?

19 One angle in an isosceles triangle is one hundred and twenty degrees. How large is each of the other two angles?

20 What number is one hundred times bigger than nought point six?

Test 2

1 How many sides has a pentagon?

2 What is nought point one as a percentage?

3 How much change from a ten pound note will I receive if I spend three pounds and ninety-nine pence?

4 What are eight thirties?

5 What number is nineteen more than twenty-six?

6 Write in figures the number two thousand and fifteen.

7 What is one quarter of eighty-eight?

8 What is the sum of sixty-three and twenty-nine?

9 How many sevens are there in sixty-three?

10 A DVD costs §9.50. How much change do you get from a §20 note?

11 What is fifty per cent of fifty pounds?

12 How many sides has an octagon?

13 I think of a number, double it and the answer is seven. What was the number I thought of?

14 What is four thousand four hundred and fifty-nine to the nearest hundred?

15 What is nought point two multiplied by one hundred?

16 Two angles of a triangle add up to one hundred and fifteen degrees. What size is the third angle?

17 Write noon in twenty-four hour clock time.

18 You are facing east and turn through three right angles clockwise, what direction are you now facing?

19 A thermometer in a room shows twenty-two degrees. The temperature outside the room is minus 8 degrees. What is the difference in temperature between inside and outside?

20 If you have four thousand and eleven pennies, how much do you have in pounds and pence?

UNIT 5

5.1 Rotation

In section 5.1 you will learn about:

- rotating shapes
- rotational symmetry

In these diagrams the blue shape has been rotated onto the yellow shape.

In the first diagram the blue shape is rotated 90° (1 right angle) anti-clockwise around point A.

In the second diagram the blue shape is rotated 180° (2 right angles) around point B.

Notice that for a 180° rotation it makes no difference whether you turn clockwise or anti-clockwise.

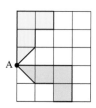

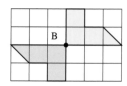

Exercise 1M

1   These pictures have been hung incorrectly. Give instructions to turn them the right way round. Remember to give both the angle and the direction.

(a)

(b)

(c)

(d) 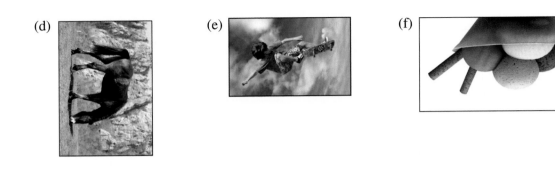 (e) (f)

In questions ② to ⑩ copy each diagram and then draw its new position after it has been turned. You can use tracing paper if you wish.

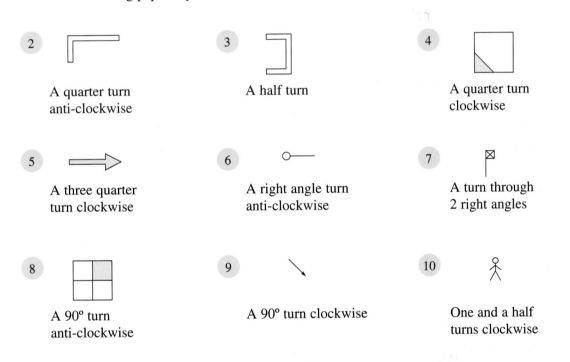

② A quarter turn anti-clockwise

③ A half turn

④ A quarter turn clockwise

⑤ A three quarter turn clockwise

⑥ A right angle turn anti-clockwise

⑦ A turn through 2 right angles

⑧ A 90° turn anti-clockwise

⑨ A 90° turn clockwise

⑩ One and a half turns clockwise

In questions ⑪ to ⑯ describe the rotation. Give the angle and the direction.

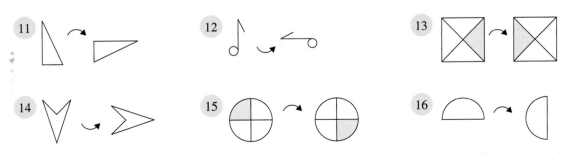

11 12 13

14 15 16

258

Rotate this
shape 90°
clockwise around
the point A.

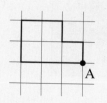

A

Here is
the result.

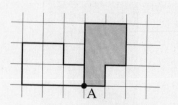

A

The pink shape is called the *image*.

Exercise 1E   (Use tracing paper if you wish)

1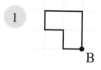

B

(a) Copy this shape on squared paper

(b) Draw the image of the shape after a quarter turn clockwise around the point B.

In questions 2 to 4 copy the shape on squared paper and then draw and shade its new position.

2

C

Half turn around
the point C

3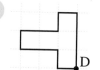

D

Quarter turn clockwise
around the point D

4

E

Turn 90° anti-clockwise
around the point E

5 The diagram shows shapes which have been rotated about the points A, B, C, D and E.

Which shape do you get when you:

(a) rotate shape R 90° clockwise about A

(b) rotate shape R 90° clockwise about B

(c) rotate shape Q 180° about C

(d) rotate shape S 90° anti-clockwise about D

(e) rotate shape P 180° about E

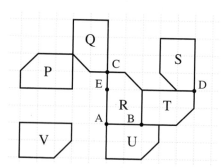

6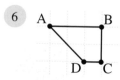

A   B

D   C

Draw this shape on squared paper.

Draw the image of the shape

(a) after a 90° rotation clockwise about A

(b) after a 180° rotation about B

(c) after a 90° rotation anti-clockwise about C

Rotational symmetry

The shape B fits onto itself three times when rotated through a complete turn. It has *rotational symmetry of order three*.

The shape C fits onto itself six times when rotated through a complete turn. It has rotational symmetry of order six.

Exercise 2M

For each diagram decide whether or not the shape has rotational symmetry. For those diagrams that do have rotational symmetry state the order.

1
2
3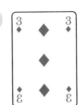
4

5
6
7
8

9
10
11
12

13
14
15
16

260

Exercise 2E

1 (a) If this umbrella was viewed from above would it have rotational symmetry?

(b) If so what is the order of rotational symmetry?

In questions 2 to 7 copy each diagram and complete it so that the final design has rotational symmetry of the order stated.

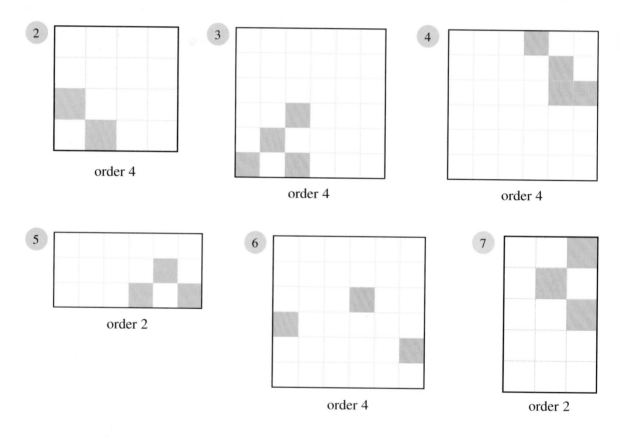

2
order 4

3
order 4

4
order 4

5
order 2

6
order 4

7
order 2

8

This shape is made using coloured pencils.

If you ignore the different colours, what is the order of rotational symmetry of the shape?

5.2 Line Symmetry

In section 5.2 you will learn about:

- line symmetry
- reflections

Paper folding activities

1 Take a piece of paper, fold it once and then cut out
a shape across the fold. This will produce a shape
with one line of symmetry, which is a mirror line.

cut along
the broken line →

2 Fold another piece of paper twice so that the second
fold is at right angles to the first fold. Again cut
across the fold to see what shapes you can make.

This will produce a shape with two lines of
symmetry. [i.e. two mirror lines]

3 Fold the paper three times and cut.

This will produce a shape with four lines of symmetry.

Below are three shapes obtained by folding and cutting as above.
Try to make similar shapes yourself.
Stick the best shapes into your exercise book.

1

one line of symmetry
(or one mirror line)

2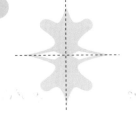

two lines of symmetry
(or two mirror lines)

3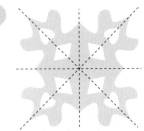

four lines of symmetry
(or four mirror lines)

Exercise 1M

Copy each of the following shapes and mark on the diagram all lines of symmetry.

1

2

3

4

5

6

Exercise 1E

1 Copy these shapes on square 'dotty' paper (or ordinary squared paper). Complete the shapes with the lines of symmetry shown.

(a)

(b)

(c)

2 **N   Z   E   H   T**

(a) Which of these letters have 1 or more lines of symmetry?

(b) Which letters have rotational symmetry?

(c) Do any of these letters have both line symmetry and rotational symmetry?

3 Make a list of all the capital letters in the alphabet which have line symmetry.

4

(a) Does this shape have rotational symmetry?

(b) Does this shape have line symmetry?

5 Draw a 4 × 4 grid like the one above. Shade four squares to make a pattern with rotational symmetry but not line symmetry.

6 Draw a 3 × 3 grid. Shade three squares to make a pattern with line symmetry but not rotational symmetry.

7 Draw a 4 × 4 grid and shade four squares to make a pattern with no line symmetry and no rotational symmetry.

Reflection

A reflection is a transformation in which points are mapped to images by folding along a mirror line.

Shade in as many squares as necessary so that the final pattern has mirror lines shown by the broken lines.

(a)

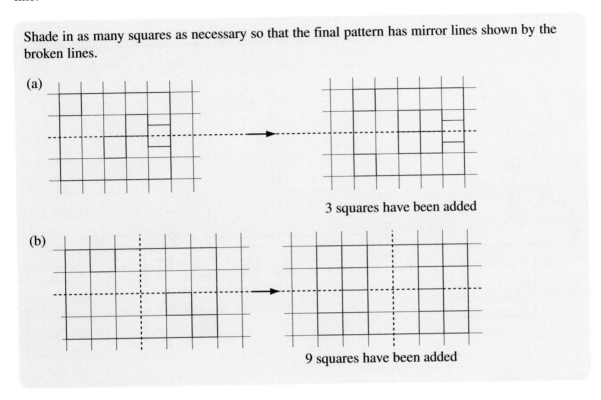

3 squares have been added

(b)

9 squares have been added

Exercise 2M

Copy each diagram and, using a different colour, shade in as many squares as necessary so that the final pattern has mirror lines shown by the broken lines. For each question write down how many new squares were shaded in.

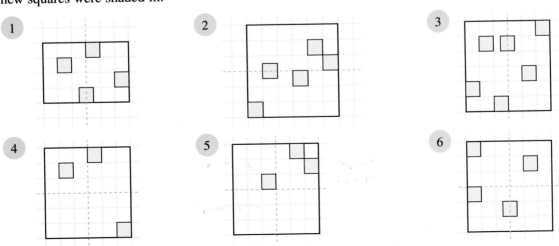

Exercise 2E

Copy each diagram and, using a different colour, shade in as many squares as necessary so that the final pattern has mirror lines shown by the broken lines. For each question write down how many new squares were shaded in.

Be careful when the mirror line is a diagonal line. You can check your diagram by folding along the mirror line.

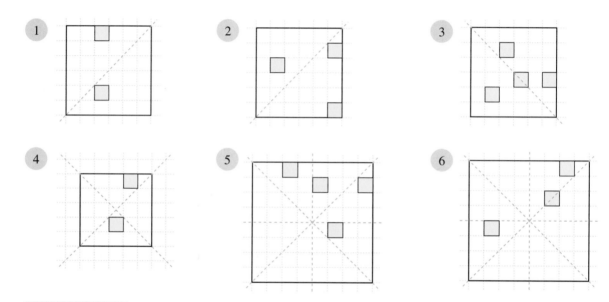

Exercise 3M

1   You have 3 square yellow tiles and 2 square white tiles, which can be joined together along whole sides.

So this ▨☐ is allowed but this ☐▨ is *not* allowed.

Draw as many diagrams as possible with the 5 tiles joined together so that the diagram has line symmetry.

For example fig. 1 and fig. 2 have line symmetry but fig. 3 does not have line symmetry so fig. 3 is not acceptable.

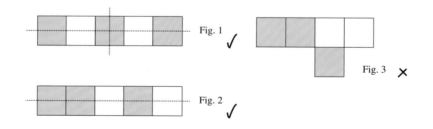

2 Now you have 2 yellow tiles and 2 white tiles. Draw as many diagrams as possible with these tiles joined together so that the diagram has line symmetry.

3 Finally with 3 yellow tiles and 3 white tiles draw as many diagrams as possible which have line symmetry.

Here is one diagram which has line symmetry

4 Shape A is a single square.   Shape B consists of four squares.

Draw three diagrams in which shapes A and B are joined together along a whole edge so that the final shape has line symmetry.

5 Shape C is a single square.   Shape D consists of five squares.

Draw four diagrams in which shapes C and D are joined together along a whole edge so that the final shape has line symmetry.

The tile factory: an activity

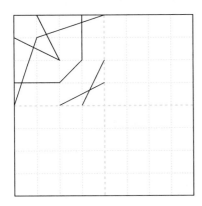

1 Copy this square and pattern onto the top left hand corner of a piece of A4 centimetre squared paper.

2 Lightly mark the reflection lines on the diagram as shown.

3 Use these lines to help you reflect
   the pattern across ...   ... and then down.

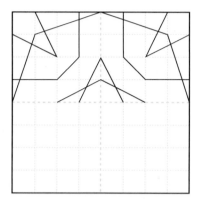

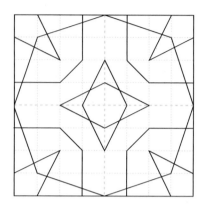

4 Repeat the process with the same tile so that your tile neatly
   covers the piece of paper →.

5 Now colour or shade in your work as neatly and symmetrically
   as you can.

5.3 Translation

In section 5.3 you will learn about:

● translations

A translation is a transformation
in which every point of the object
moves the same distance in a parallel
direction.

A translation can be described by two
instructions, the move parallel to the
x-axis and the move parallel to the
y-axis.

In the example shown, the
translation is 5 units to the right
and 1 unit up.

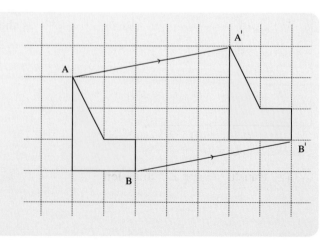

Exercise 1M

1 (a) Draw the object triangle A on squared paper.

   (b) Draw the image of A after a translation of 4 units to the right and 1 unit up. Label the image B.

   (c) Draw the image of A after a translation of 2 units to the right and 2 units down. Label the image C.

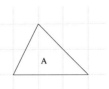

2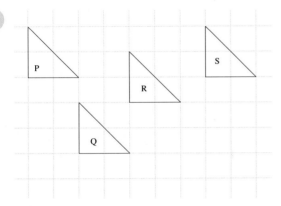

Describe the following translations.

   (a) P → Q

   (b) Q → S

   (c) R → P

   (d) S → P

3 (a) Draw shape A as shown.

   (b) Translate shape A 5 units right and label the image B.

   (c) Translate shape B 3 units down and label the image C.

   (d) Translate shape C 3 units left and 1 unit down and label the image D.

   (e) What is the single translation which would move shape A onto shape D?

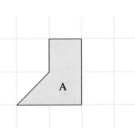

Exercise 1E

1 What shape do you move to when you:

   (a) translate shape A 2 units left, 1 unit down

   (b) translate shape E 5 units right, 3 units up

   (c) translate shape D 3 units right, 2 units down

   (d) translate shape B 5 units left

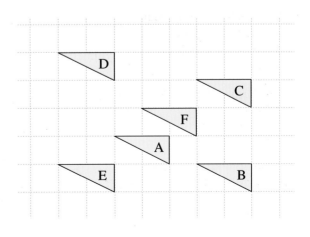

268

2

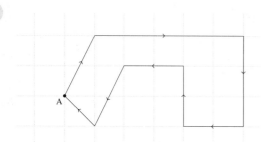

A computer controls a pen which starts at A. Describe the 8 translations required to draw the shape given.

3 Square ABCD can be moved onto square BCEF by either a translation, a rotation or a reflection.

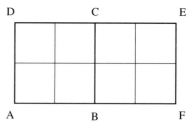

(a) Describe the translation

(b) What is the mirror line for the reflection?

(c) Describe *two* possible rotations which achieve the result given.

TEST YOURSELF ON UNITS 5.1, 5.2 and 5.3

1   Rotating shapes

Draw the shape on squared paper.

(a) Draw the new position after it is turned clockwise through one right angle around the point A.

(b) Draw the new position after it is turned anticlockwise through one right angle about the point B.

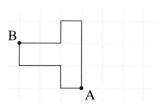

2   Rotational symmetry

State the order of rotational symmetry of each shape

(a) 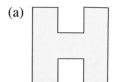   (b) 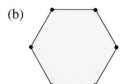   (c)    (d)

(e) Draw the two patterns on the right and shade in more squares so that the final patterns have rotational symmetry of order 2.

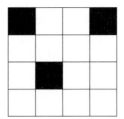 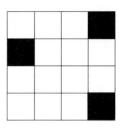

3   Line symmetry

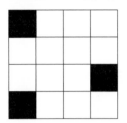 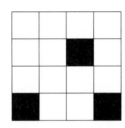

Draw the two patterns on the left and shade in one more square
so that the final patterns have symmetry.

4   Reflections

In each of the following diagrams, mirror lines are shown as broken lines. Copy each diagram and complete the reflections.

(a)   (b)   (c)

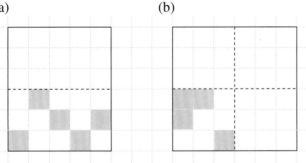 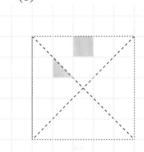

5   Translation

(a) Copy the diagram shown.

(b) Describe the translation.

    (i) A → C   (ii) C → D   (iii) B → E

(c) Draw the new position of shape A after the translation 4 units right and 3 units up.

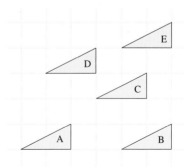

5.4 Number review

In section 5.4 you will review:

- multiples, factors, prime numbers, HCF and LCM
- fractions, decimals and percentages
- long multiplication and division
- adding, subtracting, multiplying and dividing decimals
- finding a 'fraction of' or a 'percentage of' a quantity.

Multiples, factors and prime numbers

The first six *multiples* of 5 are   5, 10, 15, 20, 25, 30

The factors of 8 are   1, 2, 4, 8

The first five prime numbers are   2, 3, 5, 7, 11

Exercise 1M

1   Continue the list below to write down the first seven multiples of 4

4, 8, 12, ☐, ☐, ☐, ☐

2   Write down the first five multiples of

(a) 3   (b) 7   (c) 2   (d) 10

3   Write down the odd one out

(a) Multiples of 9:   18, 27, 54, 83, 99

(b) Multiples of 8:   18, 32, 40, 64

(c) Multiples of 7:   7, 35, 56, 69

4   Copy and complete

(a) The factors of 6 are: 1, 2, ☐, 6

(b) The factors of 15 are: 1, 3, 5, ☐

(c) The factors of 36 are: 1, 2, 3, 4, ☐, 12, ☐, 36

5   Write down the odd one out.

(a) Factors of 24:   2, 3, 8, 24, 48   (b) Factors of 50:   2, 5, 10, 20, 25

(c) Multiples of 11: 22, 66, 88, 111   (d) Multiples of 15: 1, 15, 30, 45

6   Write down the first eight prime numbers in order of size.

7   11   21   31   51   71   81

Which of the numbers above are prime numbers?

8   Write down two prime numbers whose sum is a prime number.

Exercise 1E

1   In the diagram below the factors of the numbers from 1 to 25 are to be shaded in.

For example:

4 has factors 1, 2 and 4 so shade in those factor boxes above the number 4.

5 has factors 1 and 5 so shade in those factor boxes above the number 5.

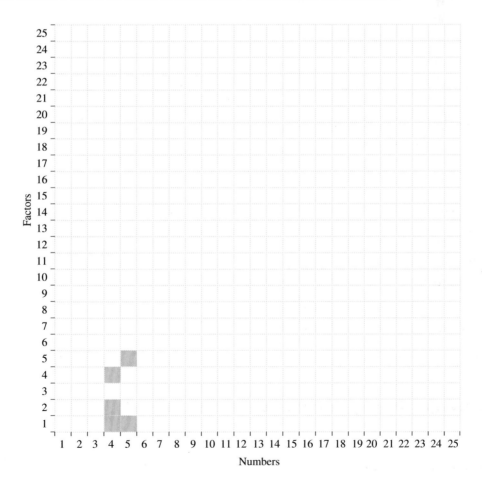

Numbers

Complete your chart for all the numbers.

Count up how many boxes you have shaded and write down the answer.

2   Write down the 1-digit numbers that have three factors.

3   What is the smallest number with two factors?

4    Write down the numbers in the hoop which are

20   65   2
1   30   5

    (a) factors of 10

    (b) multiples of 10

5   Find three numbers that are multiples of both 2 and 3

6   Find three numbers that are multiples of both 3 and 5

7   (a) Copy the diagram shown.

    (b) Shade in red the section which contains
        factors of 22

    (c) Shade in green the section which contains
        multiples of 7

    (d) Shade in blue the section which contains
        multiples of 3

    (e) Shade in orange the section which
        contains prime numbers.

    (f) Shade in any colour of your choice the
        section which contains factors of 4

8   (a) Write down the first six multiples of 4

    (b) Write down the first six multiples of 5

    (c) Write down the lowest common multiple (L.C.M.) of 4 and 5

Reminder:
The L.C.M. is
the lowest number
which is in both lists.

9   (a) Write down the first seven multiples of 3

    (b) Write down the first seven multiples of 7

    (c) Write down the L.C.M. of 3 and 7

10   Find the L.C.M. of 3 and 5

11   The table shows the factors and common factors of 12 and 18

number	factors	common factors
12	1, 2, 3, 4, 6, 12	1, 2, 3, 6
18	1, 2, 3, 6, 9, 18	

The H.C.F. is
the highest number
which is in both
lists.

Write down the highest common factor (H.C.F.) of 12 and 18.

12 Find the H.C.F. of

(a) 9 and 12   (b) 24 and 36   (c) 12 and 16

Fractions, decimals, percentages

Exercise 2M

1 Find the missing number to make these fractions equivalent.

(a) $\dfrac{3}{4} = \dfrac{\square}{12}$ (b) $\dfrac{4}{7} = \dfrac{\square}{35}$ (c) $\dfrac{6}{10} = \dfrac{\square}{5}$ (d) $\dfrac{3}{8} = \dfrac{\square}{24}$

(e) $\dfrac{3}{8} = \dfrac{9}{\square}$ (f) $\dfrac{4}{5} = \dfrac{12}{\square}$ (g) $\dfrac{8}{9} = \dfrac{16}{\square}$ (h) $\dfrac{1}{3} = \dfrac{5}{\square}$

2 Cancel down each fraction to its lowest terms

(a) $\dfrac{8}{10}$ (b) $\dfrac{9}{12}$ (c) $\dfrac{15}{25}$ (d) $\dfrac{7}{28}$ (e) $\dfrac{28}{36}$

(f) $\dfrac{45}{50}$ (g) $\dfrac{30}{70}$ (h) $\dfrac{56}{64}$ (i) $\dfrac{27}{63}$ (j) $\dfrac{18}{72}$

3 Work out

(a) $\dfrac{1}{5} + \dfrac{2}{5}$ (b) $\dfrac{3}{7} + \dfrac{2}{7}$ (c) $\dfrac{5}{9} - \dfrac{2}{9}$ (d) $\dfrac{5}{8} + \dfrac{1}{4}$

(e) $\dfrac{2}{5} + \dfrac{1}{4}$ (f) $\dfrac{1}{5} + \dfrac{1}{2}$ (g) $\dfrac{5}{6} - \dfrac{1}{2}$ (h) $\dfrac{2}{5} + \dfrac{1}{7}$

4 Convert these fractions into decimals

(a) $\dfrac{3}{10}$ (b) $\dfrac{1}{4}$ (c) $\dfrac{3}{5}$ (d) $\dfrac{3}{4}$ (e) $\dfrac{9}{100}$

(f) $\dfrac{27}{100}$ (g) $\dfrac{35}{70}$ (h) $\dfrac{3}{12}$ (i) $\dfrac{24}{200}$ (j) $\dfrac{4}{25}$

5 Copy and complete

(a) $\dfrac{1}{5} = \dfrac{20}{100} = \square\%$ (b) $\dfrac{3}{20} = \dfrac{15}{100} = \square\%$ (c) $\dfrac{1}{25} = \dfrac{4}{100} = \square\%$

(d) $\dfrac{9}{20} = \dfrac{\square}{100} = \square\%$ (e) $\dfrac{11}{50} = \dfrac{\square}{100} = \square\%$ (f) $\dfrac{11}{25} = \dfrac{\square}{100} = \square\%$

Exercise 2E

1 Change these decimals into fractions (cancel down when possible).

(a) 0.2   (b) 0.9   (c) 0.03   (d) 0.11   (e) 0.43

(f) 0.03   (g) 0.15   (h) 0.85   (i) 0.24   (j) 0.05

2 Change these percentages into fractions (cancel down where possible).

(a) 30%   (b) 75%   (c) 12%   (d) 35%   (e) 4%

3 In different tests Isabel got $\frac{7}{10}$ and Dani got $\frac{15}{25}$. Change these marks into percentages.

4 Write down each fraction with its equivalent percentage.

(a) $\frac{1}{3}$ (b) $\frac{2}{5}$ (c) $\frac{3}{4}$ (d) $\frac{3}{100}$ (e) $\frac{2}{3}$ (f) $\frac{1}{1000}$

5 Change these percentages into decimals.

(a) 42%   (b) 67%   (c) 9%   (d) 7%   (e) 94%

6 Copy and complete the table

	fraction	decimal	percentage
(a)			40%
(b)		0.15	
(c)	$\frac{3}{25}$		
(d)			16%
(e)		0.04	

7 Write the following in order of size, smallest first

(a) $\frac{3}{4}$, 60%, 0.7   (b) 5%, $\frac{1}{50}$, 0.03   (c) $\frac{3}{9}$, 0.3, 23%

8 Copy and complete

(a) $\frac{7}{35} = \square\%$ (b) $0.55 = \frac{\square}{20}$ (c) $0.08 = \square\%$ (d) $24\% = \frac{\square}{\square}$

Long multiplication and division

Exercise 3M

Work out

1 23×14 **2** 35×17 **3** 27×23 **4** 52×24

5 56×35 **6** 72×41 **7** 125×19 **8** 214×36

9   Copy and complete.

(a) ☐ ÷ 25 = 15   (b) ☐ ÷ 33 = 17   (c) ☐ ÷ 27 = 42

10   Work out

(a) 784 ÷ 14   (b) 544 ÷ 32   (c) 806 ÷ 31   (d) 1035 ÷ 23

Exercise 3E

1   There are 47 seats on a coach. How many coaches will be needed to transport 206 people to a concert?

2   There are 23 seats in each row at a football stadium. How many seats are there in 35 rows?

3   Find the remainder when 276 is divided by 11.

4   There are twenty-two balls in a set of snooker balls. Each ball weighs 154 grams. Calculate the total weight of the set of snooker balls.

5   Chocolates are packed eighteen to a box. How many boxes are needed for 648 chocolates?

Calculations involving decimals

Exercise 4M

1   Work out.

(a) 4 + 5.2   (b) 6.1 + 18.7   (c) 9.54 − 7   (d) 0.74 + 3.4

(e) 0.65 + 0.888   (f) 11 − 3.2   (g) 4.2 + 7.4 + 6   (h) 32.7 − 19

2   Copy and complete.

(a)   6 . ☐ 4   (b)   4 . 7 ☐   (c)   6 . ☐ 7 2
    + ☐ . 7 ☐   + 4 . ☐ 5   ☐ . 2 ☐ 9
    ─────────   ─────────   ───────────
      8 . 2 7   ☐ . 1 0   8 . 0 9 ☐

3   A CD costs £5.99, a book costs £4.75 and a calculator costs £7.50. Work out the total cost of the three items.

4   I started with 0.756 and then added a number. The answer was 0.777. What number did I add?

5   What five different coins make £1.77?

6 Copy and complete

(a) $\quad 6 \ . \ \Box \ 9$

$\quad - \ \Box \ . \ 3 \ \Box$

$\quad \overline{\ \ 5 \ . \ 5 \ 7\ }$

(b) $\quad \Box \ . \ 7 \ \Box$

$\quad - \ 3 \ . \ \Box \ 6$

$\quad \overline{\ \ 5 \ . \ 4 \ 7\ }$

(c) $\quad 7 \ . \ 4 \ 8$

$\quad - \ 6 \ . \ \Box \ \Box$

$\quad \overline{\ \Box \ . \ 7 \ 0\ }$

7 Copy and complete the cross number.

Clues across

1. $5.7 \div 3$

3. 0.8×3

5. $(17 - 8) \times 2$

6. $44.8 \div 8$

7. $4.9 + 3.5$

8. $16.7 - 9.8$

10. $(10 \times 10) - (10 \times 1)$

11. $46.4 + 47.6$

Clues down

1. $203 - 86$

2. $7 \times 2 \times 7$

3. $(1000 \div 4) + 4$

4. $7 \times 7 - 3$

7. $44.5 \div 5$

8. $3 \times 2 \times 5 \times 2$

9. 11×0.4

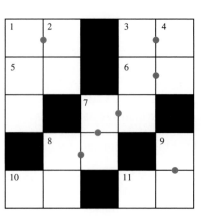

Exercise 4E

1 Work out.

(a) 3.26×10

(b) 11.4×10

(c) 0.415×100

(d) 1.2×100

(e) $17.6 \div 10$

(f) $427 \div 100$

(g) $16.53 \div 10$

(h) $0.42 \div 10$

2 Answer true or false: $0.8 \times 100 = 8000 \div 10$

3 Copy and complete.

(a) $0.72 \times \Box = 7.2$

(b) $\Box \times 100 = 170$

(c) $10 \times \Box = 16$

(d) $100 \times \Box = 85.4$

(e) $3.2 \times \Box = 3.2$

(f) $\Box \times 100 = 2$

4 Find the cost of 5 cakes at £2.40 each.

5 What is the total weight of 7 eggs, if each egg weighs 8.2 grams?

6 Copy and complete.

(a) $\boxed{2.4} \xrightarrow{\times 10} \boxed{} \xrightarrow{\div 100} \boxed{} \xrightarrow{\times 10} \boxed{}$

(b) $\boxed{0.43} \xrightarrow{\times 100} \boxed{} \xrightarrow{\div 1000} \boxed{} \xrightarrow{\times 100} \boxed{}$

(c) $\boxed{1.4} \xrightarrow{\times 5} \boxed{} \xrightarrow{\times 3} \boxed{} \xrightarrow{\div 10} \boxed{}$

7   What number when divided by five gives an answer of 3.2?

8   What number when multiplied by 7 gives an answer of 16.8?

9   Work out

(a) 8.23×4 (b) $3.12 \div 4$ (c) $6.2 \div 5$ (d) 0.85×4

(e) $31.8 \div 6$ (f) 7×1.23 (g) $9.94 \div 7$ (h) 6×8.02

10 Five people share the cost of a meal which costs £42.
    How much does each person pay?

Fraction or percentage of a number

Exercise 5M

1   Work out.

(a) $\frac{1}{3}$ of 69   (b) $\frac{2}{3}$ of 69   (c) $\frac{1}{4}$ of 64   (d) $\frac{3}{4}$ of 64

(e) $\frac{1}{5}$ of 80   (f) $\frac{4}{5}$ of 80   (g) $\frac{1}{10}$ of 750   (h) $\frac{3}{10}$ of 750

2   Copy and complete

(a) $\frac{1}{\square}$ of 35 = 5   (b) $\frac{1}{\square}$ of 121 = 11   (c) $\frac{1}{\square}$ of 74 = 37

(d) $\frac{2}{5}$ of 45 = $\square$ (e) $\frac{2}{\square}$ of 12 = 8   (f) $\frac{1}{\square}$ of 3000 = 30

3   There are four hundred and fifty mushrooms in a garden and
    $\frac{1}{50}$ of them are poisonous. How many of the mushrooms are
    poisonous?

4   In one week 400 people took their driving test and three
    fifths of them passed. How many people passed the test that
    week?

5   Work out.

(a) 10% of £800   (b) 25% of £60   (c) 20% of £55   (d) 1% of 200 kg

(e) 75% of 400   (f) 5% of 600   (g) 2% of 900 g   (h) 25% of 84 cm

6   Answer true or false:

(a) 25% of 60 = 15   (b) $33\frac{1}{3}$% of 60 = 20   (c) 10% of 9000 = 90

(d) 1% of 5000 = 50   (e) 20% of 45 = 8   (f) 2% of 200 = 4

Exercise 5E

1. Write down which fractions are greater than the percentage.

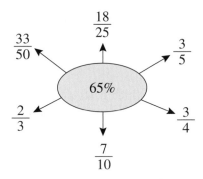

2. Copy and complete.

   (a) $\frac{1}{4} = \boxed{}\%$ (b) $\frac{2}{5} = \boxed{}\%$ (c) $\frac{1}{3} = \boxed{}\%$ (d) $\frac{1}{50} = \boxed{}\%$

3. Work out

   (a) 3% of £250   (b) 7% of 400 km   (c) 20% of £685

   (d) 11% of £90 000   (e) 16% of 1200 kg   (f) $33\frac{1}{3}\%$ of 660 miles

4. A factory produces forty-five thousand clocks every week and, when tested, two per cent of them are not accurate. How many inaccurate clocks are made each week?

5. Write in order of size, smallest first.

   (a) 20%, $\frac{1}{4}$, 0.15   (b) $\frac{3}{5}$, 52%, 0.05   (c) 0.7, $\frac{2}{3}$, 66%

6. Which is greater: 5% of 800 or 18% of 300?

7. Work out 22% of $\frac{2}{3}$ of 480.

8. Work out (5% of £30) + (4% of £200) + (11% of £1200)

5.5 Probability 2

In section 5.5 you will learn to:

- find the probability of an event

Equally likely outcomes

(a) When you roll a fair dice there are six *equally likely outcomes*.
You can get a 1, 2, 3, 4, 5 or 6

The probability of rolling a 4 is $\frac{1}{6}$

(b) On this spinner there are five equal sections and two of these are blue.

The probability of spinning blue is $\frac{2}{5}$

Exercise 1M

1   What is the probability of spinning pink on this spinner?

2   What is the probability of spinning pink on each of these spinners?

(a)   (b)   (c)   (d)

3      This spinner has five equal sections with 3 yellow and 2 pink.

What is the probability of spinning?

(a) yellow   (b) pink

4   A hat contains 1 red ball, 1 blue ball and 1 orange ball. One ball is selected at random.
What is the probability of selecting?

(a) a blue ball   (b) an orange ball.

5   Cards with the letters of the word O C T O P U S are placed in a bag. One letter is selected at random.

What is the probability of selecting?

(a) a T   (b) an O

6   Bags A and B contain red and yellow balls as shown. Gary wants to get a yellow ball.

From which bag does he have the better chance of selecting a yellow ball?

A   B

7   The cards below are placed in a bag and then one card is selected at random.

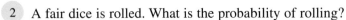

What is the probability of selecting?

(a) the number 4

(b) an even number

(c) a number less than 5

Exercise 1E

1   Children in France count up to five using their fingers and thumb as shown.

Michelle displays one number at random.

Find the probability that she shows

(a) the number three,
(b) an even number.
(c) How do *you* count from 1 to 5 using your fingers?

2   A fair dice is rolled. What is the probability of rolling?

(a) a 5

(b) an even number

(c) a number greater than 7

3   Four cards numbered 1, 2, 3, 4 are placed face down. One card is chosen at random.

(a) What is the probability of selecting an even number?

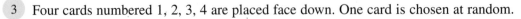

(b) A card numbered 5 is added to the cards above. What is now the probability of selecting an even number?

4  These balls are placed in a bag and then one ball is selected at random. What is the probability of selecting?

(a) a purple ball

(b) a purple ball or a red ball

5 These cards are shuffled and turned over. One card is picked at random. What is the probability of picking?

(a) the number 6

(b) the number 4

(c) the number 8

| 2 | 5 | 6 | 8 | 8 |

6 A raffle has tickets numbered from 1 to 150. Maggie has ticket number 37. What is the probability that Maggie wins the raffle?

7 There are 16 pens in a box. All of them are black. Steve chooses one of the pens at random. What is the probability that the pen is?

(a) black (b) red

8 There are 54 white cubes and 1 red cube in the pile shown. The cubes are jumbled up in a box and then one cube is selected at random.

What is the probability of selecting the red cube?

A pack of playing cards, without Jokers, contains 52 cards.
There is Ace, King, Queen, Jack, 10, 9, 8, 7, 6, 5, 4, 3, 2 of four suits.
The suits are…

spades  hearts  diamonds  clubs

A pack of cards is shuffled and then one card is chosen at random.

(a) The probability that it is a King of hearts is $\frac{1}{52}$

(b) The probability that it is an ace is $\frac{4}{52}\left(=\frac{1}{13}\right)$

(c) The probability that it is a spade is $\frac{13}{52}\left(=\frac{1}{4}\right)$

Exercise 2M

1. One card is picked at random from a pack of 52.
   Find the probability that it is

   (a) a Queen

   (b) the King of diamonds

   (c) a spade

2. One card is selected at random from a full pack of 52 playing cards.
   Find the probability of selecting

   (a) a heart   (b) a red card   (c) a '2'

   (d) any King, Queen or Jack   (e) the ace of spades

3. A small pack of twenty cards consists of the Ace, King, Queen,
   Jack and 10 of spades, hearts, diamonds and clubs. One card is
   selected at random. Find the probability of selecting

   (a) the ace of hearts   (b) a King   (c) a '10'

   (d) a black card   (e) a heart

4. One card is selected at random from the cards shown.
   Find the probability of selecting

   (a) a red card

   (b) a 5

   (c) a card of the 'club' suit

5. A bag contains 3 black balls, 2 green balls, 1
   white ball
   and 5 orange balls.

   Spades

   Find the probability of selecting

   (a) a black ball

   (b) an orange ball

   (c) a white ball

6. A bag contains the balls shown. One ball is taken out at random.
   Find the probability that it is

   (a) yellow   (b) blue   (c) red

   One more blue ball and one more red ball are added to the bag.

   (d) Find the new probability of selecting a yellow ball from the bag.

283

7   If Jake throws a 1 or a 4 on his next throw of a dice when
    playing 'Snakes and Ladders' he will climb up a ladder on the board.
    What is the probability that he will *miss* a ladder on his next throw?

8   A box contains 11 balls: 3 green, 2 yellow, 4 red and 2 blue

    (a) Find the probability of selecting

        (i) a blue ball   (ii) a green ball

    (b) The 3 green balls are replaced by 3 blue balls. Find the
        probability of selecting

        (i) a blue ball   (ii) a yellow ball.

9   Here are two spinners. Say whether the following statements are true or false.
    Explain why in each case.

    (a) 'Sarah is more likely to spin a 6 than Ben'.

    (b) 'Sarah and Ben are equally likely to spin an even number.'

    (c) 'If Sarah spins her spinner six times, she is bound to get
        at least one 6.'

Exercise 2E

In questions 1 to 4 a bag contains a certain number of red balls and a certain number of white
balls. The tally charts show the number of times a ball was selected from the bag and then
replaced. Look at the results and say what you think was in the bag each time.

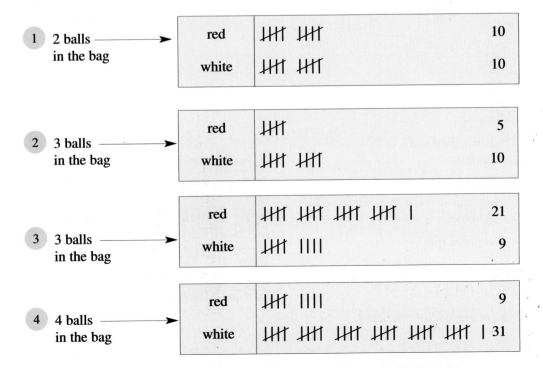

5   A bag contains 9 balls, all of which are black or white.
Jane selects a ball and then replaces it. She repeats
this several times. Here are her results (B = black, W = white):

B   W   B   W   B   B   B   W   B   B   W   B   B   W   B

B   B   W   W   B   B   B   B   W   B   W   B   B   W   B

How many balls of each colour do you think there were in the bag?

6   Cards with numbers 1, 2, 3, 4, 5, 6, 7, 8, 9, 10 are shuffled and
then placed face down in a line. The cards are then turned over
one at a time from the left. In this example the first card is a '4'.

Find the probability that the next card turned over will be

(a) 7   (b) a number higher than 4.

7   Suppose the second card is a 1

Find the probability that the next card will be

(a) the 6   (b) an even number   (c) higher than 1.

8   Suppose the first three cards are   4   1   8   ...

Find the probability that the next card will be

(a) less than 8

(b) the 4

(c) an odd number.

9   Three friends Alf, Ben and Curtis sit next to each
other on a bench.

(a) Make a list of all the different ways in
which they can sit. (Use A = Alf, B = Ben
and C = Curtis).

Find the probability that

(b) Alf sits in the middle.

(c) Alf sits next to Curtis.

(d) Ben sits at one end of the bench.

10 Debbie, Alan and Nicky were asked to toss a fair coin 16 times.
Here are the results they wrote down.

Debbie   H T H T H T H T H T H T H T H T

Alan   H H T H T T H T T T H H T H H T

Nicky   H H H H H H H H T T T T T T T T

One of the three did the experiment properly while the other two just made up results.
Explain what you think each person did.

5.6 Interpreting graphs

In section 5.6 you will learn to:

- read information from line graphs
- draw line graphs in real life situations

Exercise 1M

1 This graph converts miles into
   kilometres.

   (a) Convert 20 miles into km

   (b) Convert 64 km into miles

   (c) Sharon's journey to work is 10
       miles. How far is that in
       kilometres?

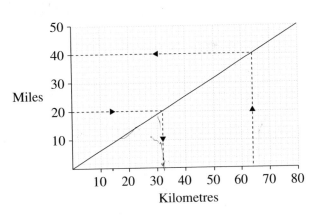

2 This graph converts rupees into pounds. The rupee is the currency in India

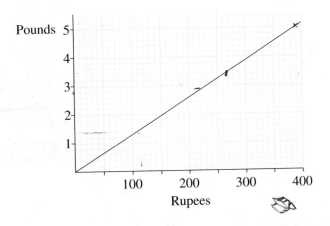

(a) Convert into pounds

   (i) 280 rupees   (ii) 110 rupees   (iii) 250 rupees   (iv) 360 rupees

(b) Convert into rupees

   (i) £5.00   (ii) £2.40   (iii) £4.20   (iv) £0.80

(c) On holiday in India, Jason bought fish and chips for 300 rupees. How much did the meal cost in pounds?

3 Jerome was not well one day. The graph shows his temperature between 07.00 and 13.00 one day.

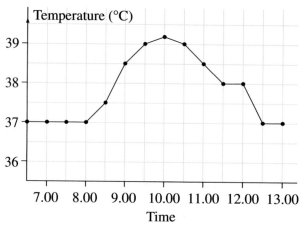

(a) What was his temperature at   (i) 8.00   (ii) 10.30?

(b) At what time was his temperature highest?

(c) At what two times was his temperature 38.5°C?

(d) Between which two times did his temperature rise most quickly?

4 A man climbing a mountain measures his height above sea level after every 30 minutes; the results are shown below.

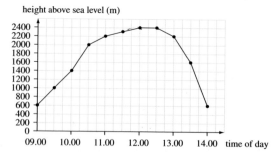

(a) At what height was he at 10.00?

(b) At what height was he at 13.30?

(c) Estimate his height above sea level at 09:45.

(d) At what two times was he 2200 m above sea level?

(e) How high was the mountain? (He got to the top!)

(f) How long did he rest at the summit?

(g) How long did he take to reach the summit?

Exercise 1E

1 The cost of hiring a tank for filming depends on the duration of the hire.

(a) How much does it cost to hire the tank for

    (i) 1 day   (ii) $5\frac{1}{2}$ days   (iii) 3 days

(b) What is the minimum hire charge?

2 The graph shows the cost of making calls to two directory enquiry numbers.

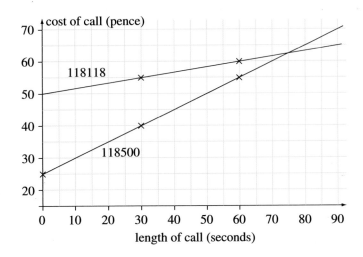

(a) How much does it cost for a 50 seconds call to 118500?

(b) Using 118118, for how long can you call for 55p?

(c) At what length of call do both numbers cost the same?

3 A car went on a five hour journey starting at 12.00 with a full tank of petrol. The volume of petrol in the tank was measured after every hour; the results are shown below.

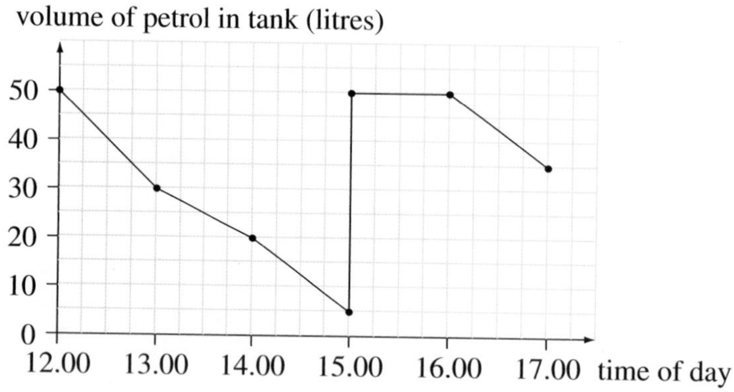

(a) How much petrol was in the tank at 13.00?

(b) At what time was there 5 litres in the tank?

(c) How much petrol was used in the first hour of the journey?

(d) What happened at 15.00?

(e) What do you think happened between 15.00 and 16.00?

(f) How much petrol was used between 12.00 and 17.00?

Exercise 2M

1 Draw a graph to convert kilograms into pounds. Draw a line through the point where 3 kg is equivalent to 6.6 pounds. Use a scale of 1 cm to 1 pound across the page and 2 cm to 1 kg up the page.

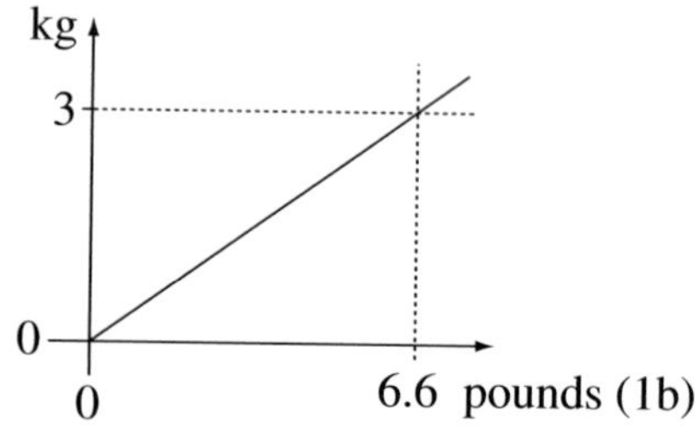

Use your graph to convert

(a) 1.2 kg into pounds

(b) 2 pounds into kg

2

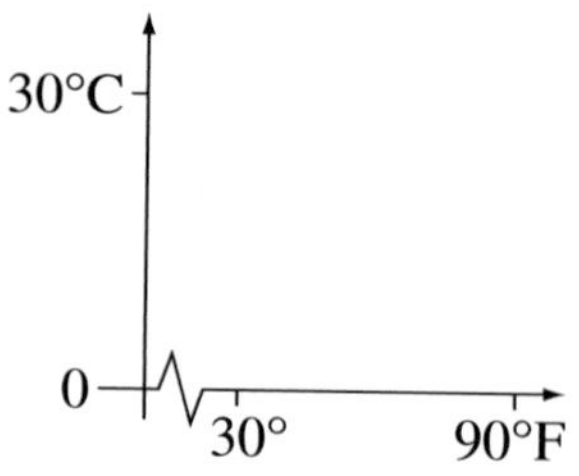

Draw a graph to convert temperatures from °F to °C.

Draw a line through the points 50°F = 10°C.

and 86°F = 30°C.

Use the graph to convert:

(a) 77°F into °C (b) 15°C into °F

3   A mobile phone company charges £10 a month rental plus 20p per minute for calls.

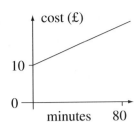

minutes of calls	0	20	40	60	80
cost in £	10	14	18	22	26

(a) Draw a graph to show this information.

(b) Use your graph to find the total cost of making 65 minutes of calls

Travel graphs

● This graph shows the details of a cycle ride that Jim took starting from his home.

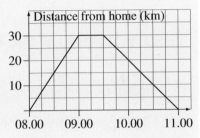

(a) In the first hour Jim went 30 km so his speed was 30 km/h.

(b) He stopped for $\frac{1}{2}$ hour at a place 30 km from his home.

(c) From 09:30 until 11:00 he cycled back home. We know that he cycled back home because the distance from his home at 11:00 is 0 km.

(d) The speed at which he cycled home was 20 km/h.

Exercise 2E

1   The graph shows a car journey from A to C via B.

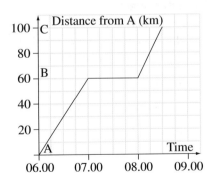

(a) How far is it from A to C?

(b) For how long does the car stop at B?

(c) When is the car half way between B and C?

(d) What is the speed of the car

(i) between A and B?

(ii) between B and C?

2   The graph shows the motion of a train as it accelerates away from Troon.

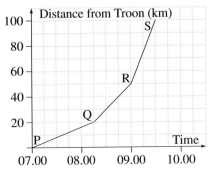

(a) How far from Troon is the train at 08.45?

(b) When is the train half way between R and S?

(c) Find the speed of the train

(i) from R to S

(ii) from Q to R

(d) How long does it take the train to travel 100 km?

3   The graph shows a car journey from Lemsford.

(a) For how long did the car stop at Mabley?

(b) When did the car arrive back at Lemsford?

(c) When did the car leave Mabley after stopping?

(d) Find the speed of the car

(i) from Mabley to Nixon

(ii) from Nixon back to Lemsford.

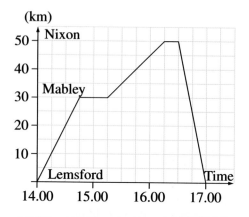

TEST YOURSELF ON UNITS 5.5 AND 5.6

1   Finding the probability of an event

(a) One ball is selected at random from the bag shown.

Write down the probability of selecting

(i) a red ball

(ii) a green ball

(b) There are eight balls in a different bag.
The probability of taking a white ball from the bag is 0.5

A white ball is taken from the bag and put on one side.

What is the probability of taking a white ball from the bag now?

2   Reading information from line graphs

This line graph shows the average daily temperature in Sweden.

(a) What was the temperature in June?

(b) In which month was the temperature 7°C?

(c) In which two months was the temperature 3°C?

(d) Between which two months was there the largest increase in temperature?

(e) What was the range of temperature over the year?

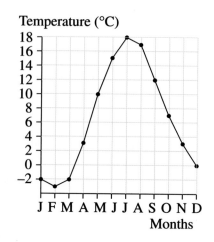

3   Drawing line graphs in real life situations

Draw a graph to convert kilometres into miles.

Draw a line through the point where 80 km is equivalent to 50 miles. Use a scale of 1 cm to 10 units.

Use the graph to convert:

(a) 60 km into miles   (b) 20 miles into km.

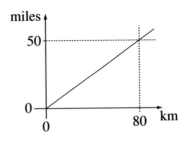

5.7 Algebra review

In section 5.7 you will look at:

● algebraic expressions and formulas

Exercise 1M

Simplify the expressions where possible.

1   $3x + 2y + 5x$

2   $3a + c + a$

3   $5m + 2n - 2m + n$

4   $6h + 7x - 3x + 3h$

5   $6e + 7e - 8e$

6   $3a + 7b + 2b - 3a$

7   Write down each statement and write whether it is true or false.

(a) $x + x + x + x = 4x$

(b) $2a + a = a^3$

(c) $2 \times a \times b = 2ab$

(d) $m \times 3 = 3m$

(e) $3a + 3b = 3ab$

(f) $m \times m = m^2$

8   Simplify the expressions.

(a) $\dfrac{3a}{3}$

(b) $a \times a$

(c) $\dfrac{m^2}{m}$

(d) $5 \times a \times b$

(e) $\dfrac{8a}{2}$

In questions 9 to 20 substitute the values for a, b and c to find the value of each expression below.

$a = 5$

$b = 2$

$c = 10$

9   $a + 2b$

10   $3c - a$

11   $a + b + c$

12   $b(c - a)$

13   ab

14   $5a + 2c$

15   $2b + 3c$

16   $c - 4b$

17   $2(c + b)$

18   $\dfrac{c}{a} - b$

19   $\dfrac{ab}{c}$

20   $\dfrac{c + 5b}{a}$

21 Write down any pairs of expressions below which are equal.

$$m + m + m$$

$$m \times m$$

$$m - 2$$

$$m \div 2$$

$$\frac{m}{2}$$

$$3m$$

$$2 - m$$

$$m^2$$

Exercise 1E

In question **1** to **8** you are given a formula. Find the value of the letter required in each case.

1 $m = 3a + 5$

Find m when $a = 3$

2 $c = 5d - 1$

Find c when $d = 0$

3 $z = 3x + 7$

Find z when $x = 22$

4 $e = 2m + n$

Find e when $m = 7$ and $n = -2$

5 $h = 3(a + b)$

Find h when $a = 3$ and $b = -3$

6 $t = ab$

Find t when $a = 5$ and $b = -3$

7 $w = \frac{x}{y}$

Find w when $x = 24$ and $y = 3$

8 $z = 5(2a + b)$

Find z when $a = 4$ and $b = -1$

9 You are given $a = 8$, $b = 4$, $c = -2$

Write down each statement and say whether it is true or false.

(a) $ab = 12$

(b) $a + b + c = 10$

(c) $bc = -8$

(d) $b(a + c) = 24$

(e) $b + c = -2$

(f) $ac = -16$

10 Highly trained mosquitoes can be used to find oil.

The annual profit in pounds, P, made by the mosquitoes is given by the formula.

$P = 500m - 2$, where m is the number of mosquitoes.

Find the profit when 10000 mosquitoes are employed.

5.8 Rounding numbers

In section 5.8 you will learn how to:

● round numbers

● calculate using estimates

Here are cuttings from two newspapers

A. '360 mm of rain makes summer 2007 the wettest ever'

B. '358.4 mm of rain fell from June to August 2007 to make the summer of 2007 the wettest on record'

In A the figure 360 has been rounded off because the reporter thinks that his readers are not interested in the exact amount of rainfall.

Rounding to the nearest whole number

● The arrow points at 8.8 on the scale. 8.8 is nearer to 9 than to 8. So 8.8 is rounded to 9 to the *nearest whole number*.

● This arrow points at 13.5 which is half way between 13 and 14. We have to decide whether to round up or down. The rule is:

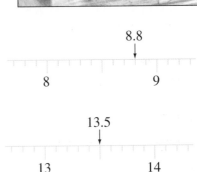

If the first digit after the decimal point is *5 or more* round *up*.
Otherwise round down.

$$57.3 \rightarrow 57$$
$$89.8 \rightarrow 90$$
$$5.5 \rightarrow 6$$

Rounding to the nearest ten, hundred, thousand

● Rounding to the nearest **ten**.
If the digit in the units column is 5 or more round up.
Otherwise round down.

$$27 \rightarrow 30$$
$$42 \rightarrow 40$$
$$265 \rightarrow 270$$

● Rounding to the nearest **hundred**.
If the digit in the tens column is 5 or more round up.
Otherwise round down.

$$593 \rightarrow 600$$
$$247 \rightarrow 200$$
$$2643 \rightarrow 2600$$

294

- Rounding to the nearest **thousand**.
  If the digit in the hundreds column
  is 5 or more round up.
  Otherwise round down.

  $1394 \rightarrow 1000$

  $502 \rightarrow 1000$

  $11\,764 \rightarrow 12\,000$

Exercise 1M

1 Round these numbers to the nearest whole number.

(a) 8.2 (b) 9.7 (c) 11.4 (d) 8.5 (e) 11.8

(f) 57.4 (g) 20.8 (h) 108.2 (i) 0.7 (j) 16.5

2 Answer 'true' or 'false' when the numbers are rounded to the nearest whole number.

(a) $7.7 \rightarrow 8$ (b) $3.4 \rightarrow 3$ (c) $11.5 \rightarrow 12$ (d) $9.6 \rightarrow 9$

(e) $11.1 \rightarrow 11$ (f) $6.5 \rightarrow 6$ (g) $0.7 \rightarrow 1$ (h) $27.5 \rightarrow 28$

3 Write these numbers to the nearest ten.

(a) 73 (b) 88 (c) 22 (d) 36 (e) 77

(f) 128 (g) 253 (h) 18 (i) 29 (j) 187

4 1680   1690   1700   1710   1720

Use the scale to round these numbers to the nearest ten.

(a) 1682 (b) 1718 (c) 1694 (d) 1704 (e) 1722

5 Round off these numbers to the nearest hundred.

(a) 584 (b) 293 (c) 607 (d) 914 (e) 706.5

(f) 285 (g) 655 (h) 222 (i) 1486 (j) 28 374

6 Round off these numbers to the nearest thousand.

(a) 4555 (b) 757 (c) 850 (d) 2251 (e) 6511

(f) 614 (g) 2874 (h) 25 712 (i) 13 568 (j) 294 888

Exercise 1E

1 (a) Round to the nearest whole number.

(i) 8.4 (ii) 26.5 (iii) 9.8

(b) Round to the nearest ten.

    (i) 88   (ii) 307   (iii) 5274

(c) Round to the nearest hundred.

    (i) 680   (ii) 5275   (iii) 12684

2 Copy and complete.

(a) $17 \to 20$ to the nearest   ☐   (b) $31.4 \to 31$ to the nearest   ☐

(c) $516 \to 500$ to the nearest   ☐   (d) $35.4 \to 40$ to the nearest   ☐

(e) $6741 \to 7000$ to the nearest   ☐   (f) $654.7 \to 655$ to the nearest   ☐

3 Work out the following using a calculator and then round the answer to the *nearest hundred.*

(a) 67.5×841 (b) 173×11.4 (c) $25000 \div 241$

(d) $6781.4 + 374$ (e) $784 \div 0.92$ (f) $9801 - 416.2$

(g) 18.6×18.7 (h) $501000 \div 6751$ (i) $\sqrt{623000}$

4 Work out these answers on a calculator and then round off the answer to the *nearest whole number.*

(a) $235 \div 7$ (b) $4714 \div 58$ (c) $2375 \div 11$ (d) $999 \div 17$

(e) 5.62×7.04 (f) 19.3×1.19 (g) 53.2×2.3 (h) 12.6×0.93

(i) $119.6 \div 5.1$ (j) $109 \div 0.7$ (k) $63.4 \div 11$ (l) $1.92 \div 0.09$

5 How long is this rod to:

(a) the nearest cm   (b) the nearest 10 cm   (c) the nearest metre

Round to one decimal place

- Using a calculator to work out $25 \div 9$, the answer is 2.777777.

  On a number line we can see that the answer is nearer to 2.8 than to 2.7. We will *round off* the answer to 2.8 correct to 1 *decimal place.*

- Using a calculator to work out 11% of 21.23, the answer is 2.3353.

  On a number line we can see that the answer is nearer to 2.3 than to 2.4. So the answer is 2.3, correct to 1 decimal place (1 d.p. for short).

● Suppose the calculator shows 1.75. This number is exactly half way between 1.7 and 1.8. Do we round up or not?

The rule for rounding off to 1 decimal place is:

> If the figure in the 2nd decimal place is 5 or more, round up. Otherwise do not.

$$3.7538 = 3.8 \text{ to 1 d.p.}$$
↑

$$14.287 = 14.3 \text{ to 1 d.p.}$$
↑

$$17.9582 = 18.0 \text{ to 1 d.p. (We need the zero!)}$$
↑

7.96 rounded to the nearest whole number is 8

7.96 rounded to 1 decimal place in 8.0 [The zero is needed.]

Exercise 2M

1   Round these numbers to 1 decimal place.

(a) 2.41   (b) 8.94   (c) 4.65   (d) 12.47   (e) 16.35

2   Round these numbers to 1 decimal place.

(a) 1.924   (b) 4.065   (c) 9.997   (d) 65.374   (e) 14.043

3   Write the following numbers correct to 1 decimal place.

(a) 18.7864   (b) 3.55   (c) 17.0946   (d) 0.7624

(e) 5.421   (f) 11.27   (g) 10.252   (h) 7.084

4   Write the following numbers correct to the nearest whole number.

(a) 3.75821   (b) 11.64412   (c) 0.38214   (d) 138.2972

(e) 11.444   (f) 7.058   (g) 6.5781   (h) 5.3092

5   Work out these answers on a calculator and then round the answer to one decimal place.

(a) $65 \div 7$ (b) 85×0.7 (c) $8.64 \div 11.014$ (d) 8×16.22

(e) 1.4×0.97 (f) $82 \div 7$ (g) $113 \div 5$ (h) $0.6 \div 0.022$

Exercise 2E

1   Round each number:

(a) to the nearest whole number,

(b) to one decimal place

(i) 8.41   (ii) 0.782   (iii) 7.92   (iv) 4.95

2 Work out the following on a calculator and write the answers correct to 1 decimal place.

(a) $11 \div 7$ (b) $213 \div 11$ (c) $1.4 \div 6$ (d) $29 \div 13$

(e) 1.3×0.95 (f) 1.23×3.71 (g) $97 \div 1.3$ (h) 0.95×8.3

3 Measure the lines below and give the lengths in cm correct to one decimal place.

(a) ————————————————————————

(b) ————————

(c) ——————————————————————————————

(d) ————————————————————

(e) ——————————————————————————————————

4 Measure the dimensions of the rectangles below.

(a) Write down the length and width in cm, correct to one decimal place.

(b) Work out the area of each rectangle and give the answer in cm², correct to one decimal place.

(i)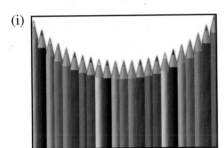

(ii)

Calculating with estimates, checking results

● Hazim worked out 38.2×10.78 and wrote down 41.1796. He can check his answer by working with estimates.

Instead of 38.2 use 40, instead of 10.78 use 10.

So $40 \times 10 = 400$.

Clearly Hazim's answer is wrong. He put the decimal point in the wrong place.

● Here are three more calculations with estimates.

(a) 27.2×51.7
$\approx 30 \times 50$
≈ 1500

(b) $78.9 \div 1.923$
$\approx 80 \div 2$
≈ 40

(c) 12% of £411.55
$\approx$ 10% of £400
$\approx$ £40

[The symbol $\approx$ means 'approximately equal to']

298

Exercise 3M

Do not use a calculator. Decide, by estimating, which of the three answers is closest to the exact answer. Write the calculation and the approximate answer for each question (use ≈).

	Calculation	A	B	C
1	102.6 × 9.7	90	500	1000
2	7.14 × 11.21	30	70	300
3	1.07 × 59.2	6	60	200
4	2.21 × 97.8	200	90	20
5	8.95 × 42.1	200	400	4000
6	4.87 × 6.18	15	10	30
7	789 × 12.3	8000	4000	800
8	978 × 9.83	1 million	100 000	10 000
9	1.11 × 28.7	20	30	60
10	9.8 × 82463	8 million	1 million	800 000
11	307.4 ÷ 1.97	50	100	150
12	81.2 ÷ 0.99	8	0.8	80
13	6121 ÷ 102.4	60	300	600
14	59.71 ÷ 3.14	10	20	180
15	1072 ÷ 987.2	0.2	1	10
16	614 − 297.4	300	100	3000
17	0.104 + 0.511	0.06	0.1	0.6
18	8216.1 + 1.44	800	4000	8000
19	51% of £8018.95	£40	£400	£4000
20	9% of £205.49	£10	£20	£200

Exercise 3E

1 A 'Pritt Stick' costs £1.99.

(a) Without a calculator, estimate the cost of twelve Pritt Sticks.

(b) Find the exact cost of twelve Pritt Sticks.

2 A box of drawing pins costs £3.85

Estimate the cost of 20 boxes of drawing pins.

3 A painting measures 12.2 cm by 9.7 cm.

(a) Without a calculator, estimate the area of the painting.

(b) Use a calculator to work out the exact area of the painting.

4 A new band's first demo CD was sold at £2.95 per copy.

Estimate the total cost of 47 copies.

5 Desmond has to pay £208.50 per month for 2 years towards the cost of his car. Estimate the total cost of his payments.

6 Two hundred and six people share the cost of hiring a train. Roughly how much does each person pay if the total cost was £61 990?

In questions 7 and 8 there are six calculations and six answers.

Write down each calculation and insert the correct answer from the list given. Use estimation.

7 (a) 6.9×7.1 (b) $9.8 \div 5$ (c) 21×10.2

(d) $0.13 + 15.2$ (e) $3114 \div 30$ (f) 4.03×1.9

| Answers: | 1.96 | 15.33 | 48.99 | 103.8 | 7.657 | 214.2 |

8 (a) $103.2 \div 5$ (b) 7.2×7.3 (c) 4.1×49

(d) $3.57 \div 3$ (e) $36.52 \div 4$ (f) $1.4 \div 10$

| Answers: | 52.56 | 1.19 | 9.13 | 200.9 | 20.64 | 0.14 |

TEST YOURSELF ON UNITS 5.7 AND 5.8

1 Algebraic expressions and formulas

Simplify the expressions.

(a) $3a + 7c + a$ (b) $2 \times a \times b$ (c) $3m - n + 5m + 3n$

(d) $\dfrac{x^2}{x}$ (e) $\dfrac{10c}{5}$ (f) $2a + 4a + ab$

(g) $s = 3u - 6$

Find s when $u = 5$

(h) $h = 4(2a - b)$

Find h when $a = 8$ and $b = 9$

---

2 Rounding numbers

(a) Round these numbers to the nearest ten.

(i) 561   (ii) 2045   (iii) 68.5

(b) Round these numbers to one decimal place.

(i) 5.67   (ii) 9.15   (iii) 0.77   (iv) 5.4072

---

3 Calculating using estimates

Decide, by estimating, which of the three answers is closest to the exact answer.

(a) 81.5×2.24 [1500   150   40]

(b) 0.97×38.4 [40   4   0.4]

(c) $98.1 \div 11.7$ [1   1000   10]

(d) A tin of blackcurrants cost 95p. Estimate the cost of 63 tins.

UNIT 5   MIXED REVIEW

Part one

1   Trisha, Stella and Vikky have lunch together and agree to share the cost equally. If lunch costs £24.99, how much should each pay?

2   How many 20 pence coins can I exchange for £3.60?

3   What fraction of the whole figure is shaded green in this diagram?

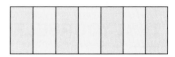

4   Simplify the following expressions.

(a) $5n + 3 + 2n - 1$

(b) $6m + 2n - 2m + 7n$

(c) $3a + 7c - 3a + 5$

(d) $10n + 3 + 10n + 13$

5 An advert for toothpaste used a photo of a model's teeth. Sales of the toothpaste rose from 25 815 per week to 31 880. How many extra tubes were sold?

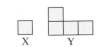

6 A rowing machine costs £360 plus 10% delivery charge. How much extra do you pay for the delivery charge?

7 Look at this group of numbers…

10, 19, 25, 30, 21

(a) Which of the numbers is a multiple of both 3 and 5?

(b) Which of the numbers is a prime number?

(c) Which of the numbers is a square number?

(d) Which number is a factor of another number in the group?

8 In how many ways can you join the square X to shape Y along an edge so that the final shape has line symmetry?

9 On a coordinate grid, plot the points A(1, 4) B(2, 1) C(5, 2) What are the coordinates of D if ABCD is a square?

10 Two books cost £13.50 in total. One book is one-and-a-half times the price of the other. How much does each book cost?

11 The temperature in a centrally heated house is recorded every hour from 12.00 till 24.00; the results are shown below.

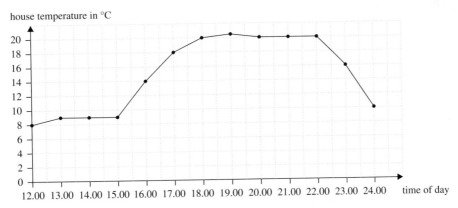

(a) What was the temperature at 20.00?
(b) Estimate the temperature at 16.30.
(c) Estimate the two times when the temperature was 18°C.

(d) When do you think the central heating was switched on?

(e) When do you think the central heating was switched off?

12  Crash dummies do have feelings!
Just before being 'tested' a dummy's
heart rate increased from 60
beats per minute by 75%.
What is the raised heart rate?

13 Write down these calculations and find the missing digits.

(a)
```
   5 · □ 5
 + 3 · 7 □
 ─────────
   9 · 0 9
```

(b)
```
   7 · □ 8
 − 3 · 8 □
 ─────────
   □ . 1 5
```

(c)
```
   □ 3 · □
 + 2 □ · 3
 ─────────
   7 0 · 0
```

14 (a) Copy the diagram.

(b) Rotate triangle A 90° clockwise around
the point (0, 0). Label the image ΔB.

(c) Rotate triangle A 90° anti-clockwise around
the point (4, 3). Label the image ΔC.

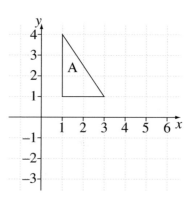

Part two

1 Work out:

(a)
```
   £3.87
 + £2.43
```

(b)
```
   £5.00
 − £1.67
```

(c)
```
   £3.75
 ×     3
```

(d) 4)£2.16

2 Look at the following numbers… 2, 3, 8, 9, 11, 15

(a) How many numbers are odd?

(b) How many numbers are even?

(c) Write down the prime numbers.

(d) Write down the number that is a multiple of five.

(e) Write down the numbers that are factors of twenty-four.

(f) Write down the number that is a square number.

3 In the box is a formula for working out heights. Lindsey's mother is 162 cm tall and her father is 180 cm tall. What is the greatest height to which Lindsey is likely to grow?

> Add the height of each parent.
> Divide by 2
> Add 6 cm to the result.
>
> A girl is likely to be this height plus or minus 7 cm.

4 A normal pack of 52 playing cards (without jokers) is divided into two piles

Pile A has all the picture cards (Kings, Queens, Jacks) 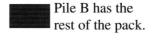 Pile B has the rest of the pack.

Find the probability of selecting
(a) any 'three' from pile B
(b) the King of hearts from pile A
(c) any red seven from pile B.

5 The star shape is made from four triangles like the one shown.

(a) Calculate the area of the star shape.

(b) Calculate the perimeter of the star shape.

(c) Describe the symmetry of the star shape.

6 Copy and complete by filling in the boxes. You can use any of the numbers 1, 2, 3, 4, 5 but you cannot use a number more than once.

(a) $\square + \square - \square = 7$

(b) $(\square + \square) \div \square = 3$

(c) $(\square + \square) \div (\square - \square) = 1\frac{1}{2}$

(d) $(\square + \square + \square) \times \square = 33$

7 Mr Gibson the famous balloonist was at a height of 3.2 km when a fault developed and he started to descend at a speed of 10 m/s. How long does Mr Gibson have to fix the problem?

8 Which fraction is closer to one: $\frac{7}{8}$ or $\frac{8}{7}$?
Show your working.

9   Work out the total cost. You may use a calculator.

13 kg of sand at 57p per kg.
2 tape measures at £4.20 each
2000 screws at 80p per hundred
250g of varnish at £6.60 per kg.

10 Use a calculator to work out the following and give your answers correct to 1 decimal place.

(a) $8.62 - \dfrac{1.71}{0.55}$

(b) $\dfrac{8.02 - 6.3}{1.3 + 4.6}$

(c) $\dfrac{5.6}{1.71} - 1.08$

11 Here are some number cards. $\boxed{6}$ $\boxed{3}$ $\boxed{8}$ $\boxed{2}$ $\boxed{7}$

(a) Use two cards to make a fraction which is equal to $\dfrac{1}{3} = \dfrac{\square}{\square}$

(b) Use three of the cards to make the smallest possible fraction $= \dfrac{\square}{\square\square}$

12 Numbers are missing on four of these calculator buttons. Copy the diagram and write in numbers to make the answer 30.

13 This shape has $\dfrac{1}{3}$ shaded green.

Copy each diagram and shade the given fraction.

(a)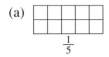

$\dfrac{1}{5}$

(b)

$\dfrac{1}{4}$

(c)

$\dfrac{2}{3}$

14 Simplify these fractions.

(a) $\dfrac{12}{16}$

(b) $\dfrac{20}{25}$

(c) $\dfrac{48}{50}$

(d) $\dfrac{28}{42}$

15 Copy the diagrams onto squared paper.
Draw reflections of the shapes in both mirror lines.

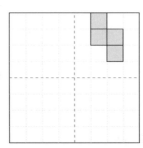

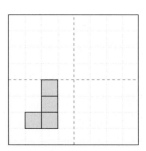

Puzzles and Problems 5

Cross numbers

Make three copies of the pattern below and complete the puzzles using the clues given. To avoid confusion it is better not to write the small reference numbers 1, 2–18 on your patterns.

1		2		3			4
				5			
	6		7			8	
9					10		
		11					12
				13	14		
15	16				17		
			18				

Part A

Across

1. Days in a year

3. 6524 − 4018

5. 20% of 400

6. 43 328 ÷ 8

8. 82.74 to the nearest whole number

9. 126 ÷ 7

10. $4^2 + 5^2$

11. 164 + 57 + 8

13. Half of a half of 104

15. $10^3 + 10^2 + 1$

17. 4 × (58 + 6 × 7)

18. Next in the sequence 8, 16, 32, 64

Down

1. 6^2

2. 7 × 72

4. 285 + 338

7. $8^2 \times 3$

8. 269 + 270 + 271

9. 5 × 5 × 5 × 10 + 1

11. 2 × 3 × 5 × 7

12. 967 × 9

14. 1000 − 352

16. Two fifths of 45

Part B

Across

1. 3.25 m in cm
3. 4567 − 123
5. Area of a square of side 7 cm
6. $50^2 + 555$
8. Total of the numbers on a dice
9. One fifth of 475
10. Find n, if $n − 23 = 37$
11. Angle sum of a triangle
13. Next in the sequence 3, 7, 15, 31
15. $100 \times 100 − 100$
17. $5^4 − 5$
18. Find n, if $\frac{n}{85} = 10$

Down

1. $2 \times 2 \times 2 \times 2 \times 2$
2. 1% of 50 000
4. $41 + 10 \times 41$
7. $4116 \div 7$
8. 9×23
9. $10\,001 − 2$
11. $11^2 − 5^2 + 2^2$
12. 3.3 km in metres
14. Angle sum of a quadrilateral
16. $10^2 − 1^2$

Part C

Across

1. Next square number after 100
3. $15 + 200 \times 7$
5. Minutes between 1.55 pm and 2.50 pm
6. 7416 − 4533
8. $\frac{4}{5}$ as a percentage
9. Smallest two digit prime number
10. $1^1 + 2^2 + 3^3$
11. $180 − 65 \div 5$
13. Factor of 60
15. 6874 to the nearest 100
17. Find n, if $n \div 11 = 11$
18. Number of 2p coins in £10

Down

1. Half of a third of 66
2. Perimeter of a square of side 27 cm
4. Next in the sequence 70, 140, 280
7. Double 125 plus treble 202
8. $30^2 − 2^6 − 3^2$
9. William the Conqueror
11. Maximum score with three darts
12. $\frac{3}{7}$ of 3528
14. 17×30
16. Multiple of 8

Part D

Design you own crossnumber puzzle. Start with the answers and then write clues to the puzzle. Try to make your clues as varied and interesting as possible.

A long time ago!? 5

The Königsberg Problem

In the 18th century, the city of Königsberg
(in Prussia) was split into parts by the
river Pregel. There were seven bridges.
The people of Königsberg tried to walk
across all seven bridges without crossing
the same bridge twice.

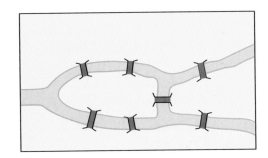

Exercise

1 Sketch the diagram above to show the river and the bridges. Use a pencil to show how you
   could walk across each bridge without crossing the same bridge twice.
   If you make a mistake, rub out the pencil and try again.
   If you find a way, show somebody else then show your teacher.

2 Make up a map of a city which has more than seven bridges. Get somebody else to copy your
   map and try to show you how to walk across each bridge without crossing the same bridge
   twice.

3 **RESEARCH:**

A famous mathematician, Leonhard Euler,
examined the Königsberg problem.
(a) Find out when Euler lived.
(b) Find out what Euler said about the Königsberg
     problem.
(c) Königsberg is now called Kaliningrad and is in
     Russia. Find out how many of the seven
     bridges still exist.
(d) Discuss as a class your main findings about the
     Königsberg problem.

Mental Arithmetic Practice 5

There are two sets of mental arithmetic questions is this section. Ideally a teacher will read out each question twice, with pupils' books closed. Each test of 20 questions should take about 20 minutes.

Test 1

1. Jack has £330 and spends £295. How much money does he have left?

2. What is the sum of 73, 42 and 7?

3. Sarah is given a bonus of 5% of £440. How much is the bonus?

4. Write 0.07 as a fraction.

5. How many halves make up six whole ones?

6. What is eight squared?

7. What is the probability of getting an even number if you throw one dice?

8. A triangle has three equal sides. What is its special name?

9. Subtract 0.3 from 5.

10. Write down three factors of 6.

11. Penny leaves Norwich at 1:40 p.m. and gets to Cambridge at 3:15 p.m. How long did the journey take?

12. A rectangle of length 10 cm has an area of 35 cm². What is the width of the rectangle?

13. What is 300 multiplied by 8?

14. Write down a prime number between 15 and 20.

15. What is the mean average of 9, 6 and 15?

16. If $n = 4$, which is larger: $3n$ or n^2?

17. £420 is shared equally between seven people. How much does each person get?

18. What is three-fifths of 40?

19. 39° and 52° are added together. Is the answer acute or obtuse?

20. I think of a number. If I treble it and subtract 6, the answer is 21. What number did I think of?

Test 2

1. What is 54 divided by 9?

2. Work out 301 – 102.

3. Round off three hundred and seventy-six to the nearest ten.

4. Find 25% of 880.

5. 38% of children at Wallis School travel by bus and 49% walk. The remainder travel by car. What percentage of the children travel by car?

6. What number is one less than two thousand?

7. What is the difference between six squared and two squared?

8. Write 20% as a fraction.

9. Don buys a book for £5.99 and a drink costing 50p. How much change does he get from a £10 note?

10. Hannah walks for 200 minutes and Ben walks for three hours ten minutes. Who walks for the longest time and by how much?

11 What is 400 divided by 20?

12 What is the product of 3, 4 and 5?

13 A triangle has two angles of 40° and 65°. What is the size of the third angle?

14 What is the median of 1, 2, 3, 4 and 5.

15 What is 4 – (–4)?

16 There are 12 beads in a bag. Seven of the beads are red. I take out one bead from the bag. What is the probability that the bead is red?

17 How many lines of symmetry does a rectangle have?

18 What is half of 370?

19 How many fifty pence coins make £100.50?

20 How many seconds in one hour?

6.1   More equations

In section 6.1 you will:

● review equations covered in section 4.6

Remember with equations:

You may do the same thing to both sides

Exercise 1M

1   Solve the equations below.

(a) $n - 7 = 9$ (b) $4x = 28$ (c) $19 + m = 27$

(d) $8y = 40$ (e) $w - 15 = 17$ (f) $6n = 42$

2   Now solve these equations:

(a) $3n + 4 = 19$ (b) $2w + 8 = 24$ (c) $7y - 5 = 9$

(d) $5m + 12 = 62$ (e) $6x - 8 = 16$ (f) $4m - 5 = 31$

3   I think of a number, multiply it by 9 and add 14. The answer is 68. Write down an equation then solve it to find the number.

4   Solve these equations:

(a) $\dfrac{x}{5} = 8$ (b) $\dfrac{w}{3} = 12$ (c) $5 = \dfrac{n}{7}$

(d) $3 = \dfrac{m}{10}$ (e) $11 = \dfrac{n}{6}$ (f) $\dfrac{x}{9} = 9$

5   Solve

(a) $6x - 2 = 34$ (b) $10m + 17 = 47$ (c) $6w - 30 = 9$

(d) $9n + 8 = 71$ (e) $4x - 20 = 28$ (f) $6m - 15 = 33$

6 Lois thinks of a number. She multiplies it by 7 and
   subtracts 13. The answer is 50. Write down an
   equation then solve it to find the number.

7 Solve

   (a) $3m + 7 = 22$ (b) $4x - 9 = 15$

   (c) $4w + 80 = 200$ (d) $20n - 6 = 74$

   (e) $3w + 20 = 95$ (f) $5y - 75 = 425$

Sometimes the answers are not whole numbers.

(a) Solve $5n - 3 = 1$

$$\overset{\large\textcircled{\scriptsize +3}}{} \quad \overset{\large\textcircled{\scriptsize +3}}{}$$
$$5n = 4$$
$$\overset{\large\textcircled{\scriptsize \div5}}{} \quad \overset{\large\textcircled{\scriptsize \div5}}{}$$
$$n = \frac{4}{5}$$

(b) Solve $9 = 6 + 2n$

$$\overset{\large\textcircled{\scriptsize -6}}{} \quad \overset{\large\textcircled{\scriptsize -6}}{}$$
$$3 = 2n$$
$$\overset{\large\textcircled{\scriptsize \div2}}{} \quad \overset{\large\textcircled{\scriptsize \div2}}{}$$
$$\frac{3}{2} = n$$
$$1\frac{1}{2} = n$$

Exercise 1E

1 Copy and complete the boxes:

   (a) $7n + 4 = 6$ (b) $5 = 2 + 4n$

   $7n = \square$ $\square = 4n$

   $n = \dfrac{\square}{\square}$ $\dfrac{\square}{\square} = n$

2 Solve these equations:

   (a) $5n - 1 = 3$ (b) $7y - 2 = 2$ (c) $3m - 1 = 1$

   (d) $7x + 5 = 8$ (e) $13n + 10 = 12$ (f) $5w - 2 = 1$

3 Now solve these equations:

   (a) $5 = 6x + 4$ (b) $10 = 7 + 8m$ (c) $6 = 5 + 2w$

   (d) $13 = 10n + 6$ (e) $6 = 12m - 1$ (f) $2 = 8x - 5$

4   Abbie is 3 years older than her sister. The sum of their ages is 27. Let Abbie's age be x. Write down an equation involving x then solve it to find Abbie's age.

5   The perimeter of this rectangle is 44 cm. Write down an equation involving n then solve it to find the actual length and width of this rectangle.

n

$2n + 7$

6   Solve

(a) $5x + 4 = 7$

(b) $25 = 9 + 8m$

(c) $52 = 3 + 7p$

(d) $4 = 9w - 3$

(e) $6a - 17 = 43$

(f) $2n + 6 = 11$

(g) $21 = 12 + 2q$

(h) $13 = 5b - 3$

(i) $6d - 3 = 8$

6.2   Sequence rules

In section 6.2 you will learn how to:

● find rules for sequences

● Here is a sequence of shapes made from sticks

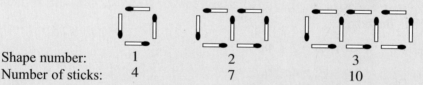

Shape number: 1   2   3
Number of sticks: 4   7   10

● There is a *rule* or *formula* which we can use to calculate the number of sticks for any shape number.

'*The number of sticks is three times the shape number add one*'.

Check that this rule works for all the shapes above and also for shape number 4 which you can draw.

● We could also write the rule using symbols. Let n stand for the diagram number and let s stand for the number of sticks.

The rule (or formula) is '$s = 3n + 1$'.

Exercise 1M

1 Here is a sequence of triangles made from sticks.

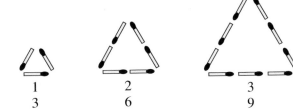

Shape number: 1   2   3
Number of sticks: 3   6   9

(a) Draw shape number 4 and count the number of sticks.

(b) Write down and complete the rule for the number of sticks in a shape: 'The number of sticks is ____ times the shape number'.

2 Here is a sequence of 'steps' made from sticks

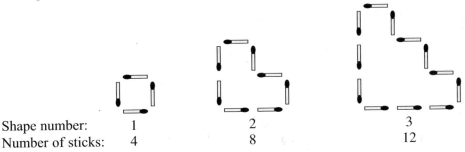

Shape number: 1   2   3
Number of sticks: 4   8   12

(a) Draw shape number 4 and count the number of sticks.

(b) Write down the rule for the number of sticks in a shape. 'The number of sticks is ____ times the shape number'.

3 Louise makes a pattern of triangles from sticks.

Shape number: 1   2   3
Number of sticks: 3   5   7

(a) Draw shape number 4 and shape number 5

(b) Make a table:

shape number	1	2	3	4	5
number of sticks	3	5	7		

(c) Write down the rule for the number of sticks in a shape.

'The number of sticks is ____ times the shape number and then add ____.'

314

4 Crosses are drawn on 'dotty' paper to make a sequence.

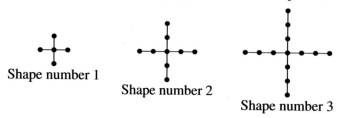

Shape number 1

Shape number 2

Shape number 3

(a) Draw shape number 4

(b) Make a table:

shape number	1	2	3	4
number of dots	5	9	13	

(c) Write down the rule.

'The number of dots is ____ times the shape number and then add ____ .'

5 In these diagrams pink squares are surrounded on three sides by yellow squares. Let the number of pink squares be p and let the number of yellow squares be y.

$p = 1$
$y = 5$

$p = 2$
$y = 6$

$p = 3$
$y = 7$

(a) Draw the next diagram which has 4 black squares.

(b) Write down the rule.

'The number of yellow squares is ....'

6 Look again at questions 1 2 3 and 4 . Use n for the shape number and s for the number of sticks or dots. For each question write the rule connecting n and s without using words. In each question write '$s =$.'

● Here is a sequence 4, 8, 12, 16, ...

The first term is 4×1

The second term is 4×2

The third term is 4×3

⋮   ⋮

The 30th term is 4×30

Consider a term n. We call this the nth term.

The nth term is $4 \times n$ in this sequence.

$$n^{\text{th}} \text{ term} = 4n$$

This formula can be used to find any term in the sequence

eg. 15th term = $4n$ = 4 × 15 = 60

$\quad$ 100th term = $4n$ = 4 × 100 = 400

● In another sequence the nth term is $3n + 2$

$\quad$ 1st term = 3 × 1 + 2 $\qquad\qquad$ 2nd term = 3 × 2 + 2 $\qquad\qquad$ 3rd term = 3 × 3 + 2

$\quad$ ($n = 1$) $\;$ = 5 $\qquad\qquad\qquad$ ($n = 2$) $\;$ = 8 $\qquad\qquad\qquad$ ($n = 3$) $\;$ = 11

Exercise 2M

1 The nth term of a sequence is $6n$. What is the value of:

(a) the first term $\qquad\qquad$ (use $n = 1$)

(b) the second term $\qquad\quad$ (use $n = 2$)

(c) the tenth term $\qquad\quad$ (use $n = 10$)

2 The nth term of a sequence is $2n + 5$. What is the value of:

(a) the first term $\qquad\qquad$ (use $n = 1$)

(b) the fifth term $\qquad\qquad$ (use $n = 5$)

(c) the one hundredth term $\quad$ (use $n = 100$)

3 Write down the first four terms of each sequence using the nth term given.

(a) $7n$ $\qquad\quad$ (b) $n + 3$ $\qquad\quad$ (c) $3n + 1$

(d) $25 - n$ $\quad$ (e) $4n + 7$

4 Match up each sequence and the correct formula for the nth term from the list given.

(a) 10, 20, 30, 40, ...

(b) 3, 6, 9, 12, ...

(c) 5, 9, 13, 17, ...

(d) 50, 100, 150, 200, ...

(e) $1^2, 2^2, 3^2, 4^2, ...$

(f) 8, 10, 12, 14, ...

(g) 11, 14, 17, 20, ...

(h) 12, 24, 36, 48, ...

$3n$

$4n + 1$ $\qquad\qquad$ $50n$

$10n$

$12n$ $\qquad\qquad$ $2n + 6$

n^2 $\qquad$ $3n + 8$

316

5

		N1			N2			N3			N4	
		↓			↓			↓			↓	
		6			10			14			18	
	5		7		9		11		13	15	17	
	4			8			12			16		
		↑			↑			↑			↑	
	M1			M2			M3			M4		

The numbers N1, N2, N3, N4 and M1, M2, M3, M4 form two sequences.

(a) Find M5, M6, N5, N6.

(b) Think of rules and use them to find M15 and N20.

6 Here is a sequence of touching squares.
Copy and complete the table.

Square number	Coordinates of centre
1	(2, 2)
2	(4, 4)
3	
5	
40	
45	

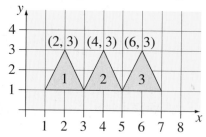

7 Here is a sequence of touching triangles.

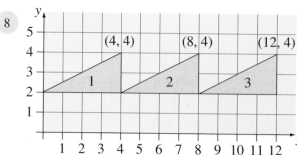

(2, 3) (4, 3) (6, 3)

Find the coordinates of:

(a) the top of triangle 5

(b) the top of triangle 50

(c) the bottom right corner of triangle 50

(d) the bottom right corner of triangle 100.

8

(4, 4)   (8, 4)   (12, 4)

Find the coordinates of the top vertex of:

(a) triangle 4

(b) triangle 20

(c) triangle 2000.

Investigation – count the crossovers

Two straight lines have a maximum of one crossover

Three straight lines have a maximum of three crossovers.

Notice that you can have less than three crossovers if the lines all go through one point. Or the lines could be parallel.

In this work we are interested only in the *maximum* number of crossovers.

Four lines have a maximum of six crossovers.

Part A   Draw five lines and find the maximum number of crossovers.
Does there appear to be any sort of sequence in your results? If you can find a sequence, use it to *predict* the maximum number of crossovers with six lines.

Part B   Now draw six lines and count the crossovers to see if your prediction was correct (remember not to draw three lines through one point).

Part C   Predict the number of crossovers for seven lines and then check if your prediction is correct by drawing a diagram.

Part D   Write your results in a table:

Number of lines	Number of crossovers
2	1
3	3
4	6
5	
6	

Predict the number of crossovers for 20 lines.

CHECK YOURSELF ON SECTIONS 6.1 AND 6.2

1   Review of equations

Solve the equations below.

(a) $5n - 17 = 28$

(b) $\dfrac{m}{7} = 8$

(c) $34 = 3y + 10$

(d) $4 = 6w - 1$

(e) $9x + 16 = 34$

(f) $10 = 4p + 7$

2   Finding rules for sequences

In these diagrams blue squares are surrounded by green squares.

 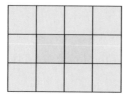 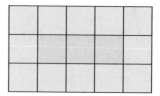

(a) Draw the next diagram which has 4 blue squares.

(b) Make a table. Fill in the missing values.

number of blue squares	1	2	3	4
number of green squares	8	10		

(c) Complete the rule:

'The number of green squares is _____ times the number of blue squares and then add _____.'

(d) The nth term of a different sequence is $4n + 3$. What is the value of the tenth term of this sequence?

6.3   Metric and imperial units

In section 6.3 you will learn how to:

● convert metric units

● convert between metric and imperial units

● read scales

● change units for some problems

Metric units

Length	Mass	Volume
1 cm = 10 mm	1 kg = 1000 g	1 millilitre (ml) = 1 cm^3
1 m = 100 cm	1 tonne = 1000 kg	1 litre = 1000 ml
1 km = 1000 m		

Converting metric units

Divide or multiply by 10, 100, 1000 and so on.

(a) 1.6 m = 160 cm   (b) 4300 g = 4.3 kg   (c) 59 litres = 59000 ml

$\times 100$ $\div 1000$ $\times 1000$

Exercise 1M

1 Write each length in cm.

(a) 4 m   (b) 2.6 m   (c) 30 mm   (d) 0.9 m

2 Write each length in km.

(a) 2000 m   (b) 4600 m   (c) 750 m   (d) 300 000 m

3 Write each mass in grams.

(a) 8 kg   (b) 1.8 kg   (c) 0.2 kg   (d) 0.035 kg

4 Write each mass in kg.

(a) 7 tonnes   (b) 20 tonnes   (c) 6500 g   (d) 400 g

5 Percy the pig weighs 38 kg.

How many grams does Percy weigh?

Copy and complete questions 6 to 25

6   5 m =   cm   7   9 kg =   g   8   600 g =   kg   9   3.5 km =   m

10   6 cm =   mm   11   40 mm =   cm   12   70 cm =   m   13   4 litres =   ml

14   2.4 kg =   g   15   6 tonnes =   kg   16   0.2 m =   cm   17   500 g =   kg

18   7 litres =   ml   19   62 litres =   ml   20   8.4 kg =   g   21   2500 ml =   litres

22   46 mm =   cm   23   6.3 m =   cm   24   0.85 kg =   g   25   300 g =   kg

26 Write each mass in kg.

  (a) 950 g (b) 25 tonnes (c) 20 g

27 Write each length in m.

  (a) 40 cm (b) 0.9 km (c) 6 cm

Converting between metric and imperial units

We still use imperial units. Imperial measurements were made by using appropriately sized bits of human being. The inch was measured using the thumb (we still sometimes say 'rule of thumb' when we mean rough measurement), the foot by using the foot.

1 foot ≈ 30 cm 1 kg ≈ 2.2 pounds

8 km ≈ 5 miles 1 gallon ≈ 4.5 litres

'≈' means 'is approximately equal to'

Divide or multiply by the appropriate number shown above.

  (a) 3 feet ≈ 90 cm (b) 11 pounds ≈ 5 kg (c) 3 gallons ≈ 13.5 litres

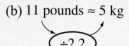 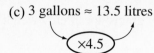

  ×30 ÷2.2 ×4.5

Exercise 1E

1

Danny puts 8 gallons of petrol into his car. *Roughly* how many litres of petrol did Danny put into his car?

Copy and complete questions **2** to **13**.

2 4 kg ≈ pounds **3** 5 feet ≈ cm **4** 10 gallons ≈ litres

5 120 cm ≈ feet **6** 18 litres ≈ gallons **7** 16 km ≈ miles

8 30 miles ≈ km

9 6 gallons ≈ litres

10 25 miles ≈ km

11 44 pounds ≈ kg

12 80 km ≈ miles

13 3 m ≈ feet

14 Phil has cycled 24 km from his house. His total journey will be 19 miles. How many *more* miles does he have to cycle?

15 The maximum height limit for children on a bouncy castle is four feet. Julie is 130 cm tall. Is Julie inside the limit?

16 Luke uses 9 gallons of water to wash his car. Jenny uses 40 litres of water to wash her car. Who uses more water?

17 The distance from Calais to Paris is about 240 km. About how many miles is this?

18 A restaurant needs 9 kg of potatoes for one evening. It has 20 pounds of potatoes. Will the restaurant have enough potatoes?

19 A helicopter can fly up to 500 miles from its base. How far is this in km?

20 The perimeter of a farm is about 36 km. What is the approximate perimeter of the farm in miles?

Reading scales

Exercise 2M

For each of the scales work out:

(a) the measurement indicated by each of the arrows.

(b) the difference between the two arrows.

1

2

3

4

322

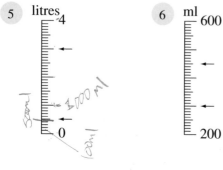

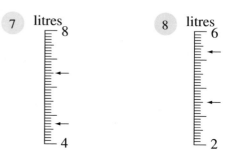

9   200   ↓   ↓1000

10   0   ↓   ↓   4

11

12

13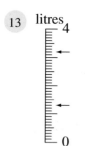

14

15   Read the measurement shown by the arrow on each dial.

(a)   (b)   (c)   (d)

16   Here are scales for changing:
A kilograms and pounds,
B litres and gallons.

In this question give your answers to the *nearest whole number.*

(a) About how many kilograms are there in 5 pounds?

(b) About how many litres are there in 2.2 gallons?

(c) About how many pounds are there in 1.8 kilograms?

Changing units

When a problem has quantities measured in different units the first
thing you must do is change some of the units so that all quantities
are in the same units.

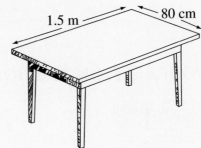

● Find the area (in cm²) of the rectangular
  table top shown.

  Write 1.5 m as 150 cm.

  area of table = 150 × 80

  = 12000 cm².

Exercise 2E

1   Work out

(a) 3 m + 45 cm (in cm)   (b) 0.2 kg + 600 g (in g)   (c) 5 km + 326 m (in m)

(d) 4 cm + 8 mm (in cm)   (e) 2.3 kg – 735 g (in kg)   (f) 6 cm – 5 mm (in mm)

2   Work out

(a) 5 litres + 700 ml (in ml)   (b) 0.6 m + 31 cm (in m)   (c) 4 tonnes – 300 kg (in kg)

(d) 9 kg – 100 g (in g)   (e) 14 g + 0.6 kg (in g)   (f) 35 mm + 4.5 cm (in cm)

3   Find the area of each shape in cm².

(a)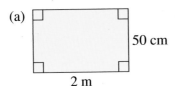
50 cm
2 m

(b)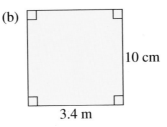
10 cm
3.4 m

(c)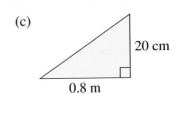
20 cm
0.8 m

4   Find the perimeter of each shape in cm.

(a)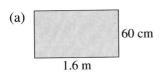
60 cm
1.6 m

(b)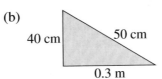
40 cm
50 cm
0.3 m

(c)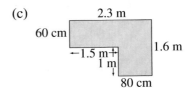
2.3 m
60 cm
←1.5 m→
1 m
1.6 m
80 cm

5 A postage stamp measures 22 mm by 2 cm.
Calculate the area of the stamp in cm².

CHECK YOURSELF ON SECTION 6.3

1 Converting metric units

Copy and complete:

(a) 7 km =   m   (b) 0.4 m =   cm   (c) 7500 ml =   litres   (d) 4.8 kg =   g

2 Converting between metric and imperial units

Copy and complete:

(a) 3 kg ≈   pounds   (b) 8 gallons ≈   litres   (c) 40 miles ≈   km

(d) Ed is 6 feet tall. Mo is 1.75 m tall. *Roughly*
how many cm is Ed taller than Mo?

3 Reading scales

For each scale below write down the measurement indicated by the arrow.

(a)   (b) litres   (c)

4 Changing units for some problems

(a) What is the sum of 5.8 kg and 340 g (in g)?

(b)

70 cm   P   Which rectangle has the
larger area and by how
much?   Q   30 cm

0.9 m   2 m

6.4 Angles and constructions

In section 6.4 you will learn how to:

- review angle work from unit 2
- construct a triangle with three sides given
- construct bisectors

Review of angle work

Exercise 1M

1

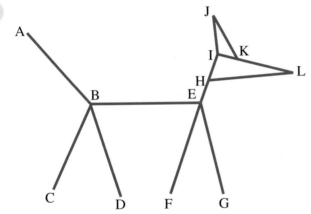

Write down true or false for each statement below.

(a) AB̂C is acute.

(b) FÊG is acute.

(c) BÊH is obtuse.

(d) AB̂E is obtuse.

(e) HL̂K is acute.

(f) IĴK is obtuse.

2 Use a protractor to draw the following angles accurately

(a) 65°   (b) 110°   (c) 170°   (d) 300°   (e) 73°   (f) 285°

3 Which angles in question 2 are *reflex*?

4 Find the angles marked with letters.

(a)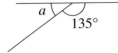

(b)

(c)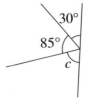

(d)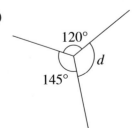

326

5 Find the angles marked with letters.

(a)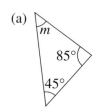

(b)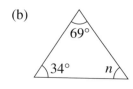

(c)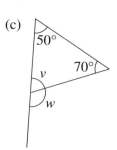

(d)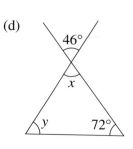

6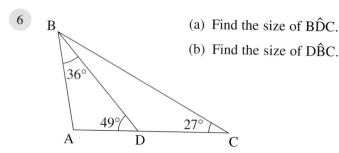

(a) Find the size of BD̂C.

(b) Find the size of DB̂C.

Exercise 1E

Find the angles marked with letters.

1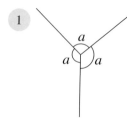

2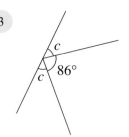

3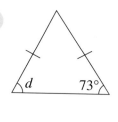

4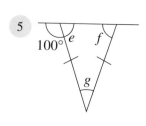

5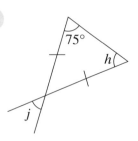

6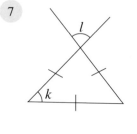

7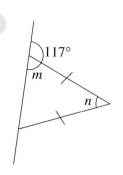

8

9   If you add together two acute angles, will the answer always be an obtuse angle?
    Give a reason for your answer.

10 If you add together two obtuse angles, will the answer always be a reflex angle? Explain
    your answer.

11

Find the size of AD̂B

12

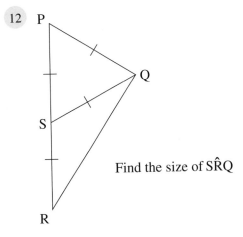

Find the size of SR̂Q

Constructing a triangle with three sides given

Draw triangle XYZ and measure XẐY.

(a) Draw a base line longer than 7 cm
    and mark X and Y exactly 7 cm
    apart.

(b) Put the point of a pair of compasses
    on X and draw an arc of radius 8 cm.

(c) Put the point of the pair of compasses
    on Y and draw an arc of radius 5 cm.

(d) The arcs cross at the point Z so the
    triangle is formed.

Measure XẐY = 60°

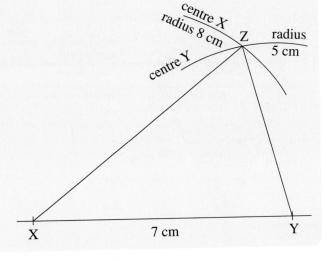

328

Exercise 2M

Use a ruler and a pair of compasses to construct the triangles in questions ① to ⑥ . For each triangle, measure the angle *x*.

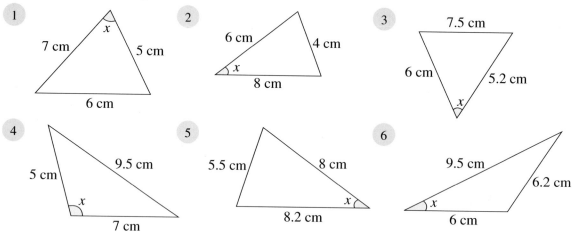

1

2

3

4

5

6

⑦ Construct triangle XYZ where XY = 6.7 cm, YZ = 8.2 cm and ZX = 7.9 cm. Measure XẐY.

⑧ Construct this shape and measure the angle *x*.

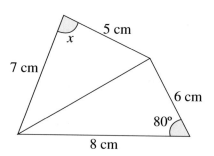

Draw accurately the diagrams in Questions ⑨ and ⑩ .

9

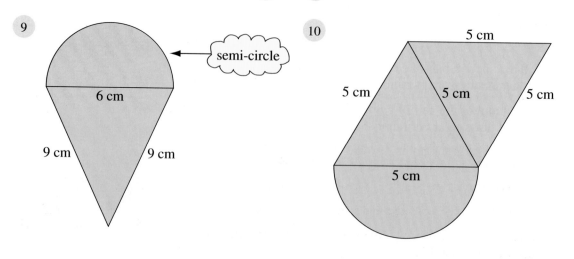

semi-circle

10

Constructing bisectors

Perpendicular bisector

Draw a line AB 8 cm long.

Set the pair of compasses to more
than 4 cm (half the line AB).
Put the compass point on A
and draw an arc as shown.

Put the compass point on B
(*Do not let the compasses slip*)
Draw another arc as shown.

Draw a broken line as shown.

This broken line cuts line AB in half
(*bisects*) and is at right angles to line AB
(*perpendicular*)

The broken line is called the *perpendicular
bisector* of line AB.

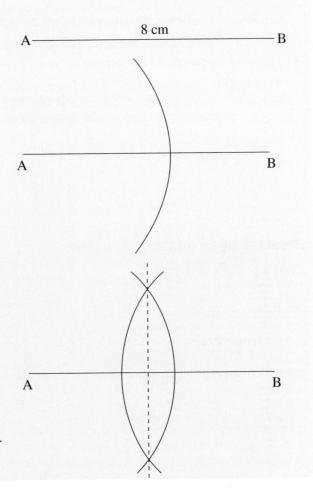

Exercise 3M

1   Draw a horizontal line AB of length 8 cm. Construct the perpendicular bisector of AB.

2   Draw a vertical line CD of length 6 cm. Construct the perpendicular bisector CD.

3   Draw a vertical line EF of length 5 cm. Construct the perpendicular bisector EF.

4   (a) Use a pencil, ruler and a pair of compasses *only* to
        construct the triangle ABC shown opposite

    (b) *Construct* the perpendicular bisector of line AB.

    (c) *Construct* the perpendicular bisector of line AC.

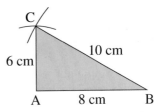

If done accurately, your two lines from (b) and (c) should cross
exactly on the line BC.

5 Draw *any* triangle KLM and construct

(a) The perpendicular bisector of KM.

(b) The perpendicular bisector of KL.
    Mark the point of intersection X.

Take a pair of compasses and, with centre at X and
radius KX, draw a circle through the points K, L
and M. This is the *circumcircle of triangle KLM*.

Repeat the construction for another triangle of
different shape.

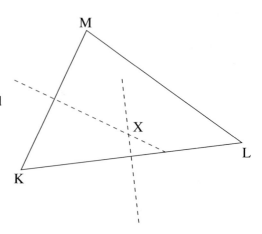

Bisector of an angle

Draw any angle as shown.

Put the compass point on A and draw an arc as shown.

Put the compass point on P
and draw an arc as shown.
Put the compass point on Q
and draw an arc as shown.

Draw a broken line as shown.

This broken line cuts the angle in half (*bisects*).

This broken line is called the *angle bisector*.

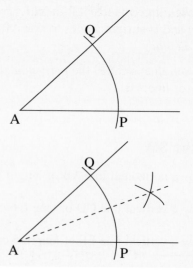

Exercise 4M

1 Draw an angle of 60°. Construct the bisector of the angle (use a protractor to measure the
   angles to check that you have drawn the angle bisector accurately).

2 Draw an angle of 40°. Construct the bisector of the angle.

3   Draw an angle of 130°. Construct the bisector of the angle.

4   Draw an angle of 50°. Construct the bisector of the angle.

5   Draw any triangle ABC and then construct the bisectors of angles A, B and C. If done accurately the three bisectors should all pass through one point.

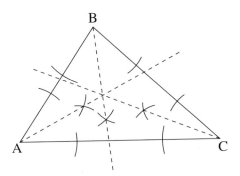

6   Draw any triangle ABC and construct the bisectors of angles B and C to meet at point Y.

With centre at Y draw a circle which just touches the sides of the triangle.
This is the *inscribed circle of the triangle*.

Repeat the construction for a different triangle.

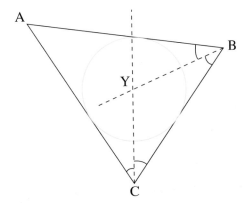

6.5   Three dimensional objects

In section 6.5 you will learn how to:

- recognise common solid objects

- count faces, edges and vertices

- make shapes with nets

Common solid objects

Prisms

A *prism* has the same cross section throughout its length.

Here is a triangular prism.

If you cut through the prism parallel to its end, (the face marked A in the diagram) you produce a shape exactly the same as A (marked A').

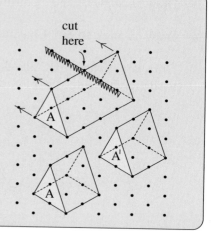

You should *learn* the names below.

cube

cuboid

cylinder

triangular prism

square based pyramid

cone

sphere

hexagonal prism

Faces, edges and vertices

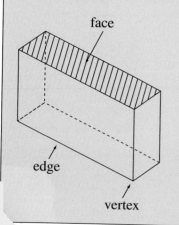

face

edge

vertex

Many three-dimensional shapes have faces, edges and vertices.

'vertices' is the plural of 'vertex'.

The *faces* of the cuboid are the flat surfaces on the shape. A cuboid has 6 faces.

The *edges* of the cuboid are the lines where the faces meet. A cuboid has 12 edges.

The *vertices* are where the edges meet at a point. A cuboid has 8 vertices (corners).

Exercise 1M

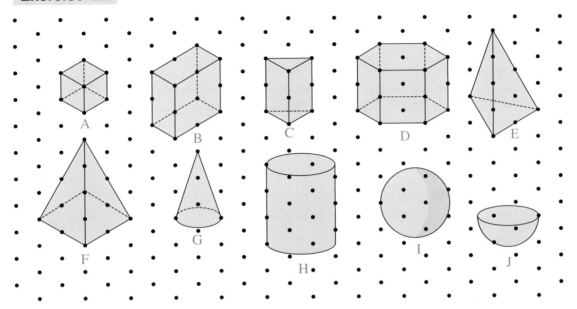

1. Write down the letters of all the objects above that are prisms and write next to the letter the name of the object.

2. Write down the letters of all the objects that are not prisms and write next to the letter the name of the object.

3. (a) For objects A to F, state the number of faces, edges and vertices. Write your answers in a table with columns for 'shape', 'faces', 'edges' and 'vertices.'

   (b) Try to find a connection between the number of faces, edges and vertices which applies to all the objects A to F.

4. Draw 3 pictures of a cube and label them A, B, C.
   On A, colour in a pair of edges which are parallel.
   On B, colour in a pair of edges which are perpendicular.
   On C, colour in a pair of edges which are parallel nor intersect each other.

Exercise 1E

1. Imagine a large cube which is cut in half along the dotted lines. Describe the two new solids formed. How many faces, edges and vertices does each solid have?

2. Suppose the same large cube is now cut in half along a different dotted line. Describe the two new solids formed.

   How many faces, edges and vertices does each solid have?

3   Suppose you cut off one corner from a cube. How many
    faces, edges and vertices has the remaining shape? How
    about the piece cut off?

4   These diagrams show different solids when viewed from
    directly above. Describe what each solid could be. [There may be
    more than one correct response but you only have to give one].

5   Describe two different ways in which you could cut a cylinder into two
    identical pieces. Describe and/or sketch the solids you would obtain in each case.

6   Sit back to back with a partner. Look at one of the models below but don't tell
    your partner which one. Tell your partner how to make the model. Now swap over.
    With practice you can design harder models of your own.

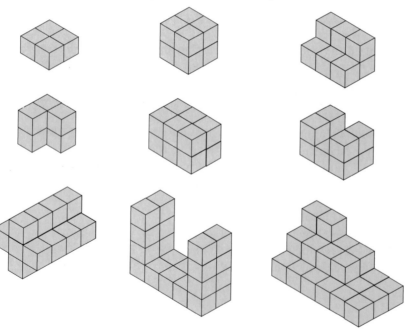

7   Here is an object made from four cubes.

    (a) Copy the drawing on isometric paper (Make sure
        you have the paper the right way round.)

    (b) Make as many *different* objects as you can using
        four cubes. Draw each object on isometric paper.

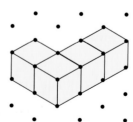

Nets for making shapes

- If the cube shown was made of cardboard, and you cut along some of the edges and laid it out flat, you would have a *net* of the cube.

  There is more than one net of a cube as you will see in the exercise below.

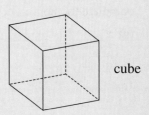
cube

- To make a cube from card you need to produce the net shown below complete with the added 'tabs' for glueing purposes.

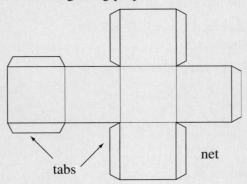
tabs   net

- In this section you will make several interesting 3D objects. You will need a pencil, ruler, scissors and either glue (Pritt Stick) or Sellotape.

Exercise 2M

1 Here are several nets which may or may not make cubes. Draw the nets on squared paper, cut them out and fold them to see which ones do make cubes.

(a)

A	B	C		
		D	E	F

(b)

		A	
B	C	D	E
		F	

(c)

A			
B	C		
	D	E	F

(d)

A	B	
	C	D
	E	F

(e)

			E
A	B	C	D
			F

2 For the nets, which *did* make cubes in question 1 , state which of the faces B, C, D, E or F was opposite face A on the cube.

3 Each diagram below shows *part* of the net of cube. Each net needs one more square to complete the net.

(a) 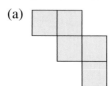   (b)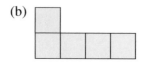

Draw the four possible nets which would make a cube with each one.

4 Draw a net for each of the following:

(a) a closed cuboid measuring 5 cm × 3 cm × 2 cm
(b) a square-based pyramid.

5 Use triangle dotty paper. Draw a net for a triangular based prism.

Exercise 2E

Ask your teacher for cardboard.

1 Use a ruler and compasses to construct this triangle in the middle of the cardboard. All lengths are in cm.

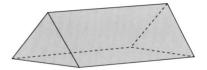

2 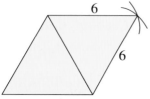 Use a ruler and compasses to construct this triangle joined to the first triangle.

3 Use a ruler and compasses to draw 2 more triangles joined to your first triangle.

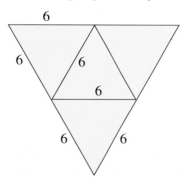

4 Draw on some flaps like this.

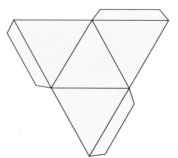

5 *Score* all the lines then cut out the net. Fold and glue to make a triangular pyramid (called a *tetrahedron*).

6 Use triangle dotty paper. Draw each net then make the solid shown.

(a) Octahedron (octa: eight; hedron; faces)

(b) Icosahedron (an object with 20 faces)

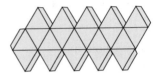

CHECK YOURSELF ON SECTIONS 6.4 AND 6.5

1 Review of angle work from unit 2

Find the angles marked with letters

(a)

109°

a

172°

(b)

49° b

(c)

c 35°

97°

26°

2 Constructing a triangle with three sides given

Construct this triangle with a ruler and compasses only.
Use a protractor to measure the angle x

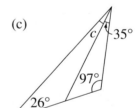

5 cm x 5.5 cm

7 cm

3 Constructing bisectors

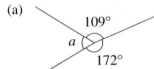

B

4 cm

70°

A   6 cm   C

Use a ruler and protractor to draw this triangle accurately. Construct the perpendicular bisector of AC and the angle bisector of angle A. Mark with a P the point where the two bisectors meet. Measure and write down the length of AP.

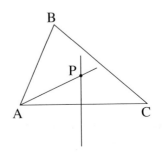

B

P

A   C

4   Recognising common solid objects

Write down the names of these solids

(a)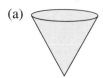

(b)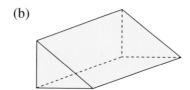

(c)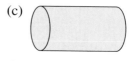

5   Counting faces, edges and vertices

For each solid below, write down how many faces, edges and vertices there are

(a)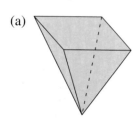

(b)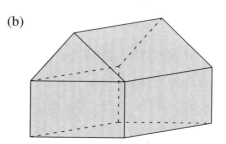

6   Making shapes with nets

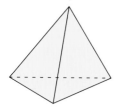   This is a tetrahedron (a triangular pyramid)

Which of these nets will make a tetrahedron?

(a)

(b)

(c)

(d) If time, copy these nets onto triangle dotty paper. Cut them out and see if you were right.

UNIT 6   MIXED REVIEW

Part one

1. Write the missing number in this sequence:

   5, 18, ☐, 44.

2. What is the reading in kilograms shown in this scale?

3. Name the 3D shape whose faces are all squares.

4. What number, when divided by 7 and then multiplied by 12, gives an answer of 144?

5. Listed below are various items that can be measured. Copy the list and insert next to each item the most suitable unit of measurement.

   (a) The fuel tank of an aircraft.

   (b) The mass of a packet of crisps.

   (c) The height of your bedroom.

   (d) The distance from London to Edinburgh.

   (e) The amount of cough mixture on a teaspoon.

   (f) The width of a postage stamp.

Units
1. centimetres
2. millilitres
3. grams
4. kilometres
5. litres
6. metres

6. Solve the equations.

   (a) $n - 8 = 13$ (b) $5n = 20$ (c) $2n + 4 = 12$

   (d) $3n - 7 = 14$ (e) $\frac{n}{9} = 4$ (f) $8n - 15 = 33$

7. A metal rod is 14 cm long. A piece 2 cm 3 mm is cut off. What length of rod is left in centimetres?

8. What is the mathematical name for a snooker ball?

9. Here is the net for a cube.

   (a) When the net is folded up, which edge will be stuck to the edge JI?

   (b) Which edge will be stuck to the edge AB?

   (c) Which corner will meet corner D?

   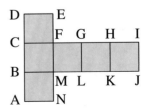

10. Sarah is 14 years old and her father is 35 years older than her. Sarah's mother is 4 years younger than her father. How old is Sarah's mother?

11

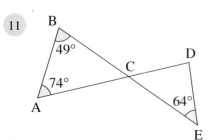

(a) Find the size of AĈB.

(b) Find the size of CD̂E.

12

P ———————— 7 cm ———————— Q

Draw a line PQ of length 7 cm. *Construct* the perpendicular bisector of PQ.

13 If 8 km is about 5 miles, how many miles is 56 km?

14 Answer true or false:

(a) $2n + n = 3n$ (b) $3n - 2n = 1$ (c) $n^2 = 2 \times n$

(d) $n \times 3 = 3n$ (e) $n \div 3 = \dfrac{n}{3}$ (f) $n \times 0 = n$

15 Unifix cubes can be joined together to make different sized cuboids.

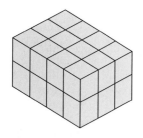

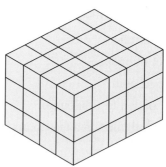

If the smaller cuboid weighs 96g, how much does the large cuboid weigh?

Part two

1 Write each of the following in the units shown, using decimals when needed.

(a) 3 m 65 cm = ☐ m   (b) 850 g = ☐ kg   (c) 0.49 m = ☐ cm

(d) 4.2 kg = ☐ g   (e) 38 cm = ☐ m   (f) 46 mm = ☐ cm

2 What is the name of the shape which has one square face and four triangular faces?

3

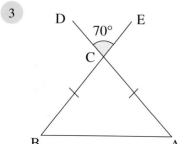

Find the size of AB̂C.

4   Here is a sequence of diagrams showing an arrangement of counters…

   Diagram 1   Diagram 2   Diagram3

(a) Draw diagram number 4.

(b) Copy and complete this table for diagrams so far.

Diagram Number	Counters used
1	7
2	
3	
4	

(c) Without drawing, how many counters will be needed for diagram number 5?

(d) Write in words how you found your answer without drawing.

5   Draw a net for a cuboid 2 cm × 3 cm × 4 cm.

6   (a) How many 7 centimetre pieces of string can be cut from a piece of string which is 2 metres in length?

   (b) How much string is left over?

7   A jar with 8 chocolates in it weighs 160g.
    The same jar with 20 chocolates in it weighs 304 g. How much does the jar weigh on its own?

8   Solve the equations.

   (a) $3n + 7 = 9$ (b) $7n - 3 = 3$ (c) $4 = 5n - 3$

9   These nets form cubical dice. Opposite faces of a dice always add
   up to 7. Write down the value of a, b, c, d, e and f so that opposite
   faces add up to 7.

	c		
a	b	1	3
	2		

2			
d	e	1	3
	f		

10 The tenth number in the sequence 1, 4, 16, 64…… is 262 144.
    What is (a) the ninth number,
            (b) the twelfth number?

11 *Construct* this triangle with a ruler and compasses only.
    Use a protractor to measure the size of AB̂C.

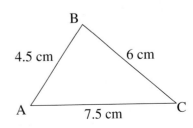

342

12 What is the name of the solids which have the same cross-section throughout their length?

13 Each pace of an Egyptian warrior is 90cm. How far does he walk, in km, when he walks 100 000 paces?

14 A car travels 10 miles on a litre of petrol and petrol costs 98p per litre. In six months the car is driven a total of 6500 miles. Find the cost of petrol to the nearest pound.

15 In a code the 25 letters from A to Y are obtained from the square using a 2 digit grid reference similar to coordinates. So letter 'U' is 42 and 'L' is 54. The missing letter 'Z' has code 10.

	1	2	3	4	5
5	G	A	P	C	Q
4	O	F	R	H	L
3	N	K	B	M	Y
2	D	S	I	U	E
1	J	T	V	W	X

[Second digit] (vertical axis)   [First digit] (horizontal axis)

Decode the following messages:

(a) 41, 52
    13, 52, 52, 12
    43, 14, 34, 52
    22, 42, 43, 22

(b) 44, 25, 31, 52
    25
    13, 32, 45, 52
    12, 25, 53

(c) 22, 35, 42, 34, 22
    25, 34, 52
    34, 42, 33, 33, 32, 22, 44

In part (d) each pair of brackets gives one letter

(d) ($\frac{1}{4}$ of 140), ($7^2 + 5$), ($7 \times 8 - 4$), ($4^2 + 3^2$), ($\frac{1}{5}$ of 110), ($26 \div \frac{1}{2}$)
    ($3 \times 7 + 1$), ($83 - 31$), ($2 \times 2 \times 2 \times 2 + 5$).
    ($100 - 57$), ($4^2 - 2$), (17×2), ($151 - 99$)
    ($2 \times 2 \times 2 \times 5 + 1$), ($\frac{1}{4}$ of 56), ($2 \times 3 \times 2 \times 3 - 2$), ($5^2 - 2$).

(e) Write your own message in code and ask a friend to decode it.

Answers to 'check yourself' questions

Page 18 sections 1.1 and 1.2

1. (a) 2011 (b) 23201 (c) 9500
2. (a) 60234 (b) 8207 (c) 5587 (d) 7209 (e) 903
3. (a) 533 (b) 282 (c) 369 (d) 2206 (e) 975
4. (a) 63 (b) 518 (c) 1968 (d) 168
5. (a) $54 \div 6 = 9$ (b) $45 \div 5 = 9$ (c) $252 \div 7 = 36$
   (d) $414 \div 9 = 46$ (e) $256 \div 4 = 64$ (f) $216 \div 8 = 27$
6. (a) 12 (b) 12

Page 30 sections 1.3 and 1.4

1. (a) 630 (b) 1701 (c) 13272
2. (a) 23 (b) 24
3. (a) 5 (b) 87 (c) 8 (d) 55 (e) 5 (f) 30
4. (a) 99 (b) 15.9 (c) 8.61 (d) 1.07 (e) 9

Page 37 section 1.5

1. (a) 17 (b) 8 (c) 37 (d) 8 (e) 1.3
2. (a) 29 (b) 7,17 (c) $6 \rightarrow 15 \rightarrow 33 \rightarrow 69$
3. (a) $\frac{1}{3}$ (b) 4×5^2 (c) 31 (d) 6
   (e) (i) [diagram] (ii) [diagram]

Page 47 section 1.6

1. (a) 52 cm (b) 50 m (c) 62 cm (d) 7 m
2. (a) 40 cm^2 (b) 81 cm^2 (c) 92 cm^2 (d) 7 m
3. (a) 33 cm^2 (b) 28 m^2 (c) 30 cm^2
   (d) 132 cm^2 (e) 20 m

Page 64 section 2.1

1. (a) 9 (b) 8.5 (c) 8 2. 37
3. Warriors : mean = 23.8, range = 14
   Sabres:mean = 22.7, range = 12

Page 81 sections 2.2 and 2.3

1. (a) $\frac{7}{42}$ (b) $\frac{28}{36}$ (c) $\frac{2}{3}$ (d) $\frac{30}{42}$ (e) $\frac{49}{56}, \frac{63}{72}$
2. (a) 4 (b) 20 (c) 42 (d) 16
3. (a) $\frac{7}{9}$ (b) $\frac{29}{35}$ (c) $\frac{1}{12}$ (d) $\frac{13}{16}$
4. $\frac{1}{20}, 0.05, 5\%; \frac{9}{20}, 0.45, 45\%;$

   $\frac{3}{4}, 0.75, 75\%; \frac{2}{5}, 0.4, 40\%$

Page 92 section 2.4

1. (a) 85° (b) 30° (c) 100° 2. (a) 62° (b) 115°
3. (a) about 40° (b) about 75° (c) about 150°

4. (a) true (b) false (c) true
5. (a) 65° (b) 125° (c) $X\hat{W}Y = 100°, V\hat{W}X = 80°$
5. (a) 28° (b) 102° (c) $P\hat{R}Q = 64°, P\hat{R}S = 116°$

Page 107 section 2.5

1. (a) $4x$ (b) $n - 6$ (c) $2w + 24$
2. (a) $2m + 6n$ (b) $7y$ (c) $4p + 6$ (d) $2a + 2b$
3. (a) 645 (b) 33 (c) 6
4. (a) 8 (b) $\square = 12$, $\bigcirc = 3$

Page 155 sections 3.1, 3.2, 3.3, 3.4 and 3.5

1. (b) 4 (d) parallelogram
2. (a) (5, 3) (b) (7, 5) (c) (4, 3)
3. (a) 432 (b) 1944 (c) 144
4. (a) £39 (b) £24
5. (a) 2.0 cm (b) 4.2 cm (c) 2.6 cm
   (d) 0.7 (e) 0.03 (f) 0.15
6. (a) 0.08, 0.31, 0.411, 0.5 (b) 0.007, 0.1, 0.602, 0.62
   (c) A = 0.27, B = 0.5
7. (a) 5.27 (b) 3.45 (c) 9.43 (d) £3.82
8. (a) 36.1 (b) 1.194 (c) 140 (d) 0.06
   (e) 1000 (f) 1000 (g) 10
9. (a) 13.5 (b) 3.84 (c) 12.32 (d) £6.10
10. (a) 4.71 (b) 5.3 (c) 5.5 (d) 0.32 kg
11. (a) 17 (b) 55 (c) 9 (d) 12 or 18
12. (a) 49 (b) 1 (c) 43 (d) 92
    (e) 36, 49 (f) 9, 25 (g) 1, 100

Page 184 sections 3.6, 3.7 and 3.8

1. (a) (1, 4) (b) $x = 1$ (c) $y = 2$ (d) (3, 3)
2. (a) $y = x - 2$ (b) $y = x + 3$ (c) $y = 2x$ (d) P and R
3. (a) (i) 18 (ii) £3.50 (iii) Prawn
   (b) (i) 10 (ii) 80
   (iii) You cannot have , for example, $2\frac{1}{2}$ bedrooms.
4. (a) Frequencies:2, 3, 7, 14, 8, 3, 3
   (b) AB no rain and no use, BC it rains, CD no rain and no use, DE water used, EF no rain, FG it rains, GH no rain and no use.
5. (a) $\frac{1}{3}$ (b) 30
7. (a) $\frac{1}{4}$ (b) $\frac{5}{8}$ (c) $\frac{3}{8}$
   (d) $\frac{1}{3}$ (e) $\frac{1}{52}$ (f) $\frac{1}{13}$ (g) $\frac{1}{2}$
8. (a) (i) true (ii) true (iii) false
   (b) (i) white (ii) $\frac{7}{11}$ (iii) $\frac{3}{11}$ (iv) 0 (v) $\frac{1}{11}$

Page 213 sections 4.1 and 4.2

1. (a) 70° (b) 5.3/5.4 cm
2. (a) AB or CD (b) AB or CD (c) AD or BC
3. (a) equilateral (b) scalene (c) isosceles
   (d) right-angled (e) two equal sides and two equal angles
4. (a) trapezium (b) square (c) rhombus (d) kite
   (e) parallelogram (f) parallelogram with four equal sides
5. (a) P, R (b) 10 (c) regular octagon

Page 228 sections 4.3 and 4.4

1.

(a)	$\frac{2}{25}$	0.08	8%
(b)	$\frac{4}{5}$	0.8	80%
(c)	$\frac{9}{10}$	0.9	90%
(d)	$\frac{8}{25}$	0.32	32%
(e)	$\frac{18}{25}$	0.72	72%

2. (a) 75% (b) 60% (c) $33\frac{1}{3}$%
3. (a) £18 (b) £285 (c) £96
4. (a) £56 (b) £2 5. (a) $\frac{1}{3}$ (b) $\frac{9}{22}$
6. (a) 2:3 (b) 3:8 (c) £35:£5 (d) 9

Page 246 sections 4.5 and 4.6

1. (a) 2°C, 1°C, –3°C, –4°C, –8°C, –9°C (b) –5
2. (a) –15 (b) 8 (c) –3 (d) 32
3. (a) –4 (b) –7 (c) –3 (d) –2
4. (a) 28 (b) 4
5. (a) 26 (b) 30 (c) 10 (d) 7
6. (a) $5x + 35$ (b) $np - 3n$ (c) $x^2 + 8x$

Page 268 sections 5.1, 5.2 and 5.3

2. (a) 2 (b) 6 (c) 3 (d) 2
(e)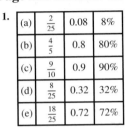

3.

5. (b) (i) 3 units right and 2 units up
   (ii) 2 units left and 1 unit up (iii) 4 units up

Page 290 sections 5.5 and 5.6

1. (a) (i) $\frac{3}{7}$ (ii) $\frac{2}{7}$ (b) $\frac{3}{7}$
2. (a) 15°C (b) October (c) April and November
   (d) April, May (e) 21°C
3. (a) 37.5 miles (b) 32 km

Page 299 sections 5.7 and 5.8

1. (a) $4a + 7c$ (b) $2ab$ (c) $8m + 2n$ (d) x
   (e) $2c$ (f) $6a + ab$ (g) 9 (h) 28
2. (a) (i) 560 (ii) 2050 (iii) 70
   (b) (i) 5.7 (ii) 9.2 (iii) 0.8 (iv) 5.4
3. (a) 150 (b) 40 (c) 10 (d) £60

Page 317 sections 6.1 and 6.2

1. (a) 9 (b) 56 (c) 8 (d) $\frac{5}{6}$ (e) 2 (f) $\frac{3}{4}$
2. (b) 12, 14 (c) 2 times _____ add 6 (d) 43

Page 324 section 6.3

1. (a) 7000 m (b) 40 cm (c) 7.5 litres (d) 4800 g
2. (a) 6.6 pounds (b) 36 litres (c) 64 km (d) 5 cm
3. (a) 2.5 (b) 0.25 (c) 1.6
4. (a) 6140 g (b) P by 300 cm²

Page 337 sections 6.4 and 6.5

1. (a) 79° (b) 82° (c) 22° 2. 83°/84°
3. 3.7 cm 4. (a) cone (b) triangular prism
   (c) cylinder 5. (a) 5 faces, 8 edges, 5 vertices
   (b) 8 faces, 16 edges, 10 vertices
6. (a) and (c) make tetrahedrons

INDEX